MINES OF DE

DF'

Pleas

The term fathom (6ft/1.829m) is used throughout, this being until recently the standard measure of length and depth common to all Westcountry mines.

Imperial currency is used throughout.
1/- (1 shilling) = 5p.
6d (sixpence) = $2^1/_2$p.

LANDMARK COLLECTOR'S LIBRARY

MINES OF DEVON

A. K. Hamilton Jenkin

Landmark Publishing

Published by

LANDMARK
Publishing Ltd ● ● ● ●

Ashbourne Hall, Cokayne Ave
Ashbourne, Derbyshire DE6 1EJ England
Tel: (01335) 347349 Fax: (01335) 347303
e-mail: landmark@clara.net
web site: www.landmarkpublishing.co.uk

Landmarks 1st edition

ISBN: 1-84306-174-0

British Library Cataloguing in Publication Data: a catalogue
record for this book is available from the British Library.

Printed by Cromwell Press, Trowbridge, Wiltshire

Design & reproduction by James Allsopp

Front cover: Wheal Betsy engine house
Back cover Top & page 3: Shaft head gear and tram road at Bedford United Mine.
© rcm VM BED 002
Back cover Bottom: Below: Dressing floors at Lady Bertha Mine, c.1890. © rcm VM LBE 001

Contents

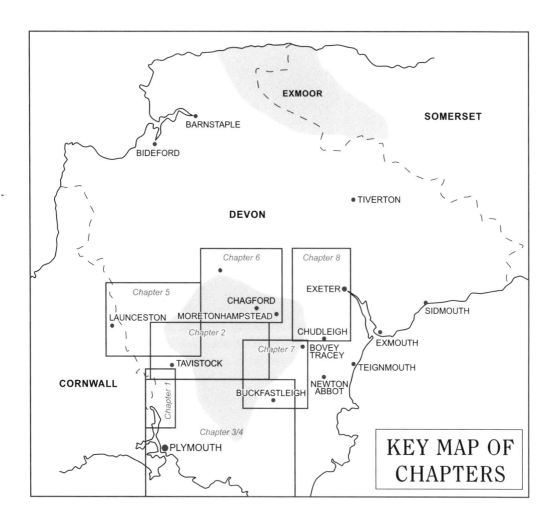

EXMOOR

SOMERSET

BARNSTAPLE

BIDEFORD

DEVON

TIVERTON

Chapter 6

Chapter 8

Chapter 5

EXETER

CHAGFORD

SIDMOUTH

LAUNCESTON

MORETONHAMPSTEAD

Chapter 2

CHUDLEIGH

EXMOUTH

Chapter 7

BOVEY
TRACEY

TAVISTOCK

TEIGNMOUTH

CORNWALL

Chapter 1

NEWTON
ABBOT

BUCKFASTLEIGH

Chapter 3/4

PLYMOUTH

KEY MAP OF CHAPTERS

Introduction to the 1ST Edition (South Devon)

In recent years the growing appeal of industrial archaeology has reawakened interest in the subject of mining in Devon. The first fruits of this was seen in the publication by Mr Frank Booker of his now standard work on the mining and industries of the Tamar Valley. Since then further contributions have appeared on the Birch Tor tin complex of Dartmoor and the lead mines of the Teign Valley. Valuable as these special studies have proved, the fact remains that no book has yet been written on the mines of Devon as a whole, although the need for such a work has long been recognised. Having waited in vain for some Devon historian to supply this need it has now fallen to me, a Cornishman, to attempt the task.

Among the countless number of visitors who pour into the West Country each summer, few realise that Devon once 'possessed a metal mining industry almost as diversified as that of Cornwall, although in general on a much smaller scale. In 1862 too mines are known to have been at work and as late as 1870 the number was not less than sixty. In addition to these the heyday of the industry witnessed an incalculable number of prospecting trials, many of which are described for the first time in this book.

That tin has been worked in Cornwall since the Bronze Age is now generally agreed. Less well known is the fact that for a period in the Middle Ages the greater part of the metal supplying the needs of Europe and the Near East was derived from the alluvial gravels of Dartmoor where from a mere sixty tons in 1156 production rose to over 340 tons a year between 1171 and 1189. By the thirteenth century, however, the richest deposits of the moor were showing signs of exhaustion and the main centre reverted to Cornwall which thenceforth maintained its predominance until, in the sixteenth century, alluvial 'streaming' gradually gave way to the beginnings of underground mining. In this new development Devon played only a minor role, the county possessing no tin lodes comparable in size and productiveness to those of Cornwall.

In lead and silver mining, Devon was early to the forefront. Exploitation of the argentiferous lead ores of Combe Martin was already in full swing in the reign of Edward I when it is recorded that over 300 men were brought down from Derbyshire to work them. For a considerable period the mines proved very productive and according to Lysons provided funds for the wars of Edward III. They were still active in 1485, but a few years later were said to be 'deep and almost worn out. Reopened in the reign of Elizabeth fresh deposits were discovered, but the ore was found difficult to treat and on reaching a depth of 32 fathoms values showed a falling off. Subsequent trials initiated during the 19th century had little or no success.

During the thirteenth and fourteenth centuries the mining of silver-lead was similarly pursued under royal patronage in the Bere Alston peninsula in the south-west of the county. Operations are known to have been started here by 1290 and four years later it is recorded that 370lb of refined silver was sent up to London from Martinstow (now Maristow) near the mouth of the Tavy. Between 1292 and 1297 returns amounted to £4,000 worth of silver and £360 of lead, the maximum output apparently being reached in 1305 when the exports of silver and lead were valued at

£1,773 and £180 respectively. These figures should be multiplied by at least 120 to give some idea of their worth in present-day money values.

During the above period large numbers of miners were drafted into the region from the Peak District of Derbyshire and also from Wales. By 1340, however, the boom years were over, although working continued on a reduced scale until nearly the end of the fifteenth century. After this the Bere mines lapsed into obscurity and remained dormant until their revival in the eighteenth century.

In copper mining Devon was a late starter compared with Cornwall where the industry was already well established by the middle of the eighteenth century. Although trials had been made for copper in the North Molton area during the latter part of the seventeenth century, and some years later on the banks of the Tamar and Tavy, the output at that period was insignificant. As late as the year 1801 production in Devon totalled little more than 1,000 tons and although this had risen to over 6,000 tons by 1837 it still lagged far behind Cornwall where sales in those years amounted to 56,611 and 140,753 tons respectively. By 1840 returns showed a considerable increase mainly due to the rapid growth of Devon Friendship Mine which from 1800 to 1885 yielded ores in excess of 155,000 tons.

Meantime in 1844 work had started at Devon Great Consols which in the course of the next twenty years was destined to become the richest copper mine in Europe, with an output of 736,000 tons of ore valued at more than £3 million sterling. In its later years the mine had the further distinction of being one of the world's largest producers of arsenic. The spectacular achievements of Devon Great Consols stimulated the search for copper throughout the county. Although few of the mines resulting from this proved outstandingly rich, their combined output led to a peak production of 41,513 tons in 1862. Whilst this was no mean achievement, it was wholly eclipsed by that of Cornwall where a maximum output of 198,697 tons was attained in 1857.

In this and a succeeding volume, which will cover the northern part of the county, I have followed the plan outlined in my earlier work, *Mines and Miners of Cornwall*. In the case of the larger and better-known mines, I have confined myself for the most part to adding only information antedating anything previously known of their history. My main preoccupation has been with the numerous small and now forgotten mines whose names and sites are not to be found in any readily available source. It is these which reveal the climate of the time when Devon ranked as a field of mining enterprise to an extent unrecognised today. Many of these small and ephemeral trials owed their inception to some trifling incident, a typical instance being that of Devon Burra Burra where the chance discovery of a gatepost showing traces of copper awakened a speculative fever of excitement which extended even to the City of London.

Having recounted the history of such mines, every effort has been made to locate them in the field. Wherever this has proved possible their sites have been noted in my own set of the 6in OS maps (2nd ed c.1906), but the reproduction of these is unfortunately prohibited by reason of cost. Instead – as far as is feasible – grid references are given so that they may be found on the $2^1/_2$in scale maps, but, of course, the scene is liable to change fast under the impact of new roadworks, building development and local council 'improvement' schemes.

Furthermore, Devon has long been conspicuously neglectful of the physical structures relating to its industrial past. Although endowed with far fewer engine-houses than Cornwall, it possessed at Wheal Exmouth two of the most sumptuous and imposing buildings of their kind ever erected in England. So far from placing any value on these in 1956 an order was made by the local council for their demolition on the trumped-up excuse of their being dangerous. A contractor was engaged to carry out the work but so fortress-like were the engine-houses that the attempt was soon abandoned and though sadly mutilated, the buildings still remain.

A few years later the finely proportioned engine-house and stack of West Crebor Mine, for long a conspicuous landmark on the heights above the Tamar, was senselessly destroyed; the engine-house of Wheal Betsy, now happily in the guardianship of the National Trust, was only saved from a like fate by the timely intervention of the present writer.

Due to its abundant water-power, Devon formerly owned more water-wheels than any other county in the West of England, a number of them being of outstanding size – 50, 60 and in one instance 70ft in diameter. Of these magnificent specimens of the former millwrights' art not one survives today.

In a book of this sort it is usual to make acknowledgements to a host of people who have contributed to its writing. In my case the number has been few and my indebtedness to them has for that very reason been all the greater. Foremost I would mention Mr Frank Booker who, in addition to checking my manuscript and preparing sketch maps, has been ready at all times to assist and encourage me with sound advice. My very special thanks are also due to Mr Justin Brooke, who has relieved me of the task of making an index and list of grid references, besides sharing with my cousin Ruth Phillips the typing of portions of my manuscript. To my friend Geoffrey Ordish I am once again indebted for allowing me to draw on his photographic collection of the mining scene which for the greater part of a lifetime has been a labour of love complementary to my own. Finally I wish to acknowledge the personal interest shown in my work by Mr David St John Thomas of David & Charles, but for whom this book would probably never have been written.

A. K. Hamilton Jenkin

Introduction
This edition

Twenty five years after his death, and the works of A K Hamilton Jenkin are still very much in demand. His concise accounts in the series *Mines and Miners of Cornwall* are, in some areas, being superseded by more detailed monographs but for much of Cornwall there are no real alternatives; and so it is for south Devon. For the historian, faced with a query on the smaller mines, there are still only two sources of first resort; Dines' *The Metalliferous Mining Region of South-West England*, essentially a work of economic geology, and Hamilton Jenkin's *Mines of Devon*.

Although the two volumes of *Mines of Devon* were published in 1974 and 1981, with the second published postumously, Hamilton Jenkin relied to a large extent on research done in the 1960s and earlier. Since then research carried out and published by others has increased dramatically but little has appeared in book form; most is to be found in local and special interest journals. In searching for that material the reader will find two specialist bibliographies invaluable – *Bibliography of the History of British Metal Mining* by Burt and Waite (with later material maintained on the Internet - http://www.ex.ac.uk/mhn/bibtoc.html – by the Mining History Network at the University of Exeter) and *The Industrial Archaeology and Industrial History of South Western England: A Bibliography* by Greenwood. New research has tended towards west Devon, Dartmoor and surrounding areas; where significant mines or groups of mines have been addressed by authors such as Goodridge, Richardson, Schmitz and Greeves. In addition, although Hamilton Jenkin confined himself to south Devon, new work on the north has allowed for a better coverage of the county as a whole; notably *Exmoor's Industrial Archaeology,* edited by Atkinson and published with the support of the National Park.

The National Parks, both Dartmoor and Exmoor, are amongst those organisations and individuals who have worked towards a better understanding of the historic environment; countering the trend, noted by Hamilton Jenkin in 1974, to undervalue the surviving mining features in Devon. Like his confidant Frank Booker, he was aware of the need to interpret the physical as well as the documentary evidence for mining. Today it is not only substantial structures like the Wheal Betsy engine house but the numerous earthworks and lesser features which are recognised as providing a tangible link with mining heritage; a position which reflects the amount of mining related archaeology, much of it published, in recent decades.

Hamilton Jenkin was one of the pioneers in mining history who inspired the post war, post 1945, generations to search wider and deeper into the subject. The current bibliographies bear testimont to their efforts not only to present the history of the mines but to look beyond them at the wider industry. Since the work for *Mines of Devon* was carried out, access to research resources has improved considerably. Periodicals such as the *Mining Journal*, whilst they remain important, no longer define the limits of our research. Greater depth and detail are opened up through access to primary documentary sources. Added to which, where Hamilton Jenkin could only touch on the observation of the copper industry in Devon during the early 18th century, the publication of primary material in the translation of *The Kahlmeter Journal* by Justin Brooke has brought it within easy reach. Such resources, including the published statistical records of the mining industry and access to online manuscript catalogues, allow the historian of today the tools to continue the work of A. K. Hamilton Jenkin. This book can therefore provide the starting point for a journey into the mining history of Devon to be enjoyed by all.

Abbreviations

Collins   Collins, J. H. *Observations on the West of England Mining Region* (1912)

CRO   County Record Office

Dines   Dines, H. C. *The Metalilferous Mining Region of South-West England* Vols 1-2 (1956)

MJ   *Mining Journal* (1835 onwards)

Murchison Murchison, J. H. *British Mines Considered as a Means of Investment* (1854)

RIC   Royal Institution of Cornwall

Spargo   Spargo, Thomas. *The Mines of Cornwall and Devon* (1868 ed)

Other books and sources cited in the text will be found in the Notes and Sources section.

Acknowledgements

The publishers wish to thank the following for their assistance in the provision of photographs: Exeter Central Library (Mr Ian Maxted), R. M. Ordish (re the late H. G. Ordish Collection), Royal Cornwall Museum (Mr Robert Cook)

The Introduction was kindly written by Dr. Peter Claughton

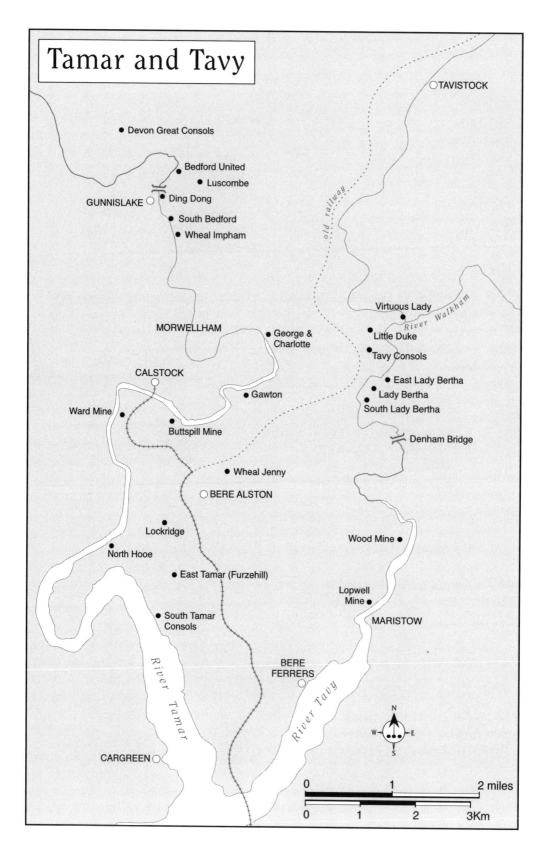

Tamar and Tavy

○TAVISTOCK

● Devon Great Consols

● Bedford United
● Luscombe
GUNNISLAKE ○ ● Ding Dong
● South Bedford
● Wheal Impham

old railway

River Walkham

Virtuous Lady ●

MORWELLHAM

● George &
Charlotte

● Little Duke

● Tavy Consols

CALSTOCK ○

● Gawton

● East Lady Bertha

● Lady Bertha
● South Lady Bertha

Ward Mine ●

● Buttspill Mine

Denham Bridge

● Wheal Jenny

○ BERE ALSTON

● Lockridge

Wood Mine ●

● North Hooe

● East Tamar (Furzehill)

Lopwell
Mine ●

● South Tamar
Consols

MARISTOW

River Tamar

BERE
FERRERS
○

River Tavy

N
W E
S

CARGREEN ○

0   1   2 miles

0   1   2   3Km

12

CHAPTER 1

TAMAR AND TAVY

No book purporting to be a record of mining in Devon could be regarded as complete without some reference to the most celebrated of all its mines – Devon Great Consols. The account that follows is condensed by Frank Booker from his standard work on the area, *The Industrial Archaeology of the Tamar Valley* (1967):

The A390 road out of Tavistock climbs over Morwell Down to dip steeply to the Tamar and cross into Cornwall at Gunnislake over a sixteenth-century bridge. Looking northwards from the bridge, a swell of land bordered by the river rises to above the 200ft contour. Although now thick with trees, glimpses can be seen of sandy dumps and heaps of calcined waste. This is the famous Blanchdown Wood (SX 426733), the site of **Devon Great Consols Mine**, once the richest copper working in Europe. In less than sixty years it produced 736,000 tons of copper ore and 72,000 tons of refined arsenic.

The story of Devon Great Consols is one of the great romances of West Country mining, but the apparent chance discovery of copper at Blanchdown in November 1844 obscures the fact that there had long been suspicions of it in the neighbourhood. The site was littered with 'good gossan', a cindery-looking stone indicating the weathered back of a copper lode. The presence of copper in the area seems certainly to have been known since Elizabethan times. William Carnsew in his memoranda c.1580 mentions copper on the borders of Devon and refers particularly to an occurrence 'at Tavistock' surpassing all that he had seen both in value and quantity – three men being able to break more than a ton of such ore per week. Eight tons of it, he says, produce one ton of copper (metal). Carnsew then goes on to say that of the several lodes the largest and most valuable is 'next the bridge'. If one assumes this to be Gunnislake bridge, the temptation to associate these lodes with those of Blanchdown is strong. But we really do not know. Carnsew's remarks might equally well refer to deposits later worked at Ding Dong or more probably Bedford United Mine, adjoining Devon Great Consols and where the so-called Marquis Lode was being explored long before Devon Great Consols began working. The existence, then, of rich mineral wealth in the area had long been known, and on the Blanchdown site widely suspected. The trouble with the latter had been getting the Duke of Bedford's consent to work it.

On 25 March 1844 permission was secured by Josiah Hugo Hitchins, a Tavistock mineral agent of great mining skill and foresight. Hitchins brought off his coup in the face of stiff competition from other mining interests, among them the Williams family of Scorrier who had developed Old Gunnislake Mine close by on the Tamar's Cornish bank. The mine had earlier interested the Williams family but their overtures had been rebuffed by the 6th Duke of Bedford with the remark that 'he did not want a gang of miners disturbing his pheasant coverts'.

Hitchins, with a lease in his pocket stipulating that at least £20,000 must be spent in developing the site and that the Duke's royalty should be one-twelfth, rapidly formed a joint stock company with five other people of 1,024 shares of which he took 144.

The Blanchdown sett was 3 miles long and 2 miles wide and contained what was to prove the longest sulphide lode in the West of England. On its extreme western edge was an oak coppice in which there already existed an old overgrown shaft 14 fathoms deep, reputed to have been sunk by Hitchins's father and known as North Wheal Bedford. Under the supervision of Captain James Phillips, manager for many years of the adjoining Bedford United mine in which Hitchins was a shareholder, work began on to August 1844 by clearing the shaft and digging a line of costeaning pits. By 4 November the shaft had been sunk a further $2^1/_2$ fathoms. Late in that afternoon there was a sudden inrush of water and the back of a 30ft wide copper lode was revealed. By the time the working shift ended at 10 o'clock that night £60 worth of ore had been recovered. The lode yielded 17 per cent of copper (metal) at a time when the average yield in Devon and Cornwall was $7^3/_4$ per cent. The new working was named Wheal Maria, after Hitchins's wife, and the shaft, marked by a stone today, became known as Gard's Shaft – after Richard Gard, MP for Exeter and a London discount broker, who was an early subscriber.

Work on proving the lode was pushed eastwards for 16 fathoms when, to everyone's consternation, it was suddenly lost, having been heaved to the right by a geological fault. It was soon found again, however, and developed east of the fault as Wheal Fanny, so called after Hitchins's infant daughter. As the strike of the lode was traced still further eastwards, other mines were established on it. These became Wheal Anna Maria, in honour of the Duchess of Bedford; Wheal Josiah (after Hitchins himself); and finally at the eastern extremity of the lode Wheal Emma, named after Mrs Morris, the wife of another shareholder. In 1845 the entire complex became known as Devon Great Consols, a title which included two subsidiary workings – South Wheal Fanny and Watson's Mine, south of Wheal Emma.

By the end of 1845 the main lode had been proved for almost its entire length of two miles. In the first full year of working, a profit of £73,622 was made and dividends of £72,704 or £71 a share were paid. The asking price of an original £1 share (which some Tavistock tradespeople had initially thought too risky to buy) was now £800.

As the mine developed, it became clear that the copper deposits deepened as they went eastwards. At Wheal Maria, on the western boundary, copper was found above the drainage adit, and between the 10 and 30 fathom levels the shoots of ore were often up to 30ft wide. At Wheal Fanny a shoot extended from surface to 55 fathoms. At Wheal Josiah lode values were found only below 50 fathoms, and at Wheal Emma between 60 and 130 fathoms. The lode in many places was embedded in arsenopyrite or mispickel which was later to be mined in quantity as arsenic. The little riverside quay of Morwellham, five miles down the Tamar, whence all the ore was sent to South Wales for smelting, was taxed to its utmost limits and additional quay space had to be improvised hurriedly at Newquay and at Gawton further down the river.

A small water-wheel had been adequate to drain the shallow Gard's Shaft, but as the lode deepened pumping and other costs increased, causing the dividend to fall in 1847 to £25 a share and immediately giving rise to rumours that the mine was on the point of collapse. In fact, its riches were only just beginning to be exploited. Four steam pumping engines were installed in 1847, but the mine became more remarkable for its use of water-power. In 1849 on the advice of Nathaniel Smith, chief engineer of the Devon Friendship Mine which was noted for its large water-wheels, it was decided to harness the Tamar for pumping and crushing wherever possible. A two-mile leat was cut from the river upstream near Latchley which eventually powered two 40ft water-wheels. From these flat rods, supported on wooden trestles, draining shafts at Wheal Maria and Wheal Josiah extended uphill for nearly three-quarters of a mile. Turning at 4rpm, this massive assemblage of hydraulic gear worked at about 60 per cent efficiency. A plunger wheel also pumped water from the Tamar to feed a reservoir and storage ponds on the higher parts of the mine, while a 35ft by 4ft wheel drove the machinery at the mine's own foundry. Altogether the river water powered thirty-three wheels, and for the first twenty years the company paid the Duchy of Cornwall £200 a year for its abstraction. This meant that in its most prosperous period the company's basic source of power cost less than £5 a week.

Throughout the fifties and into the middle sixties the wealth of the mine was a byword, and as 'rich as Devon Great Consols' became the yardstick by which every other mining prospect in the area was measured and compared. The lode at Wheal Maria was 47ft wide and produced 60 tons of ore a running fathom. At Wheal Anna Maria, where the ore occurred in two shoots, most of the lode was removed throughout the full length of the sett between the 60 and 124 fathom levels. In the mine's first twelve years of working, ore sales realised £1,400,000 or £35,000 more than Dolcoath's total output in the forty years after Waterloo. In ten years dividends totalled over £475,000, and it was estimated in 1855 that there were sufficient reserves (35,943 tons) to keep the mine going for over a year without fresh discoveries. By 1857 the Duke of Bedford had received over £100,000 in dues and had even been paid £2,050 for the despoilation of his pheasant coverts.

On the other hand, the softness of the lode and its walls made it expensive to work. Underhand stoping, instead of the more usual and easier overhead method, had to be adopted. Ore extracted from one section left a cavity 900ft long, 240ft wide and 6ft to 50ft high – the dimensions of a small cathedral. To offset frequent runs of ground, which caused a number of fatalities, massive timbering was introduced. For this, special timber from the Baltic and Canadian Pacific coasts had to be imported, costing the company an average of £4,000 a year.

By the late 1850s the expense of haulage to and from Morwellham and the lack of quay space there (ore was often washed into the river when the Tamar flooded) forced the company to undertake a twofold development. Horse and cart hire to Morwellham was costing 5s 0d a ton and in 1854 amounted to £6,000. This was more than the working profits of many small mines. It was also slow and difficult, and on the steep approach down to Morwellham the steel skid shoes under the wheels of the laden wagons became so hot that carters were said to be able to fry fatty bacon in them. To replace this cartage a 4$\frac{1}{2}$ mile standard-gauge railway was built and opened in 1858, costing £10,355 which the company paid for out of current income, an impressive tribute to its financial stability. The railway (powered by steam) ran from Wheal Maria, with access tracks to the other mines, to a point above Morwellham from where trucks were let down over a half mile in 1 in 3 incline.

On the quay itself £5,000 was spent excavating a new dock able to hold six 300-ton vessels. At the same time several acres of new quays were reclaimed from the mud, and staging built over them to allow the 3$\frac{1}{2}$ ton ore trucks with sliding bottoms to empty their lodes into piles directly on the quays. All the quays were tiled to prevent any loss of ore, and were regularly swept. Extra cottages, still eagerly sought-after today, were built by the Duke of Bedford to house miners and dock workers, while the landlord of the Ship Inn (noted among sailors and visitors alike for its 'roast beef of old England and stout October ale') also found it necessary to enlarge his premises. Henceforth Morwellham, which probably handled over 36,000 tons of ore, mine supplies and other cargo a year, became an integral part of the mine.

By 1865 the surface area of the mines sprawled over more than 140 acres. The four principal lodes were Main, Middle Lode, South Lode (the latter branching off from the main lode at Wheal Anna Maria and uniting with it again at Wheal Josiah) and New South Lode, first cut in 1864 and worked by Wheal Emma. There were some fifteen shafts, the deepest being Richards' (230 fathoms) at Wheal Josiah where four of the chief lodes were worked. It took an hour to climb to surface from Richards' Shaft. There were 40 miles of levels and it was possible to walk uninterruptedly underground for 2$^{1}/_{2}$ miles between the extreme western and eastern boundaries of the sett. Whilst over 1,000 men, women and children were employed (a school with a paid mistress was provided on the mine for children too young to work), it was estimated the mine gave indirect employment to over 6,000 people. The mine had its own brass band and supplied a choir, widely renowned, for Ogbeare Methodist Chapel, which adjoined the mine site.

In 1864 the company paid its fourth highest dividend (£62 a share) and raised 26,947 tons of copper ore. By the end of the decade, however, there were signs that the immensely rich copper lodes were becoming exhausted. The main lode had been stoped almost continuously for much of its course. South Lode at Wheal Josiah, which had yielded very nearly £600,000, ended in barren ground at 144 fathoms. In 1872 only 16,329 tons of ore were produced, making £6,144 available for dividend. The company, in common with other mines in Devon and Cornwall, also began to face competition from Australian and American mines producing copper more cheaply from shallower deposits. In the late 1860s there was also a slump in copper prices. To offset these factors the company turned its attention to the treatment of its large dumps of low-grade ore and to the mundic or arsenopyrite which had been left standing, sometimes up to a fathom or more in width, beside the copper stopes.

This decision was also influenced by an increasing commercial demand for arsenic not only in England but also from the expanding German chemical industry. Arsenic was the principal constituent of Emerald Green and King's Yellow, both fast, strong and extremely brilliant dyes. It was also used in paint and in the glass industry. Also about this time, the first man-made insecticide was perfected. This was Paris Green, a compound of gypsum and arsenic which proved initially so successful against the cotton boll weevil and Colorado potato beetle that for a time mankind dreamed of totally eliminating insect pests. Arsenic reduction works, capable of dealing with 2,500 tons a year, were completed at Wheal Maria in 1871 and progressively enlarged until they covered eight acres. They were the largest such works in Devon and Cornwall. An unusual feature was the later use in these works of the Oxland tubular calciner as opposed to the generally adopted Brunton pyramid type. The first sales of arsenic were made in 1868. By 1871 it was providing up to 20 per cent of the mine's receipts, and by the middle 1870s the company boasted that it was producing half the United Kingdom's arsenic.

The decision to prolong the mine's life by exploiting its rich arsenic deposits was supplemented by two attempts to find tin beneath the copper zone. This had happened at Dolcoath Mine, and conditions at Devon Great Consols were thought to be similar. In the hope of making the mine a Devonshire Dolcoath, the company was financially reconstructed and Richards' Shaft at Wheal Josiah (chosen because it was nearest the granite) was deepened in the early 1870s from 230 to 300 fathoms, but without any tin being found. In 1883 a second attempt was made in the adjoining Wheal Emma sett where tin stones had been found in Railway Shaft. With the aid of rock drills this shaft was carried down from 205 to 260 fathoms but again without any success. The total reward from these two expensive operations was a mere £170 worth of tin.

Arsenic now became the mainstay of the mine for its remaining years which were clouded by the increasing unwillingness of the Duke of Bedford to co-operate with the board (although he consented to forego £1,000 of his dues in 1885), and board-room squabbles stemming from opposition to the financial policies of Mr Peter Watson, a Redruth mining personality of bluff, John Bull-like appearance, who had become managing director in 1879. Copper by now had become little more than a by-prod-uct; by 1890 the mine was selling three times as much arsenic as copper. Between 1890 and 1891 the total 'make' of arsenic was 5,883 4cwt barrels which in the following year was increased to over 6,000 barrels.

Although the whole concern was now in debt and the labour force had been re-duced to under 400, there were still cosy and jovial parties on the mine whenever the directors made their annual inspection. In October 1899, when the mine had only two more years to run, Captain William Woolcock, in charge of Wheal Emma, records a 'very nice dinner' for directors and shareholders of 'boiled leg of mutton at the head of the table, ribs of beef at the bottom, two steak pies in the middle with plain dump-lings after and apples, pears and grapes for dessert' all washed down by a 'liberal supply of claret'. The meal was cooked in the count house kitchen.

In that year the mine paid its last dividend – 25 6d a share. By 1901 a steady decline in the price of arsenic and the high price of coal had led to a loss of nearly £3,000 in the previous two years working, and the company, which had borrowed £9,000 in 1898 to cover its losses for that year, owed its bankers nearly £4,000. On 30 November 1901, all work ceased except for pumping in the upper levels and the company went into voluntary liquidation. In a last effort to get the mine working again, Mr Watson called in Captain W. H. Borlase who estimated the value of ore in sight at £57,000 and recommended a better application of the enormous water-power available and the provision of cage roads in the shafts. This scheme was defeated by a lobby antagonistic to the chairman and in May 1903 the mines were abandoned and all the materials sold off.

With their closure, the little port of Morwellham, its quays now deserted and its great dock silting up, died also.

On its south, Devon Great Consols is adjoined by **Bedford United Mine** (OS 105 SW). Although not equalling the extraordinary richness of its neighbour, the Bedford United was a highly productive sett with a recorded output of 66,000 tons of copper ore, in addition to smaller quantities of arsenic, tin and, latterly, wolfram. While generally assumed to have been started in the early 1840s, the mine, in fact, originated in the opening years of the eighteenth century, as is related by Henrik Kahlmeter, a Swedish engineer, who visited the site on 13 November 1724.[1]

'In the wood called Collingswood,' Kahlmeter records, certain workmen in 1707 obtained a lease of land from the Duke of Bedford extending 20 fathoms from the River Tamar and thence up the rising ground to the east. Here they drove an adit, and finding copper named this part of the sett the Bedford Mine. Shortly afterwards a wealthier group of adventurers obtained another sett higher up the hillside where they started a second adit seven or eight fathoms above the first and drove it 6o fathoms. Subsequently the two workings were amalgamated and became known as the Marquis Mine. On commencing the upper adit, tin was met with near the outcrop of the lode, but on excavating deeper, copper was encountered in considerable quantity and of better grade than in the first adit. At length the water gained on the workmen to such an extent that sixty men were required to drain it (presumably by means of rag-and-chain pumps) until this became too costly and the working was abandoned for some years.

In 1722 the mine was acquired by the Bristol Copper Company who erected an underground engine near the adit end. This was driven by water directed down a shaft from surface which, after passing over a pumping wheel, flowed out through the adit mouth. By such means the Company contrived to sink the shaft 39 fathoms below the adit, effectively draining the workings to that level. The lode ran due east–west and varied in width from to 1 to 4ft. At the time of Kahlmeter's visit, twenty miners were employed at a wage of 28s a month 'including free tools and lights', whilst the smith received 25s and the carpenter 40s. On being brought to surface, the ore was hammered clear of stone and impurities and then sent two miles by road to Nuttstack[2] on the Tamar. Here it was shipped to Plymouth and thence to Bristol or alternatively to the smelting house at Neath in South Wales. By way of a footnote, Kahlmeter adds that close by the Marquis there was another copper lode called the Tavistock but this had not been worked 'for the last seven years'.

The Bedford United sett in its later form commenced working in 1841 when it included the lodes of Wheal Marquis, Wheal Tavistock, Delves Kitchen, Ding Dong and South Bedford. Delves Kitchen is known to have been worked before 1799 and by 1844 had been developed for 200 fathoms at adit level, 24 fathoms below surface. The Ding Dong lode lay parallel with this and is referred to in a letter of 19th September 1807 from William Jenkin of Trewirgie, Redruth, to his friend William Phillips, mineralogist and publisher of George Yard, Lombard Street:

'I have just received from Captain Davey his report on the Ding Dong Mine on the Devonshire side of the Tamar. He says 'tis a rich lode in Mundick, with some copper ore intermixed with it – and it being a gozan lode with those appearances, he thinks it deserves a tryal. He did not express himself very strongly – as if he thought highly of it but repeated, as before mentioned, that he thought it deserved some tryal.'

By 1844 the lode had been opened up by an adit which was 42 fathoms from surface at its deepest point, and below this by a shaft drained by a 45ft water-wheel.[3]

On starting work on the northern part of the Bedford sett it was found that the lodes had been entirely worked away by the old men for a length of 200 fathoms and down to the deep adit (47 fathoms). In 1843 levels were being driven at 25, 30 and 40 fathoms below adit on the Marquis Lode where a soft pumping wheel had been erected. To drive this and the wheel on Ding Dong Lode, water was brought through a leat from the southern end of the Tavistock Canal, high above Morwellham. From here its course can still be traced through the woods for a distance of nearly two miles, passing through two tunnels cut in the projecting rock and elsewhere carried by wooden launders slung in chains from the cliff face. After serving the needs of the mine, the leat was diverted back across the main Gunnislake-Tavistock road to convey the slimes and waste to a dump near the river.[4] In 1849 a steam-whim was erected and five shafts were in use. The deepest of these was Engine Shaft on the Tavistock Lode which followed its underlie down to an eventual depth of 150 fathoms from surface. On the

Marquis Lode the shaft reached an inclined depth of 115 fathoms. Shortly after 1858 the mine was connected by a branch to the Devon Great Consols Railway over which its ores were carried at an advantageous rate to the quays at Morwellham.

In 1862 the mine was employing 200 people and by 1868 had paid dividends amounting to £54,000. The company was reconstructed in 1877 and continued in existence until 1890. Some further work was carried out above adit during the 1920s mainly for arsenic, with smaller amounts of tin and wolfram.

In Hatch Wood, about half a mile south of Gunnislake New Bridge (05 105 SW), a number of lodes have been worked in the precipitous slopes of the Tamar and thence eastwards to Luscombe Down Plantation. These were originally developed in two separate setts, the more northerly being **Wheal Luscombe** (earlier spelt and pronounced Liscombe) which, according to tradition, was the first mine in Devon to possess a steam engine. In 1816 in order to facilitate drainage the workings were connected to the Ding Dong Adit, but the lode values were said to have petered out in depth on coming up against the elvan. As East Liscombe the mine returned 3,269 tons of copper ore in the years 1821 to 1834.[5]

Adjoining this on the south, **Wheal Impham** was a very old work referred to by Kahlmeter in 1724 as 'a copper mine out of which Mr Costar from Cornwall in four years and employing five or six men took out more than 100 tons of ore. After that values decreased – however it is now said to be better again'. A cost-book formerly in the Bedford Estate Office at Tavistock shows that the mine was still in operation during the years 1799 to 1820.

At a later period the Luscombe North and South Lodes, together with the Chimney Rock Lode of Wheal Impham, were included in the sett of **Bedford United**. Being too far removed from the centre of operations to be worked effectively by that company, they were transferred in 1850 to a new company called **East Gunnislake and South Bedford**, the former situated on the Cornwall side of the river. Between 1854 and 1871 the group returned some 5,300 tons of copper ore, with lesser amounts of pyrite and tin.

In June 1860 due to an exceptionally high tide accompanied by heavy rain, the mine was partially flooded by the water entering the adit which opened close to the river bank. By dint of working all night, a barge laden with very rich ore was manoeuvered into the Tamar Canal dock and saved, but 15 tons of ore standing on Impham Quay was swept away in the flood.

In 1868 Gard's Shaft was down to 54 fathoms below deep adit (36 fathoms), and Engine Shaft, 40yd east of the river, to 75 fathoms – in both cases on the underlie of the lode. No steam-power was employed, the water being drawn by a 36ft by 5ft wheel, with a 20ft by 5ft wheel for hoisting.[6]

The majority of lodes in this area contain a proportion of wolfram. In 1950 some exceedingly rich stones were found by the late Mr Frank Choke in the surface filling of a lode about 800ft north-east of Impham farm house. Application was made to the Bedford Estate for a mining lease, but the terms which restricted operations to a maximum depth of 20ft being quite unacceptable, no further action was taken.

Between Morwellham and New Quay the deep adit of George and Charlotte may be seen opening on to the river bank. The mine developed the western end of a copper lode extending from the Tamar to the Tavy, a distance of nearly a mile. At its eastern extremity the lode was worked in the **William and Mary Mine** (OS 111 NE) which was visited by Kahlmeter in 1724. According to his statement this mine was started about 1718 when 'one Lane from Bristol'[7] in conjunction with Sir William Courtenay, the mineral owner, drove a deep adit 40 fathoms from the west bank of the Tavy. When Kahlmeter saw it this level was at a standstill due to misunderstandings between the two partners.

Higher up the hill a second adit had been driven for a length of 120 fathoms and was held under grant from the Duke of Bedford at one-seventh dues. In this the lode was 4ft wide and promising in appearance. Four shafts had been sunk here but it was thought that they would have to go five or six fathoms deeper to reach the main part of the lode. No trouble was experienced from water as this was finding its way down to the deep adit. Twelve men were employed at 28s per month, with an overseer who received 40s. In the previous six months they had recovered 56 tons or '420 ship pounds' of clean ore, whilst another 30 tons was expected before Christmas, the whole worth £5 per ton on the mine. Cost of land carriage to Goton (Gawton Quay) on the Tamar was 2s 6d per ton with a further 18d per ton for sending it by boat to Plymouth. From there part of the ore was shipped to Hitchcock's smelting house in London and the rest to Neath in South Wales.

The third or topmost adit was worked by one of the Costar family from Cornwall who had sunk a winze 4 fathoms deep, but owing to the amount of the incoming water, work had been suspended here until the following summer.

At what date **George and Charlotte** was started is not known, the earliest recorded reference to the mine being in 1806 when it was purchased as a going concern by the Tavistock Canal Company.[8]

Forty years later the deep adit had been extended 130 fathoms east from the Tamar, heading towards a similar adit, then driving west from William and Mary, with the obvious intention of establishing a communication between the two mines. The lode in the George and Charlotte adit was stated at this time to be 4ft wide 'orey but not rich'.

In September 1851 the two setts were amalgamated as the Devon and Cornwall United Mines – a misleading title since both its constituent parts lay wholly in Devon. During this working a number of shafts were sunk, the two deepest being Ley's (600yd west-south-west of Broadwell, to 34 fathoms below adit – here 83 fathoms from shaft collar), and Engine Shaft near the railway, to 46 fathoms under adit which at this point is 40 fathoms from surface.

In September 1866 a correspondent of *Mining Journal* wrote:

> 'It may not be generally known that an immense body of ore was [formerly] discovered at George & Charlotte in the deep adit, which enabled the mine to pay dividends and the huge excavations caused by its removal have been familiarly named the 'Devil's Kitchen'. A long and expensive cross-cut has been put out with a view to undermining his Satanic Majesty's cooking department which cross-cut is now near the desired object.'

It would seem, however, that no downward extension of the bunch or carbona was found, and in 1869 the property was put up for sale. The machinery consisted of three water-wheels for pumping, two of 40ft diameter and one of 29ft, together with a 12in steam-whim for hoisting.

Tradition relates that after the mines had closed woodmen from the Tamar, when engaged on work in the Tavy Valley, would 'travel' through the adit in stormy weather, thus avoiding the trek over the high country between the two rivers. Although Dines states that 100 fathoms of unexplored ground separates the mines, the plans are known to be incomplete and it is more than likely that a connection formerly existed, although inaccessible today owing to rock falls.

The Bere Alston Mines

Below Gawton Mine with its leaning arsenic stack and dual refiners, the Tamar takes a westerly course past Calstock, beyond which it turns abruptly south beneath the woodlands of Cotehele. Within the angle thus formed two parallel lead-bearing cross-courses strike north–south, the eastern one extending far down the Bere Alston peninsula.

At its northern end the western cross-course was developed in **North Ward Mine** and thence southward through Ward (or South Ward), North Hooe and South Hooe. In this last mine the lode was worked for over a quarter of a mile out beneath the bed of the river in the direction of the Cornish bank.

Some three-quarters of a mile to the east the longer eastern cross-course has been proved north–south in the mines of Buttspill, Lockridge, Furzehill, East Tamar and South Tamar, the deep levels of the latter similarly extending below the river towards Cornwall'[10] (OS Cornwall 30 SW, 38 NW).

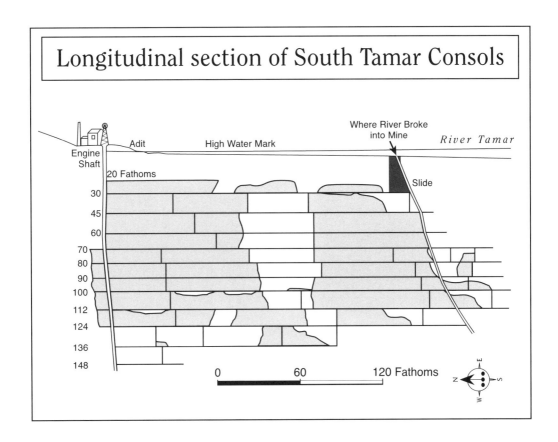

Longitudinal section of South Tamar Consols

In origin, these mines are among the oldest in Britain, having been worked as early as the thirteenth century. Due to the high proportion of silver in their lodes, they ranked as royal mines and were financed by the crown which enabled them to be developed on a scale unattainable by private enterprise in the Middle Ages. Attention was called to the documents relating to the early history of the mines by Sir Henry De la Beche in his classic *Report on the Geology of Cornwall, Devon & West Somerset* (1839), and use has been made of them in many subsequent works, including Frank Booker's *Industrial Archaeology of the Tamar Valley*.

After a long period of idleness, activity was resumed throughout the area in the 1780s, mainly through the enterprise of a certain Christopher Gullet of Tavistock. In 1781 Beer [sic] Ferrers Mine[11] was advertising for '20 good lusty hands and by 1795 it was announced that 76,000 ounces of silver and 1,400 tons of lead ore had been returned from this mine in the previous seven years, realising a sum of £45,000.' In 1788 the workings were equipped with a 20in cylinder Boulton & Watt engine which continued in operation until the latter part of 1791 when it was accidentally destroyed by fire. About this time Philip Rashleigh wrote to his fellow Cornish mineralogist, John Hawkins:

'In consequence of your telling me that some Fluors of a different Colour to mine were flung away on the Shammels [stopes] at Beer [sic] Alston Mine and that Captain John Vivian knew where to find them, I writ to him desiring he would procure me some. He properly applied to Mr. Gullet for his liberty, who writ me a most impertinent letter on the occasion – on which I shall have no further intercourse with him.'[13]

By 1812 the Beer Alston Mine had changed hands, having been taken over by a Mr Smith who formed a company consisting entirely of London shareholders. During June of that year a branch was cut in the bottom level, 5ft wide and 'calculated to produce five tons of rich ore per fathom. Should this continue in length and depth it must prove one of the greatest discoveries ever made in the two counties. We must congratulate Lord Valletort, as heir apparent to the Earl of Mount Edgcumbe (Lord of the soil) who will receive a great increase to his fortune from the dues'.[14]

In 1820 a new merger was formed entitled the Beer Alston Mines comprising the Birch and Cleave Lode (later included in South Tamar Consols), together with the **South Hooe Mine.** In the former the silver content of the lode varied from 40 to 90oz to the ton of lead, in contrast to South Hooe where it occasionally ran as high as 180oz and the lead (metal) content of the ore averaged to 11 to 12 parts in 20. The greatest output of silver in any one year amounted to 3 tons in 1814-15. After that, 'too much ore was raised by working the mine too fast – 60 tons of ore per week for a year but a large part of this did not contain more than 40oz per ton of silver'.[15]

The machinery and materials of the Beer Alston Mines as offered for sale in 1821-2 consisted of a 42in cylinder engine on Boulton & Watt's principle, several horse-whims, a 30ft water-wheel with six heads of stamps, a punching engine, iron pumps, lead moulds, two iron carts, two boats and sails and a barge of 40 tons burthen – 'the whole being conveniently situated for removal from the premises which adjoin the banks of the navigable River Tamar'.[16]

While this might suggest a final closure of the mines, such was far from being the case. In 1835 a new company was formed under the direction of Percival Norton

Johnson, celebrated as a metallurgist and assayer and later to establish the well-known firm of Johnson Matthey & Co of Hatton Garden, London. Under the name of the Tamar Silver-Lead Mine, working was resumed at South Hooe (OS Cornwall 38 NW) where in December 1835, Johnson was able to report that the surface works were in a state of 'great forwardness' and the pumping engine ready to go to work in the course of a few weeks. 'I took a sample which after dressing gave 4cwt 2qrs and 4lbs of lead to the ton which lead produced a proportion of fine silver equal to 113oz to the ton. From my knowledge of these mines when worked in the year 1814 under the name of South Hooe, and calculating the differences in the prices of materials and improvement of machinery at the present time, I have the most sanguine expectations of the undertaking.'[17]

The layout of the workings was peculiar. As the longitudinal section shows, the original shaft was sunk vertically to 226 fathoms, longer and longer levels being required to reach the ore shoot as it pitched south beneath the river. To overcome this in 1843 an incline was started from the 13 fathom level of the vertical shaft and carried down at an angle of 25° to meet the 125 level. Due to the length and weight of the hoisting chain and to facilitate drawing from deeper levels where the ore was still making down, it was decided to sink a perpendicular sub-river shaft, called Spurgin's, from the 115 to the 175 fathoms level. At the top of this shaft a 20hp steam winding and pumping engine was erected – the smoke from the boiler fire being conducted through two miles of old workings before it emerged at surface.

This primitive flue proved not without danger. In 1851 some rich ore was found by tributers in the 95 fathom level through which the flue passed and permission was given to work it, although the men were strictly cautioned by the agents that the place was dangerous because of the smoke. After working for some hours one of the 'pare', feeling unwell, decided to withdraw to the Engine Shaft where, as soon as he had reached a higher level, he fell asleep from the effects of the gas and it was two hours before he reached surface. The others, going out by another way, met the full blast of the smoke which was apparently escaping from a bricked-off level. Four of these men were overcome and died. A fifth was discovered by the rescue party and drawn up in the 'tram' through the incline shaft. After receiving treatment he recovered in due course.[18]

Shortly before this incident an improvement in the ventilation of the deep levels was brought about by the introduction of suction fans. These were at first worked manually and later by a 12ft water-wheel. Prior to this the air was so bad that a candle could scarcely be kept alight for two minutes: 'Now in traversing the levels the miners are compelled to hold their caps before them to prevent them from being blown out', as Johnson reported at the annual meeting of 1845.

In 1850 there were seven steam engines at South Hooe and 200 people were employed. The ores were smelted at Weir Quay in works which had been taken over from an earlier firm. The eighteen furnaces here could smelt over 300 tons of concentrate per month,[19] the normal returns averaging 55 to 60 per cent lead, with a silver content of 60oz to the ton of lead (metal). Occasional parcels ran as high as 145oz.[20]

In 1842 **North Hooe** (OS Cornwall 38 NW) was reopened under Johnson's direction. Never as rich a mine as South Hooe, it reached its peak in 1846 when a production of 1,200 tons of silver-lead ore was recorded. The shaft was sunk only to 10 fathoms below adit, with levels driven at 10 fathom intervals to the bottom. In the 60 fathom level north the lode was 3ft wide and consisted of fluorspar mixed with silver-lead. The cross-cut at the 10 level was stopped 2 fathoms short of the point where it should have intersected the lode. The mine was reopened in the early part of the last century by a small syndicate, but it lacked the necessary capital to lower the water below the 70 fathom level or to carry out any lateral development.[20a]

By 1854 Johnson had severed his connection with West Country mining and smelting, and the management of the South Hooe Mine was taken over by James Wolferstan. In 1861 the mine was described as the deepest lead mine in England, yet the overall costs of returning 60 tons of ore per month was not more than £800 which left a monthly profit of £300. The richest part of the mine was still in the bottom levels beneath the river bed, and the shallowest level then being worked was the 205.[21] Operations finally ceased about 1885 by which time the workings had reached a depth on the underlie of 250 fathoms below adit.

Ward Mine or more correctly South Ward stands three-quarters of a mile northward of North Hooe, adjacent to the river bank (OS Cornwall 30 SW). A 'puffing' advertisement of this property in *Mining Journal*, 7 November 1835, states that it had been formerly worked for argentiferous lead ore yielding 80 to 190oz of silver to the ton but was discontinued owing to an inundation of the river in which four or five men lost their lives.

The mine was reopened during the summer of 1869 and continued in operation until 1876. The plan as described by Dines shows Engine Shaft sunk vertically to the 60 fathom level and thence on the underlie to the 90. The machinery consisted of a 24in rotary engine for pumping and winding.[22] Recorded production relates only to the years 1873-6 when 130 tons of lead ore and 390oz of silver were returned. After the abandonment of the mine, the engine-house was converted into a farm-house. The bungalow standing nearby occupies the site of the former count-house.

Of **North Ward Mine** there is little record, its site being forgotten until 1957 when a subsidence revealed the position of the shaft about 500ft west of North Ward farm.

In a wooded valley on the south bank of the Tamar, south-east of Calstock, **Buttspill Mine** (OS Cornwall 30 SW) was the most northerly of the mines on the eastern crosscourse. The sett is an old one and is said to have been worked in Elizabethan times. It later formed part of the Old Bere group and was worked as such in the opening years of the nineteenth century when it was sunk to a depth of 67 fathoms from surface.

Operations were resumed in 1843 when under the name of Green Valley Mine an engine was erected and investigations were carried out in the 17 and 27 fathom levels. Shortly after this the sett was acquired by another small company and renamed Wheal Fancy.

In 1855 the mine was reopened as Berealston United and although work was still entirely confined to the 17 and 27 fathom levels, the returns were sufficiently large to justify the erection of a smelting furnace. During this period attention was chiefly devoted to the reserves of fluorspar which was stated to be of the 'finest quality and could be raised in any quantity at a very low rate'.[23] How long this company survived is not known for certain, but working was resumed on at least two subsequent occasions when the lode was developed to 47 fathoms below adit.

Five shafts are shown on the 1881 edition of the 6in map and the ivy-clad ruins of an engine-house and stack still stand at the southern end of Buttspill Wood. The nearby dump, now much overgrown, is estimated to contain up to 20 per cent of fluorspar. Outputs during the later periods of working are recorded as 95 tons of lead ore, 650oz of silver and 620 tons of fluorspar in 1870-6; and under the name of Tamar (or

New Tamar) Valley, 90 tons of fluorspar in 1885-6.[24]

In a tributary valley of the Tamar a quarter of a mile east of Buttspill, a north-south lead lode claimed to be rich in silver was opened up in 1846 under the name of **Philley Wood** or Tuckermarsh Mine.[25] The lode was a recent discovery and by the end of May an adit had been driven some 60 fathoms, gaining 13 fathoms of 'backs' as it entered the rising ground. The lode had an average width of 2ft and a shaft had been started with a view to taking it at 23 fathoms from surface.[26]

Five years later, a prospectus appeared of North Tamar Consols 'formerly Philley Wood or Tuckermarsh Mine'. Reports state that in the previous working the shaft had been sunk to a 10 fathom level below adit from which a few tons of ore were raised. A Mr Evan Hopkins who was called in to advise considered it unlikely that any large bunches of ore would be encountered until the mine had been developed to at least a 30 fathom level: 'the present workings being at too high an elevation to make any great discoveries'. On his recommendation an engine was erected and the shaft deepened to 44 fathoms where three levels were driven north and south. The results, however, were not encouraging, and in 1855 the adventurers decided to abandon the sett and dispose of the machinery which included a new 24in cylinder pumping engine.[27]

About a quarter of a mile from Tuckermarsh Quay lay the **Queen of Tamar** otherwise known as Great Tamar, by which latter name it is shown on C. Williams's *Map of the Tavistock Mining District* (1859). A brief notice in *Mining Journal* on 9 July of that year states that the workings were only 4 fathoms deep but had produced an abundance of highly mineralised gossan from an east-west lode. The mine is not mentioned by Dines but is said by Collins to have returned both lead and copper ores.

It is possible that the same lode may have been worked in **Wheal Jenny** a short distance south-east of Tuckermarsh hamlet where its site is marked on the 6in map, Cornwall 30 SW.

Nothing is known of its early history and most of the surface features are thought to have been obliterated when the nearby railway embankment was made. The mine is said to have been last tried in 1915 when a small portable engine was erected on the shaft. In clearing this it was found that the old men had removed all the lead ore in sight and no fresh development was carried out.[28]

From Buttspill southwards the eastern cross-course was developed on the mines of Lockridge (otherwise Goldstreet), **Furzehill** (or Whitsam Down), **East Tamar** and **South Tamar** (OS Cornwall 38 NW). Early in the 1840s the latter two were worked in concert by the Berealston Mining Company and created extraordinary excitement:

Vast quantities of silver were brought to London and, on occasions, the whole mail was engaged to carry it. The establishment in London consisted of seven directors with large salaries – in addition to two managing directors at the mines. The offices in Bishopsgate Street were like a palace and an usher with a gold stick stood at the door. That the company soon failed is not to be wondered at.[29]

A fresh start was made in 1845 when Whitsam, Lockridge and Furzehill were amalgamated under the name of East Tamar Consols. By 1847 six shafts had been cleared to depths of 30 to 40 fathoms below adit – the latter being 30 fathoms from surface in the higher part of the sett. At Whitsam (the southern portion of Lockridge) the shaft was deepened from 46 to 60 fathoms under adit, the water being drawn by a 40in cylinder engine. Five ends were then driving, all in productive ground. At Lockridge (identifiable by its tall and unusually ornamented chimney-stack) the shaft was 50 fathoms deep and was shortly after sunk to 54 fathoms in order to connect with a level then heading towards it from Whitsam. At Furzehill the shaft had been sunk from 30 to 46 fathoms and had four ends driving, all showing good values. The bottom level, south, was about to come in under the 'former Charlotte and Caroline Shafts'. The matrix of the lode consisted of fluorspar which then realised 10s a ton. The mine was equipped with a 58in cylinder pumping engine and a 36in winding and stamping engine, operating 24 heads of stamps and a crusher. Ores to the value of £10,000 had been sold.

During the commercial crisis of 1847, the holders of a majority of the shares became bankrupt. The mines, however, were taken over by a new company in April 1848, with James Wolferstan acting as general manager. By the spring of 1849 production was averaging 30 tons a month which was about paying costs. Five years later it was reported that the Furzehill Engine Shaft had been sunk below the 112 fathom level, and by 1861 the East Tamar group as a whole had returned 2,580 tons of lead ore, 19,530 ounces of silver and over 1,400 tons of fluorspar.[30]

South Tamar Consols (OS Cornwall 38 NW), the southernmost mine of the eastern cross-course, has been worked on a number of occasions, although little is known of its early history other than the tradition that it had returned large quantities of ore before 1817.

Operations were renewed in 1846 and with one short period of suspension continued for the next ten years. By May 1847 the rehabilitation of the mine was well under way, the adit had been cleared for nearly 300 fathoms and a 60in engine was being erected on Cowie's Shaft,[31] then 90 fathoms deep, adjacent to the river. First sales of ore were recorded in August 1849 and a year later the mine was making a small monthly profit and was 124 fathoms deep.[32] Engine Shaft was eventually carried down to 48 fathoms on the underlie, although no stoping was done below the 136. The deeper levels in the southern part of the mine extended fully half a mile out beneath the waters of the Tamar.

As in the case of other leading West Country mines, South Tamar was visited by a number of distinguished tourists. On 3 August 1850 *Mining Journal* recorded the arrival a few days previously of His Highness the Nepalese Ambassador and his suite. Accompanied up-river by naval officers from Plymouth, the party landed at Millshead midway between the mine and Weir Quay. After inspecting the machinery and surface operations, the ambassador and three of his suite proceeded underground. Descending Glynn's Shaft, the party passed through the 90 fathom level and thence down the Engine Shaft to the 100. While going through this level, the ambassador frequently exclaimed 'Beautiful, beautiful' as he admired the lode in the back, being no less struck with the power of the engine which drained the water from this level, 600ft below the river bed. The rapidity with which His Highness descended the ladders, climbed into the stopes and came to surface again astonished all who were present. After changing out of his underground clothes he sat in front of the account-house and partook of a basket of cherries, being the only kind of refreshment of which he might partake, presented to him by Miss Jackson who resided near the mine. For this the lady was liberally rewarded, as was also Captain Tremayne, the agent, who had accompanied him underground. On his departure from the mine which was not until

8pm, he presented his 'solumbra' (sunshade) to Mr James Wolferstan, the manager.

During 1851 the monthly output of ore rose from 45 tons in March to 80 tons in December. At the end of this year reserves were about 663 tons, enough for eight and a half months. Three years later most of the development points were still looking well. The lode in the 136 fathom level, south, was yielding 9cwt of ore per fathom, and in the end of the 124 level the yield was 15cwt. Two stopes in the back of the 112 were producing 30cwt and 25cwt respectively. In the previous month the lode in the 100 end had averaged 2 tons of ore per fathom. Somewhat lesser values were being obtained in the 80, 70, 60, 40 and 30 fathom levels, all of which, however, were being stoped at a profit. Mankin's Shaft had recently been cleared to the bottom or 90 fathom level. Some very good ore ground was standing here, but the air being bad, a winze was being sunk from the 80 level in order to improve the ventilation in this part of the mine.[33]

In the summer of 1856 a total of 144 men were employed underground and 130 men, women and children at surface; whilst returns were averaging a regular 100 tons of lead ore per month. Six weeks later came disaster. At about 8pm on 31 August 1856, the waters of the Tamar broke into the mine, completely flooding the workings. Providentially this occurred on a Sunday when there was no one underground; had it been twelve hours later some ninety-five men and boys must in all probability have lost their lives. The inrush took place through a clay-filled slide or fault about halfway out under the river, and, according to eye-witnesses, such was the force of the pent-up air as it was expelled from the workings that it burst off the capping of the disused shafts with a report resembling thunder.

The existence of the slide was, of course, well known but so little apprehension had it ever caused that a number of levels had been driven through and beyond it. At a special meeting of the company held in London on the Thursday following, the manager reported that at the time of the disaster the prospects were excellent: 'they were looking better at every point'. The richest portion of the lode lay beneath the centre of the river, where a considerable tonnage of ore was lying broken in the levels waiting to be brought to surface. Despite this he did not consider there was any hope of recovering the mine. The breach might be sealed and the water pumped out but this would take two years to complete, with an expenditure of 4,000 tons of coal, and even then the water would probably find its way in again.

However, the matter did not rest there and for weeks after the correspondence columns of *Mining Journal* were filled with suggestions for salvaging the mine. A committee was appointed consisting of leading engineers, mineral agents and practical timbermen to investigate these schemes but eventually reported that none appeared practicable. It was accordingly resolved to wind up the company and realise the assets, the whole of the machinery including five steam engines being offered for sale in Plymouth in December of that year. Today a solitary stack remains as a monument to this once-celebrated mine – one of the very few on record to be abandoned when still in full production.

East of the Tamar, the River Tavy follows a serpentine but roughly parallel course southwards, eventually uniting with its greater sister a little below Bere Ferrers. The mines of Tavy conform to the size of the valley through which it flows. More intimate in character and worked on a smaller scale than those of the Tamar, they are approachable for the most part only by steep and rugged woodland tracks and due to their seclusion are comparatively little known.

At Double Waters, near the confluence of the Tavy and the Walkham rivers the celebrated **Virtuous Lady Mine** (OS 111 NE) stands in a lovely setting of woodlands interspersed with outcrops of fern-covered rock. The mine is undoubtedly of great antiquity deriving its name, as is generally supposed, from Elizabeth I. The ore occurs in beds bearing east-west, slightly underlaying north and varying in width from a few inches to 20 or 30ft.[34] These have been exploited for 100 fathoms along the strike and 120 fathoms down the dip, the deepest workings being little more than 20 fathoms below river (Dines, p 700).

The mine was visited by Henrik Kahlmeter in November 1724 who noted that the vein then being worked 'was 8ft and is now 10ft broad'. The mineral owner was named Dean, the principal lessees being the Bristol [Copper] Company. Production at that time amounted to 9 or 10 tons of 'clean ore' in three months, the miners receiving £3 10s per ton and providing their own tools. At the most recent sale the ore fetched £4 10s per ton which Kahlmeter was informed would yield one ton of copper (metal). From this he estimated the quantity of fine copper in the ore to be 16 per cent.

The mine has been worked on many subsequent occasions. In 1849 it was stated that the 'late company' was very successful in its operations and that a Captain Williams, who held a large interest in the concern, had realised a fortune in a few years. About 1841, however, the lode had been lost and thereafter production ceased for six or seven years. Working was resumed in 1848 when in driving a cross-cut from the 24 fathom level a lode of great size was cut from which 50 tons of copper ore was sold in two months. A short time after another parcel of 54 tons was dispatched to Messrs Vivian & Son, the Swansea smelters, whilst a further 50 tons was expected to be ready for sale in January 1850, the produce varying from 6 to 8 per cent copper.[35] The mine at this period was known as Virtuous Lady and Bedford since due to its north-ward dip the ore-body was then being developed on the further side of the Tavy in a sett named **Wheal Bedford**. Here it was opened up by at least three shafts sunk near the river bank.

In December 1857 tributers searching in the side of one of the subterranean caverns excavated by former workers, cut into a new 'flat' or bed yielding more than 4 tons of ore per fathom. This discovery was made at only 15 fathoms from surface and was in 'whole' (unworked) ground. At these shallow depths 'vughs' or natural hollows in the rock were frequently lined with colourful specimens in great variety:

> 'Brilliant, well defined crystals of titanium, fishscale iron, milk and cream quartz, tetrahedral crystals of copper, red, blue, purple, yellow and violet.., which when turned about under the rays of the sun reflect a different colour from every different angle of incidence – orange, gold, crimson, violet and green'

as a local mineralogist[36] described them in 1835. Latterly the mine was worked almost solely for the value of such specimens, the men laying trusses of straw on the floor of the workings to prevent their being damaged as they were detached from the rock.[37] Throughout its history, the Virtuous Lady has always been something of a show place, as indeed it still is, although many of the caverns which inspired the Victorian sight-seer with 'fearsome awe' are no longer accessible today.

Downstream from Virtuous Lady, the Tavy passes some half-dozen other mines in its meandering course. In Blackmoorham Wood the lodes of **Little Duke**, otherwise known as North Tavy or Raven Rock (OS 111 NE), are thought to be a continuation of those worked in Bedford Consols in Maddacleave Wood on the Tamar. The mine was developed largely by adits, Deep Adit driven west from the river bank being 50 fathoms below surface on the high ground near the railway track. Near this three underlay shafts exploited the shallower parts of the lodes. Worked in its earlier days for copper ore, of which it returned some 40 tons in 1824, the mine was restarted in 1845 when it was said that £14,000 had formerly been expended and the mine as a consequence was 'very much opened'.[38] Production at this period was obtained chiefly from the 20 and 30 fathom levels where the main lode averaged 10 to 12ft in width.

The mine was again active in 1859 when as Raven Rock (formerly North Tavy) it was claimed to possess in addition to copper a large extent of tin ground standing above the 30 fathom level. In six weeks four men and four boys had raised about 2 tons of tin stuff which left a satisfactory profit for their labour.[39]

Reopened in 1907 for tin and arsenic, good values were encountered in the western part of the mine. In later years, however, little work was done below the 20 fathom level and the Deep Adit was not cleared.

At one period **Buller and Bertha Mine** was included in this last sett. The former lies nearly a mile to the east and is marked by a large slatey burrow standing between the plantations of Hele and Alston (OS 111 NE). Little is known of this mine which ceased operations in 1855 (although working resumed for a short period in 1861). Near the shaft are the remains of a count-house or possibly the miners' dry.

Hocklake Mine, a third of a mile south of Little Duke, had been started before November 1724 when it was visited by Henrik Kahlmeter on his way to Cornwall. He described the sett as being in two parts, a lower working called The Duke and an upper portion named Stocklake – both under grant to the Bristol Company from 'one Dodche [?] who receives 1/8 dues'. Drained by an adit at the foot of the hill, the Duke Lode was 6 to 10ft wide and had been developed to a depth of 14 fathoms. In the course of the previous summer 16½ tons of copper ore had been sold at £4 per ton, and they were expecting to produce another 8 tons before Christmas. Five men were then employed on tribute.

During the last century, under the name of Tavy Consols, the mine was developed to a depth of 90 fathoms below adit on the underlie and continued to be worked intermittently until 1891. The machinery consisted of a 40ft wheel for pumping and another of 30ft diameter for crushing and winding, water to drive these being brought by a continuation of the leat from Virtuous Lady Mine. The lodes were exceptionally rich in arsenical ore, the calciners on the mine commonly 'burning' 125 tons a month, with a monthly output of 15 tons of refined arsenic.'[40] The ruined furnaces, still to be seen in 1958, are now largely destroyed; the chimney-stack (OS 111 NE) was demolished in 1928.

Lady Bertha on the east bank of the river had the same lodes as those of Tavy Consols and was started as a 'new mine in 1855. In the first six months of working, 86 tons of copper ore were returned from a depth of only 15 fathoms, a fact which caused a fever of excitement in the volatile mining circles of Tavistock. During the succeeding years four shafts were sunk at Meadow, Engine, Moyle's and Eastern, the last being vertical to a 53 fathom level. The mine was worked solely by water-power, the water being conveyed through a leat three miles in length from a point on the Walkham River above Grenofen Bridge, giving a fall at the mine of nearly 180ft. A large wheel situated between the Engine and Eastern Shafts pumped from both. The water then flowed through a lobby to a second wheel which served for hoisting at Engine Shaft. Below this a third wheel operated the grinders, jigs and stamps whilst, lower down, a fourth wheel hauled the tailings up to the waste dumps.

The arsenical pyrites, of which the mine produced great quantities, was carried across the river by a suspension bridge[41] to the calciners at Tavy Consols. Here it was burnt for arsenic, the rinkle (burnt residues) being then trammed back to Lady Bertha where it was stamped and treated for tin. There were fifteen heads of stamps on the mine, five of which worked by day and ten by night (when the rolls were stopped).[42] Due to the prevailing depression in mining and the low price of arsenic, operations ceased towards the end of 1868; £35,000 worth of copper ore having been sold during this working in addition to small quantities of tin.

Operations were resumed in 1880 when a 45ft wheel was installed, with a line of flat-rods connecting to the pit-work in the shaft. On 25 November the water was turned on and 'as the massive wheel moved round for the first time, Mr Sharpe, one of the directors, dashed a bottle of champagne against it and christened it Wheal Emily'. Preparations were then being made to erect another wheel, 30ft by 4ft, to work a double-acting haulage engine, in addition to crushers. Both wheels had been manufactured by Messrs James and H. Pearce of Tavistock, under the superintendence of Matthew Loam, the engineer of the mine.[43]

During this working, which continued until 1891, fresh development was carried out both laterally and in depth. A hitherto unpublished report, dated 6 March 1895, by William Henry Clemo of Devon Great Consols shows that Eastern Shaft had been deepened prior to this time to 77 fathoms. Here a level had been driven 13 fathoms east on a lode 3ft in width, yielding 2 tons of arsenical ore per fathom. The same level extended 18 fathoms west where the values were similar and the lode was 4$\frac{1}{2}$ft wide. At the 65 east the level reached a cross-course and had been stoped in the back and bottom, producing 8 tons of mundic per fathom over a width of 5ft. Westwards the

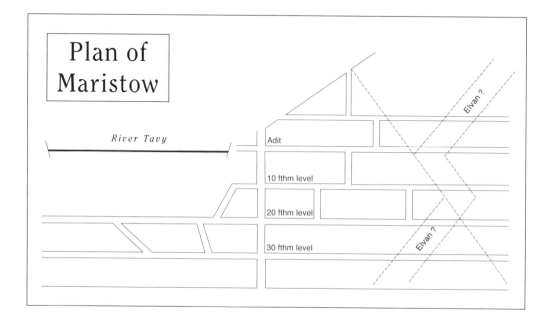

lode was 4ft wide and promising. In the 53 level east the lode had a width of 6ft and yielded 3 tons of ore per fathom. Stoping in the bottom produced 6 tons of pyrite and 2 tons of copper ore per fathom. From Western Shaft the 41, 30 and 20 fathom levels showed lode widths varying from 2^1/$_2$ to 5ft, stoping in the backs and bottoms yielding 4, 6 and 3 tons of ore per fathom. At the then ruling price of arsenic, the writer considered that there was a fair prospect of the mine being worked again at a profit.[44]

During the working of 1880 to 1891, the directors of Lady Bertha acquired the sett of **East Lady Bertha** into which the lodes of the former were believed to run. East Bertha Shaft was in course of sinking in 1860 when it reached a depth of 29 fathoms and was equipped with a 14in horizontal engine adapted for pumping and winding.[45] No plans are known of this mine, which Dines dismisses as little more than a trial. The size of the dump, however, suggests that fairly considerable development must have been carried out. The chimney-stack shown on the 1906 edition of the OS map (111 NE) has since been demolished.

About half a mile downstream on the east bank of the river **South Lady Bertha**, otherwise known as Ludbrook Mine, had three lodes, with a shaft sunk vertically to 40 fathoms from which levels were extended eastwards at 40, 30 and 20 fathoms. The mine is known to have been in operation in 1857 and despite Dines's statement that there are no records of output, there is evidence to show that 147 tons of copper ore were sold in the years 1859-61,[46] but working ceased soon after the latter date. The mine now lies in the garden of a private house and the remaining dumps are much overgrown.

Immediately opposite South Lady Bertha an old shaft situated near the west bank of the river marks the site of **Denham Bridge Mine**. According to *Mining Journal*, 20 November 1858, two copper lodes discovered here in a former working were partially explored by driving adits at river level. North Lode was thought to be an extension of the one then being worked in South Lady Bertha. From the Denham Bridge South Lode, £700 to £800 worth of ore was obtained by stoping the back of the adit for a short distance. A new company was formed soon after this, 7 tons of copper ore being sold for £13 in 1860.[47]

Output from Lady Bertha, Tavy Consols and other mines of this area was carried to the Tamar for shipment, principally from Gawton Quay which was the nearest point on the river. The journey was performed in two stages, pack animals being used to transport the ore up the steeply wooded slopes of the Tavy. At Tavisock Cross, on the Rock to Bere Alston road, midway between the two rivers, the ore was deposited on a stockpile; a cottage standing here bearing the name Orestock was formerly occupied by a caretaker who supervised the transfer of the ore to horse-drawn wagons which completed its transit to the Tamar.

Near the mouth of the Tavy, two or more lead lodes extend northwards along the west bank of the river for fully a mile. These have been developed at their southern end in **Wheal Maristow** (or the **Lopwell Mine**) and further north in the **Wood Mine** (OS 111 SE). Operations at the former are believed to have been started early in the last century when a shaft was sunk and a Cornish pumping engine erected, the ruined engine-house of which still remains. To conform with terms imposed by the mineral owner, Sir Massey Lopes, a flue was constructed 400yd in length to the summit of Whitacliffe Wood where the stack was erected out of sight of Maristow House. The dressing-floors lay a short distance upstream and near this there was a small lead smelter. No trace of the latter now remains, beyond a few large blocks of granite, whilst the engine-house stack has also been demolished, although both were remembered by old people recently living in the neighbourhood.

A plan of the mine dated 1822, in the Maristow Estate Office, shows that Engine Shaft was sunk to 40 fathoms at which depth levels were driven 30 fathoms north and 100 fathoms south. According to local tradition, the most productive part of the lode extended further south beneath the river into Maristow Park, where the miners used to boast that they would one day 'hole through' to the squire's wine cellar. On this becoming known to Sir Massey, he was so much incensed that he sent his estate carpenter over to the mine with orders to cut the main rod of the engine. The truth of this story was confirmed in 1952 by the late R. W. Toll who, on examining the shaft, noted that the rod had in fact been cut off about a foot above water level. It was subsequently learnt that there are letters in existence in the Maristow Office relating to an encroachment under the park at about this time.[48]

North of the Maristow Mine, old workings and shallow gunnises can be traced continuously to the **Wood Mine** in Great Whiterock Wood, a distance of one mile. Work was resumed at the Wood Mine in 1851 when an adit was cleared for 400 fathoms, passing through several shafts. In one of these the lode at a depth of 32 fathoms showed values of $10^1/_2$oz of silver to the ton of lead ore, whilst in White Rock Shaft the lode was 15in wide and producing fine stones of gossan. Among other shafts which were cleared Middle Shaft and South Shaft proved to be 45 and 32 fathoms deep from surface respectively. Captain Charles Thomas, who inspected the property at this time, reported that for 30 fathoms north of Middle Shaft and 20 fathoms south the back of the adit had been entirely stoped away by former workers. In the end going south the lode contained a little lead but elsewhere appeared almost worthless. Near White Rock Shaft a small dump showed some small strings of nearly pure galena. Because of the depth of the water it was impossible to examine the lodes below the adit level.[49] By 1855 the mine was at a low ebb financially, the majority of the adventurers being in default on their 'calls'. It was nevertheless agreed to give the property a further period of trial. On the advice of the agents it was decided to abandon White Rock Shaft and to enlarge Middle Shaft, subsequently attaching flat-rods to the engine in order to sink it 20 fathoms below the adit. At the same time, instructions were given that the cylinder, which had been installed without any 'clothing', should be properly lagged in order to effect a saving in fuel.[50]

The shares continued to be listed in the *Mining Journal* until the end of 1857, by which date operations had ceased. Sales of 4 tons of ore are recorded in Hunt's *Mineral Statistics* for 1852 and a further 8 tons were sold in 1856. Other sales are believed to have been made by private contract.

Above: Wheal Emma, the last discovered and most easterly extension of the Devon Great complex. This is the only known picture showing features of the surface workings in any detail.
© rcm VM DGC 002

Below: Miners cottages at Wheal Josiah
© R.M. Ordish

Above: Oxland tube arsenic calciner at Devon Great Consols – the bearded man is probably Capt. Isaac Richards.
© rcm VM DGC 007

Below: Devon Great Consols. The mill wheel and launder at the arsenic works, c.1935
© rcm VM DGC 004

Arsenic stack, Wheal Josiah, Devon Great Consols Mine, believed to have been built in the early 1920s when part of the mine was re-opened for arsenic working.
© H.G. Ordish

Shaft head gear and tram road at Bedford United Mine, probably taken in the early 1920s.
© rcm VM BED 002

Morwellham, c. 1890-1900 at a time when the port was beginning to fall into decay. The large dock in the foreground is already showing signs of silting up.
© rcm VM MOR 001

Above: Gawton Mine, showing the engine house and adjoining grinding-houses.
© H.G. Ordish

Below: An earlier view from Rumleigh works shows clearly the line of the arsenic flues of Gawton Mine and their harmful effect on vegetation. The dumps in the foreground are those of Okel Tor Mine on the Cornish bank of the River Tamar.

Above: The ruins of Butspill Mine
© rcm VM BUT 001

Below: Dressing floors at Lady Bertha Mine, c.1890. The bearded figure on the extreme left is Capt. Skewes.
© rcm VM LBE 001

All that remains of the drowned South Tamar Consols.

The stack of Lockridge Mine with its false-window effect at the top.

Above: The now destroyed engine house and stack of West Wheal Crebor, near Gulworthy. H.G. Ordish

Below: Remains of a circular buddle, Vitifer Mine
© rcm VM VIT 001

Above: A solitary stack at Wheal Julian, Plympton. Immediately behind it is the top of Wheal Sidney and in the far distance is the top of Bottle Hill Mine stack.

Below: The butt of the stack of the long-forgotten Cann Mine near Plymbridge.
Both photographs: © H.G. Ordish

Above: The engine house (c.1850s) at Ivybridge Consols Lead and Copper Mine.

Left: The stack working the end of the long underground arsenic flue at Wheal Sidney, Plympton.

Remains at Wheal Friendship (Devon Friendship) showing the huge arsenic flue and the calciners in November 1962. © H.G. Ordish

Above: The Counthouse, Wheal Friendship in November 1962. © H.G. Ordish

Below: Remains at Wheal Fanny, near Bridestowe in April 1957. © H.G. Ordish

Above: A solitary chimney at Sourton Downs Consols in September 1973. © H.G. Ordish

Below: The engine house bob wall at Collacombe Down, in autumn 1973. © H.G. Ordish

Above: The Compressor house with forge for tampering rock drills at Belstone Consols, June 1973.
© H.G. Ordish

Below: Engine house and chimney at Druid Mine near Ashburton, February 1975.
© Exeter Central Library

Top left: Silverbrook Mine, Ilsington in June 1967. © Exeter Central Library

Top right: Yarner Mine, Bovey Tracy, also in June 1967. © Exeter Central Library

Below: Remains of calciners at Atlas Mine, July 1974. © H.G. Ordish

Top left: An evocative photograph of the pump house at Wheal Exmouth in November 1955.

Top right: The engine house at Aller Mine near Christow, also in November 1955.

Below: Remains at Frank Mills, April 1959. All three photograps: © H.G. Ordish

CHAPTER 2

AROUND TAVISTOCK

During the years when Devon Great Consols was rising to its zenith, a number of trials were made in the hope of finding an extension of its phenomenally rich lodes to the east. In 1845 prospecting started on the Crease estate to the east of Millhill in the Lumburn Valley (OS 105 NE). Under the title of **Wheal Elizabeth** (late Crease) the sett was claimed to have three lodes varying in width from 2 to 10ft and likely to form a junction in depth. On one of these a shaft was sunk to 17 fathoms from which short cross-cuts were driven south in search of the Wheal Maria lode. At a depth of 4 fathoms from surface a copper lode was intersected which produced some good yellow ore. The workings, however, were only trifling in extent and carried on with 'little spirit'. Operations continued intermittently for about two years after which the search was abandoned.

Undaunted by this, the sett was taken up again in 1848, being then known as East Wheal Josiah. In driving the deep adit, a new lode was discovered producing good stones of gossan and mundic 'precisely of the same sort as that found in the Maria and Wheal Josiah mines of Devon Great Consols'. The workings on this lode, however, were little more than 36ft below surface; although stones of 'beautiful' yellow copper ore were encountered, the trial proved no more successful than those which had preceded it.'

In the 1860s more vigorous efforts were made by the East Devon Great Consols company. Three east–west lodes were opened up, two of which, underlying north, were expected to form a junction with the Devon Great Consols Lode which underlay south. In the following year work was in progress on the middle lode where an engine shaft was sunk to an ultimate depth of 70 fathoms. On this a small high-pressure puffer-engine was erected with two 9in cylinders. Some 80 fathoms south another shaft was sunk to 18 fathoms on a lead-bearing cross-course. In 1862 the mine employed eighteen people and a cross-cut was being driven from the 70 fathom level towards a copper lode which had earlier been seen in the 40 level. Although said to be producing lead and copper ores at this time, no sales appear to have been recorded. In November 1864 an unfavourable report was received from the manager and in the following month it was resolved to abandon the mine 'as it does not hold out prospects that would warrant its continuation'. The site of the engine shaft is probably identifiable with a large slaty burrow on the north side of the byroad leading from Middle Lumburn Bridge to Tavistock – nearly opposite the entrance to Crease farm house[2] (05 105 NE).

Colcharton Mine (OS 105 SE), otherwise Devon and Bedford, lay a short distance west of Lumburn. Although making no claims to possess the Devon Great Consols lodes, it was worked on a fairly considerable scale. In 1863 it was equipped with a 30in rotary engine which served for pumping, hoisting and crushing. From the vertical shaft, cross-cuts were put out at depths of 20, 30 and 40 fathoms and levels extended west on the lode to a maximum length of 115 fathoms. By 1867 no returns had been made, but twelve men were still employed in sinking the shaft, which eventually reached a 65 fathom level from surface. Soon after this the pumps were withdrawn, the outlook for the mine being considered unfavourable.[3]

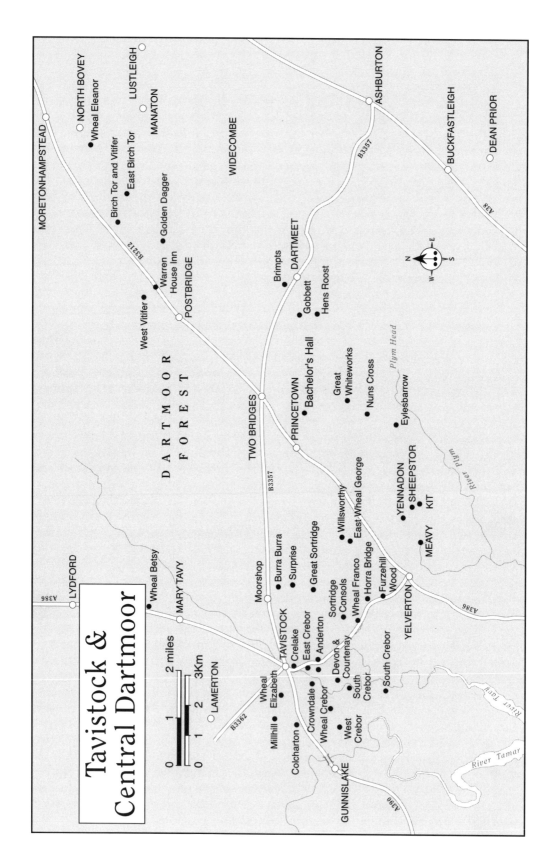

Tavistock & Central Dartmoor

DARTMOOR FOREST

LYDFORD
MORETONHAMPSTEAD
NORTH BOVEY
Wheal Eleanor
Birch Tor and Vitifer
East Birch Tor
LUSTLEIGH
MANATON
Golden Dagger
WIDECOMBE
Warren House Inn
POSTBRIDGE
West Vitifer
Brimpts
DARTMEET
ASHBURTON
Gobbett
Hens Roost
BUCKFASTLEIGH
DEAN PRIOR
Bachelor's Hall
Great Whiteworks
Nuns Cross
Plym Head
PRINCETOWN
TWO BRIDGES
Eylesbarrow
Willsworthy
East Wheal George
YENNADON
SHEEPSTOR
KIT
MEAVY
Moorshop
Burra Burra
Surprise
Great Sortridge
Sortridge Consols
Wheal Franco
Horra Bridge
Furzehill Wood
YELVERTON
Wheal Betsy
MARY TAVY
Crelake
East Crebor
Anderton
Devon & Courtenay
South Crebor
South Crebor
TAVISTOCK
LAMERTON
Wheal Elizabeth
Millhill
Crowndale
Wheal Crebor
West Crebor
Colcharton
GUNNISLAKE
River Tamar
River Tavy
River Plym

2 miles
3Km

Shortly after the commencement of work at the northern end of the Tavistock Canal tunnel in 1803, a copper lode showing good values was encountered close to the mouth. To develop this a mining company was formed entitled **Wheal Crebor**, a name derived from the adjoining farm (OS 105 SE). Further discoveries made in February and March 1805 resulted in the sale of 20 tons of ore. By 1807 the adit, which was driven beneath the floor of the canal, had been extended for more than 200 fathoms on Middle Lode and was then carried across to North Lode on which it was continued. In August 1808, Engine Shaft was down to a 12 fathom level, Cock's Shaft and Smith's Shaft had been sunk to 24 and 12 fathoms respectively, and Kelly's Shaft to adit. The outlay on the mine by this date amounted to £5,007 as against sales of only £163.

After this conditions improved rapidly. In 1811 output was averaging 150 tons a quarter, and by the following year had increased to 155 tons a month. With the price of copper falling due to (temporary) over-production, news such as this was far from welcome to the mining interests of West Cornwall. 'On the western edge of Devonshire,' wrote William Jenkin from Redruth in October 1812, 'the Canal Company have discovered (in cutting through a hill) a large Copper Lode. What will become of *this* poor County!' Crebor was losing money in that year but in 1813 showed a profit of £5,462 and paid a dividend of £15 a share.

Total costs to this date amounted to £33,449 with a net return of £32,098. About this time, rich ore was being obtained from the Georgina Lode which was intersected by the tunnel between a third and half a mile from its entrance. This lode was developed solely within the tunnel, ore from the stopes being let down through box-holes into barges drawn up to receive it. In the year ended November 1814, 3,648 tons of ore were sold at a profit of £7,000, and two dividends were paid totalling £45 per share.

The mine was abandoned in 1828 when the owner of adjoining land to the west refused to grant an extension of the sett. By that time Cock's, Smith's, Kelly's and Rundle's Shafts had been sunk to 45, 100, 135 and 104 fathoms from surface respectively, while sales of ore totalling 27,490 tons had realised £167,181. In 1844 a new company was formed, but shortly afterwards failed in the railway panic and financial depression of 1846.[4]

Working was resumed in 1851 and continued for the next fifty years, 34,900 tons of copper ore being returned between 1852 and 1893, together with considerable quantities of pyrite and mispickel during the years 1872 to 1901. The mine lasted so long mainly because of the advantages of cheap transport (the direct connection with the quays of Morwellham saving it the cost of land carriage which had crippled other mines of this district) and power which it gained from being on the canal.

Drainage was also effected by the flow of water through the canal. A 40ft wheel, 8ft breast, erected near the northern entrance of the tunnel, operated a line of flat-rods 3,000ft in length, extending up an incline to the top of the hill where by means of a T-bob it connected to the pumps in Rundle's Shaft, the most westerly on the property. Another wheel of 6ft diameter, similarly driven by the canal, drove a crusher. The only steam engine on the mine was a 22in rotary which served for hoisting, supplementing the work of the numerous horse-whims.

In 1889 a crisis arose. Due in part to a recent fall of £40 a ton in the price of copper and still more to the near exhaustion of the lodes, the mine was faced with the prospect of immediate closure. At this juncture Moses Bawden, then acting manager, came forward with an offer to lease the mine for a period of twelve months, paying the company a tribute of 2s 6d in the £ on the ores sold. As he remarked at the meeting 'We have worked the mine boldly and sunk it from the 156 to the 200 purely on speculation, though each level has proved very poor. Nevertheless, if I had the working of the mine myself; instead of stopping at the 200, I would sink another 40 fathoms. I cannot believe that the tremendous courses of ore we had from the 108 to the 144 have entirely died out.'[5] After some discussion, Mr Bawden's offer was accepted, and although the mine was never deepened below the 200, the demand for arsenic enabled it to survive until 1901, the year which also witnessed the demise of its celebrated neighbour, Devon Great Consols.

As was the case with other well-known mines, Wheal Crebor fathered a considerable progeny. Best known of these was **West Crebor** (OS 105 SE) whose engine-house, with a detached stack, until recently formed a conspicuous landmark on the high plateau of Morwell Down. The sett is separated from Wheal Crebor by 170 fathoms of ground and was connected to the workings of the latter at adit level only. Started in the 1880s, West Crebor was developed to a 60 fathom level on the underlie of the lode but without much success, the sole output recorded being 19 tons of copper ore in 1885.[6]

North Crebor produced 916 tons of copper ore between 1829 and 1835 but is otherwise unknown. Dines thought that it formed part of Crelake, a mine which in fact was not started until twenty years later. A more probable identification is that of a shaft (now obliterated but shown on the 1882 edition of the OS map 105 SE) which lay at the loop of the road, near the second milestone from Tavistock, 200yd north of the Harvest Home inn.

Information regarding **South Crebor Mine** is principally derived from a report made by C. F. Barclay and R. W. Toll[7] who worked it for a short period in the winter of 1922-3. Little is known of its early history, but the adit is said to have been started between 1830 and 1840 and was eventually driven 360 fathoms from its portal, 610yd south of Shilla Mill Bridge. About 1860 the sett was taken up by a Captain Goldsworthy, previously manager of East Wheal Russell, and continued intermittently to be worked by him until 1870 or 1880, sometimes with assistance from the adventurers of Wheal Crebor. A vertical shaft was sunk 24 fathoms from surface and at that depth a crosscut was driven north to the lode, on which a level extended a considerable distance east and west. The lode was very bunchy and had been worked mainly by tributers.

The mine is situated in the steeply sided valley of the Tavy immediately north of Lazy Bench Hill Bridge where it spans the now-disused railway. An engine-house is shown here on the 1882 edition of the OS map 105 SE. According to Barclay and Toll, the Engine Shaft 'on top of the higher dump' is vertical to 44 fathoms from surface, but being sollared over is not easily visible, a fact which no doubt accounts for its not being marked on the map. The mine's sole recorded production is stated as 226 tons of copper ore in the years 1863-7, a figure which is probably incomplete.

On the west side of the valley the South Crebor lodes have been prospected in **New East Russell**, a small mine which owed its inception to the erstwhile reputation of East Wheal Russell further to the west. In 1868 the deepest level in New East Russell was 20 fathoms below adit (40 fathoms), few men were employed and the only 'machinery' consisted of a horse-whim. Working ceased in that year with a recorded output of 67 tons of copper ore in 1865. Working was resumed in 1870 under the name of Wheal Courtenay[8] but no further development appears to have been carried out either laterally or in depth.

On the east side of the Tavy, the same lodes were explored by an adit beneath Birch Wood into the sett of **Devon and Courtenay** (OS lO5 SE) which was developed to a 90 fathom level from surface. From the 30 level downwards the plans show a number of small stopes, but according to Dines less than 15 per cent of the blocked-out ground has been removed. In 1861 the mine was employing fifty people[9] but ceased work soon after, with an output in 1852 of 1,510 tons of copper ore and 3 tons of lead ore. The burrows of the principal shaft adjacent to Middle Tor farm contain quantities of iron pyrites, together with purple fluorspar.

A mile south of Tavistock, **Crowndale Mine** (OS 105 SE), whose overgrown workings adjoin the former railway, developed an eastward extension of the Crebor main lode. The mine is an old one, resuscitated in 1799 when its machinery consisted mainly of water-wheels. These were originally driven by a leat from the Tavy and later by the flow of water through the Tavistock Canal. An old plan of the mine shows no less than eighteen shafts over a length of 500 fathoms, the deepest being sunk vertically to a 90 fathom level. The most productive part of the lode lay above the 40 fathom level – below this the values declined.[10]

During the 1830s the Tavistock Smelting Company established works on the sett, treating ores from the waste dumps of the surrounding mines, together with partially smelted residues known as Jews' tin from the ancient blowing-houses on Dartmoor. The mine continued to be worked at intervals until the 1870s, returning over 15,000 tons of copper ore, principally in the period between 1820 and 1830.

In 1924-6 the adit was reopened for arsenic when an ore shoot was found averaging $4^{1}/_{2}$ft in width and estimated to contain from 10,000 to 15,000 tons. Samples of copper pyrites assayed 4dwts of gold per ton.[12]

The Crowndale main lode crosses the Tavy south of Crowndale farm where it enters the sett of **East Crebor** (OS 105 SE). Although a comparatively small mine, the latter is said to have produced some of the richest ore ever found in Cornwall or Devon, assaying 28 per cent copper.[13] In July 1880 three men were drowned in the 70 fathom level by an influx of the Tavy through the adit, the water at the same time flooding part of the Crowndale workings. The engine shaft of that mine still registers the rise and fall of the river.[14] An undated plan of East Crebor shows two lodes, 15 fathoms apart, between which the shaft was sunk vertically to 70 fathoms below adit. Part of the engine-house, converted to a barn, was still standing here in 1958.

East Crebor had been worked at an earlier period as East Crowndale. In 1811 the latter was described as being in its infancy but had already sold ores to the value of £6,277[15] In the same year an output of 1,775 tons was recorded under the name of South Crowndale which so nearly adjoined East Crowndale as to constitute virtually one sett. Work was in progress at both mines in the middle of the nineteenth century, East Crowndale selling 605 tons of ore in the years 1852-4.[16] The machinery at this time included a 56in pumping and a 26in winding and stamps engine. South Crowndale, which was also known as West Rix Hill, was active again in 1858 when two new lodes standing 10-12 fathoms apart were discovered by surface pitting.[17]

Adjoining the above group on the east lie Rix Hill, New Anderton and Old Anderton, the two latter situated on the slopes of the Tiddy Brook (OS 105 SE). **Wheal Anderton** had been sunk to an 80 fathom level by 1849 and was subsequently deepened to the 90. Shortly before that time **Wheal Ash** was added to the sett, and the mines became known as Tavistock Consols. On the Wheal Ash Lode, the adit passed through an immense course of mundic, nearly solid, and extending for a length of 60 fathoms.

In 1850 arrangements were made for combining Wheals Anderton and Ash under the title of Tavistock United Mines. **Rix Hill** was not included in this lease, but was working independently for tin on which it was said to be making considerable profits.[18]

In 1880 a fresh amalgamation was proposed comprising the two Andertons and the Rix Hill mines under the old name of East Crowndale. The sett thus formed incorporated three east–west tin lodes, with a number of copper lodes running parallel – the latter 'extending through East Crebor, being a continuation of those extensively worked in the Old Crowndale Mine'. Five shafts had already been sunk on the Anderton and Rix Hill properties where the lodes were reported to contain between 150lb and 5cwt of tin to the ton of stuff.[19] Whether the new company ever materialised is doubtful, since no other reference to East Crowndale has been found at this period. The constituent mines, however, continued to work until 1890 returning, in the aggregate, a considerable quantity of tin for which their potential is thought to be not yet exhausted.

In the built-up area on the south side of Tavistock, a sett named **Wheal Pixon** was granted in 1834 to John Gill and John Rundle, comprising the farms of Fitzford and Beercause, with 200 fathoms on the course of the lode, east and west of Ford Street turnpike gatehouse. To this was added a length of ground north and south of the point where the Wheal Crowndale cross-course was supposed to intersect the Wheal Pixon Lode.[20] In 1838, twenty-seven people were employed on the mine of which little else is known.

Crelake Mine (OS 105 SE), closely adjoining Wheal Pixon, was started in 1857 when a copper lode was discovered in the bed of the nearby Tavy. The sett as originally granted to Richard Davey MP 'and other influential gentlemen of West Cornwall',[21] extended one mile east from the river and contained two east–west copper lodes, together with a north–south lead course. In 1860 *Mining Journal* reported that Main Lode had been opened up by Davey's Shaft, 120yd south-east of West Bridge, and sunk vertically to 50 fathoms. Cross-cuts put out north to the lode at the 15, 28 and 40 fathom levels had all been driven a considerable distance east and west. In the 40 level, west, the lode was valued at 5 to 20 tons of ore per fathom and about 700 tons had been raised. Lead Lode, 150 fathoms east of Davey's Shaft, had at this date been seen only in a shallow adit but was shortly to be tested by another vertical shaft, named the Bedford. North Lode had similarly been opened up by a shallow adit where it was 30ft wide, with very promising indications.

The machinery on the mine comprised a 30in engine designed for pumping, crushing and drawing, with a small puffing engine on Davey's Shaft. This last had hitherto served for pumping, but on the completion of flat-rods from the 30in engine to the shaft, was to be used exclusively for hoisting. Considering the mine had been at work for little more than two years, its progress was regarded as highly satisfactory. Moreover, as the *Mining Journal* correspondent remarked, 'What has been done has been carried out in a splendid, indeed I may say luxurious, style.'[22]

In the following year (1861) the 'richest young mine in the Tavistock district' as Crelake was then regarded, was visited by Joseph Yelloly Watson who was suitably impressed by the 'fine piles of ore, both lead and copper' to be seen on the floors and the 'remarkably fine pile of buildings on the sett – the chimney reminded me of the Nelson Monument – and the shareholders must have great confidence in the ultimate success of the mine to justify such an outlay at the commencement'.[23] Despite some degree of showmanship at surface, underground development proceeded in a miner-like way. In 1862, 270 people were employed and Davey's Shaft had been sunk to 86 fathoms, eventually reaching 116 fathoms from surface. From the 15 down to the 86 fathom cross-cut, levels were extended east–west, the longest being the 28 and 40 which were driven 300 and 225 fathoms west respectively, and extensively stoped in the backs.

Due to the discovery that Main Lode crossed the Tavy, an extension of the original lease was obtained at this time covering an area south of the river. Here Air Shaft was sunk on the underlie to 50 and another, unnamed, shaft to 28 fathoms. Meanwhile, Bedford Shaft on the Lead Lode had been deepened vertically to 70 fathoms, with levels driven north and south down to the 62. Above the 40 level, the ground was stoped away for 100 fathoms south of the shaft. No mention is made of any development on North Lode which seems to have failed in its early promise.

In 1868 the machinery consisted of a 36in pumping, crushing and jigging engine, with two steam-whims of 15 and 14in cylinder diameter. The returns showed a profit in 1867 and there was talk of negotiating a new lease. By 1870, however, the numbers employed had been reduced to 120,[24] and a few years later working ceased. Recorded outputs from 1856-74 comprised 12,000 tons of copper ore, 1,300 tons of lead ore, and 13,145oz of silver, added to which an unspecified quantity of arsenic and pyrite is known to have been raised.[25]

EAST OF TAVISTOCK

Two miles east of Tavistock on the Moretonhampstead road (OS 106 NW), the discovery was made in June 1851 of a gate post showing impregnations of copper. Trifling as this incident might now appear it caused a speculative fever which resulted in a company, called **Wheal Gatepost**, being formed in the following month. Within weeks, costeaning by means of trenches revealed a number of lodes and cross-courses on which, however, much work had already been done by the 'ancients'. Undeterred by this, a shaft was sunk to a depth of 8 fathoms and a start made on driving an adit. In September 1851 'the veritable gatepost 6ft high, hangings and all' was brought from Tavistock to London 'where it was pronounced by all mining men worthy of a place in the Crystal Palace'.[26]

More publicity followed, blocks of ore assaying 30 per cent fine copper being forwarded to the City where they were regarded 'with intense interest as the largest specimens of copper ore of such quality ever discovered in this country at surface'. Even *Mining Journal* was rash enough to support the claim that the Devon Great Consols Main Lode ran through the sett.

About this time the name of the property was changed to Devon Burra Burra, after the celebrated South Australia mine which was then making headlines. Additional capital was raised and an order placed with Messrs Gill & Rundle of the Tavistock Iron Works for a 60in cylinder engine, the largest ever constructed by that foundry. The mine was then being developed in two parts, the original Gatepost on the east and the Brake Section to the west. In the 10 fathom level the lode was stated to be 14ft wide and composed of quartz interspersed with yellow copper ore. Middle Lode, which was expected to junction with the Brake Lode, carried a leader of ore 3in wide, while South Lode at the same level had a width of 3-4ft, similarly interspersed with yellow ore. Pending erection of the engine on Brake Shaft, two water-wheels had been installed for pumping, one of these being connected to the Gatepost section so that shaft-sinking there could proceed without hindrance. Large returns of grey and malachite ores were expected from the Gatepost Lode, whilst stones of ore assaying 50 to 75 per cent copper had already been raised from the Brake Lode at a depth only of 11 or 12 fathoms below adit.[27]

By the summer of 1853 the gloss was beginning to wear off and shareholders were becoming restive. A Birmingham correspondent complained in the *Mining Journal* that whilst the adventure had been more frequently mentioned than any other mine in the United Kingdom the production forecasts had proved too optimistic and 'the piles of copper ore at grass at Gatepost Shaft appeared to have vanished'. Writing from Madrid, another shareholder expressed his belief that no mine in Great Britain had promised so much and performed so little.[28]

However, work continued in a desultory manner for some years after this. In 1855-66 a lode to the east of the great cross-course received a favourable report, and a drive was started towards it at the 40 fathom level. An accident to the 'clack' (pump-valve) involving the loss of the pit-work prevented further work here. Another lode had been found in the western ground, but this had not been investigated below the 40. Lead ore was also reported in the end of the 20 fathom level and 10 tons had recently been sold. About this time the mine reached its maximum depth of 60 fathoms at White's Shaft.

In 1861, due to the retirement of two of the principal shareholders, the machinery and materials were put up for sale. These included the 60in engine in a substantial engine-house, 150 fathoms of flat-rods and pulleys, two water-wheels (36ft by 4ft and 30ft by 3ft) with drawing and crushing machines, and twelve heads of stamps.[29] A document in the writer's possession records an output of 45 tons of low-grade copper ore in the years 1853-6. Dines quotes a figure of 190 tons in the period 1863-73. This, if true, implies a subsequent reworking, and a veritable instance of the 'triumph of hope over experience'.

On its south, Devon Burra Burra was adjoined by the sett of **Wheal Surprise**. Under this name, the little mine is known to have been at work in 1795 and also in 1810,[30] after which it remained in obscurity until 1851 when, due to the publicity afforded by its near neighbour, it was again taken up. The sett lay immediately west of Pennycomequick (OS 106 NW) on the south side of the stream, and was reputed to contain two copper lodes. On one of these a shaft was sunk to a 43 fathom level from surface (20 fathoms below adit) by the aid of a 30ft water-wheel erected in 1852. A few years later the mine was bankrupt but in was bought by a Mr Hill of Tavistock for £50 which, as it proved, was dear at the price. Under the new name of Whitchurch Down Consols a trifling amount of copper ore is said to have been produced, although of no marketable value. In 1859 this 'useless sett', as a contemporary critic described it, was again being offered for sale.[31]' It is hard to imagine that it found a buyer.

South of Whitchurch Down lie the **Sortridge Mines** – Great Sortridge, Great Sortridge United, Great West Sortridge, East Sortridge, North Sortridge – which sprang up like mushrooms during the 1850s. Some of them were scarcely more than names, the companies being promoted by jobbers and merchants with little serious intention of mining. **Sortridge Consols** was an exception. Earlier known as West Wheal Robert, its workings lay on high ground about half a mile north of Horrabridge and nearly adjacent to Sortridge Manor (OS 106 SW). When reopened in 1853 a rich deposit of copper ore was found only 5ft from surface, and in a matter of months £3,200 worth was sold on an outlay of £600. In 1854 the maximum depth was 30 fathoms and the lode continued as rich as ever, yielding in places 10 tons of ore per fathom. From the 20 to the 40 fathom level the course of ore returned over £50,000.[32]

At this depth the values showed a serious decline, so much so that pumping was reduced and it was actually proposed to abandon the mine. The situation was saved at the last moment by an important discovery in two of the south lodes, a fact which caused an immediate reversal of policy. In April 1855 a meeting of the shareholders authorised the installation of a new 40in engine from the Tavistock foundry of Nicholls & Williams, for the purpose of forking the old and sinking a new shaft. The existing engine, it was stated, was one of 9hp only and wholly insufficient for its task. The new engine, by contrast, was a 'noble specimen of engineering skill, combining elegance and beauty with great power'. The engine-house designed for it was similarly on the most approved principles: 'fire-proof with stairs and stair-case of iron and a flooring of slate'.

In July 1855 a colourful ceremony took place to celebrate the start of the engine's working life. At the entrance to the mine the road was crossed by a triumphal arch of evergreens, fronted by a large star formed of flowers from the four points of which floated the Union Jack and other flags. At the apex of the arch the word 'Welcome' greeted the visitors. After seeing the engine make its first stroke, the company adjourned to a dinner and settled down to listen to speeches when 'each man was supplied with his favourite beverage and a yard of clay from which quickly began to ascend clouds of smoke of the fragrant weed almost rivalling in density that issuing from the adjoining steam-engine chimney'[33]

In the following year a sale was held of the spare materials remaining on the mine. Included in these was a curious little 11 1/4in high-pressure slide-valve engine of Belgian manufacture which had originally been sent to England for the Great Exhibition of 1851.'[34]

After this the mine continued in operation for at least another twelve years during which time the main shaft was carried down on the underlie to 152 fathoms from surface. However, little stoping or driving was done below the 62 fathom level,[35] and the mine never regained the promise of its early years. By 1866 only thirty people were employed and sales of copper ore for that year realised a mere £460. Working ceased in 1868, and a few months later the machinery comprising the 40in pumping engine, 22in winder and a 24ft water-wheel was advertised for sale.[36] Output of copper ore from 1854 to the final closure is recorded as 7,792 tons. According to Barclay and Toll, the adit (50 fathoms below surface at its deepest point) was reopened in 1883 when a quantity of low-grade tin ore was found. This continued to be worked intermittently and in a small way until 1902.

Great Sortridge (or Plaister Down) which was at one period included in the Sortridge Consols sett, is shown on the OS map 106 SW as a tin mine, but it produced little of that or any other mineral. By 1846 an adit had been driven 200 fathoms and was expected to cut the lode at about 2 fathoms from surface. Three shafts were later sunk, the deepest being 25 fathoms drained by a 12in engine. At that level the lode was claimed to be 8 to 14 fathoms wide and containing small quantities of tin, native copper and spots of yellow ore. It was intended that two further shafts – one on the eastern and the other on the west side of the down – be sunk with a view to taking the lode at a depth of 50 fathoms.[37] There is no evidence to suggest that this was ever carried out. The position of the mine was formerly distinguished by a tall stack which was a landmark for many miles around (Murchison, 1856). This has long since disappeared although its base is indicated adjacent to the main shaft on the 1907 edition of the 6in map.

Immediately adjacent to Sortridge Consols on the east, but not connected underground, lay **North Wheal Robert** and **Wheal Robert**. The latter had been worked about 1825 by a local company who drove an adit 90 fathoms and sank a small shaft on one of the lodes from which 106 tons of copper ore were sold in 1825-6. Dissensions among the adventurers, coupled with the fact that the water could no longer be kept by a common hand-pump, caused the working to be abandoned.[38]

Towards the end of 1850 a London company was formed. Shortly afterwards North Wheal Robert was amalgamated with the neighbouring East Wheal Robert and the mines were subsequently operated under the general title of North Robert. Two new shafts, Murchison's and Halket's, were started at this time and orders placed for a 40ft water-wheel and 240 fathoms of flat-rods, together with the necessary pumps. Water to drive this and other wheels in the vicinity was supplied by the six-mile-long Grimstone and Sortridge leat which, as reported in the *Mining Journal,* was frozen up in the severe weather of February 1853.

Although the mines produced some tin, together with small quantities of lead ore and pyrite, their output consisted mainly of copper, of which they returned 3,674 tons in the years 1853-7[39] On the western mine, ie the original North Robert, the principal shaft was sunk on the underlie to an 80 fathom level below surface; while Murchison's Shaft on the eastern mine developed the lode vertically to 62 fathoms. By 1868 both parts of the mine had become poor, the copper shoots of the main lode having apparently been bottomed, while the tin content was too small for them to be worked solely for that mineral.'[40] The materials and machinery as advertised for sale in October and December of that year comprised a 33in engine for pumping and stamping on the western mine and the 40ft wheel on the eastern mine.

The earliest reference to **Willsworthy Mine**, which hitherto had been unidentified, occurs in the MS of John Swete in 1797-8:

> A miner (who has long been a labourer with me) informs me that between 20 and 30 years ago [say 1770] he was pursuing a copper lode on an estate belonging to Mr. Tolcher of Plymouth when on a sudden by sinking his pick axe into a sort of Gossan (which was, as it were, intermixed with the lode) a body of cobalt fell and with it a quantity of water ... From this copper mine of Sampford Spiney four tons at least of cobalt was taken, of which 1,700 lbs was sent to London and sold. Like the Bohemian ore, the cobalt was impregnated with hairs and tresses of the purest silver.[41]'

In 1775 Josiah Wedgwood, the potter, visited the mine on his way to Cornwall, being accompanied by Mr Tolcher then a lively, if somewhat querulous, old gentleman nearly ninety years of age. The mine was idle at this time but Wedgwood obtained from Mr Tolcher several specimens of 'what he called cobalt – but I never could bring any blue colour out of it. I have since had a whole cask of this mineral... from Mr Gullett of Exeter, a partner in the mine, but could not find a grain of cobalt in it'.[42] Despite this, the presence of cobalt in the ore is an established fact. In an undated letter c.1790, Phillip Rashleigh wrote to his fellow Cornishman and mineralogist, John Hawkins: 'When you returned by way of Tavistock, you might have gone to Hiccary Bridge [Huckworthy Bridge] and seen the Cobalt ore there frequently intermixed with small Capillary Native Silver. I have oftened wondered this mine has not been worked again, tho' the water is very powerful in it.'[43]

In fact, the mine was reopened sometime before 1814, in which year it appears for the first time under the name of Willsworthy and was advertising the sale of 'about Two Tons of Rich and Elegant Cobalt Ore which forms the purest Calx [cobalt oxide produced by reduction]. The ore will be shown on application to W. Willcox Esq of Huckworthy Bridge'.[44] (OS 106 SW).

Although the quantity was small and of no great economic importance, the occurrence of such an ore in a British mine aroused widespread interest in the scientific world of the day. Specimens were eagerly sought not merely by local mineral collectors, but also in London whither they were sent 'for the inspection of the learned in Chemistry and Mineralogy'. About this time Mr Mawe, the mineral dealer, was said to have had 200 such specimens at his shop in The Strand. One of the finest specimens in Cornwall was in the possession of Mr Arthur Penrose of Truro, assay master and agent for the Crown Copper Company. The capillary silver in this stone was described as 'springing from a fine white quartz intermixed with peach blossom arsenical cobalt'. In May 1816 the *Cornwall Gazette* announced that a stone weighing 124lb would shortly be exhibited at the British Museum. 'The Egyptian Museum in Piccadilly will also be enriched with some choice specimens... which although hitherto unknown in this country exactly correspond with that described by Aikin as raised in the silver mines of Peru.'[45]

A description of the ore as it was seen in the lode was given by Joseph Carne, the Cornish mineralogist, in his well-known paper 'On the Discovery of Silver in the Mines of Cornwall', published in 1818:

'It occurred in Willsworthy Mine (which, indeed, may be said to be rather on the border of Devon) in 1816. The lode in which it was found was about 12in wide, bearing NNE and SSW and underlies 2½ft to the fathom, south. In the ten fathoms level, a vein of white amethystine quartz divided the lode: between this vein of quartz... and the north wall of the lode was found a vein of rich arsenical cobalt ore, combined with native capillary silver in a ferruginous matrix from three to six inches wide. The space between the vein of quartz... and the southern wall of the lode was occupied by a vein of rich yellow copper ore, from six to nine inches wide. The silver continued about six fathoms in length and was not seen deeper. The copper was not so soon exhausted. The specimens of native silver from this mine have eclipsed all that have ever before been found in Cornwall, both in size and beauty.'[46]

It is evident from the above that Carne himself was not personally acquainted with the mine and was uncertain as to its site. This is surprising in view of the explicit statement in the contemporary Cornish press that it lay at Huckworthy Bridge in the parishes of Sampford Spiney and Walkhampton[47] – a statement which in fact has passed unnoticed to the present day. As a consequence Dines (along with others) has assumed that the mine was probably situated on a farm named Willsworthy some 2½ miles north-east of Mary Tavy although, as he admits, no trace of mining has been seen there.'[48] The Willsworthy Mine ceased working in 1817, consequent on a number of the shareholders failing to meet their calls. The materials as advertised for sale included a 35ft diameter water-wheel, 20 fathoms of pumps and a horse-whim[49]

Under the name of Huckworthy Bridge, some further activity took place in the 1840s and again in 1860-1, an output of 23 tons of copper ore being recorded in the latter period. The mine was then 40 fathoms deep from surface and had a 40ft diameter wheel driving pumps and a crusher. Operations were abandoned in December 1862 when the plant was offered for sale in *Mining Journal.*

In the immediate vicinity of Huckworthy Bridge, prospecting trials were carried out on a number of other lodes. Among these was **Wheal Collier** where, in 1846, a deep cross-cut adit was being driven north from the Walkham River to intersect the lodes of the Huckworthy Bridge Mine. Another adit was also driven on a copper lode further to the north. 'Our contiguity to the old Huckworthy Mine which returned some of the richest copper ever produced in the county and also cobalt of very 'good quality', was claimed to give added value to the Wheal Collier sett. Little more is heard of the latter mine which had earlier been worked by the Plymouth and Dartmoor Mining Company.[50]

A short distance downstream from Huckworthy Bridge, **East Wheal George** (OS 112 NW) was started in 1849 when a lode carrying a rich vein of copper was discovered at only 10ft from surface. On this a shaft was started on the southern margin of the river and was eventually sunk to a depth of 60 fathoms. In 1850-2 the mine returned 660 tons of ore, averaging nearly 14 per cent copper.[51] Most of the stoping was done between surface and the 22 fathom level, below this the values declined and the levels became successively shorter. Two dumps of considerable size were still standing near this shaft in 1959. On the further bank of the river, North Lode was opened up by a shaft sunk to 20 fathoms. The mine was drained by a 40ft water-wheel and, according to local tradition, was eventually flooded by being stoped too close beneath the river bed. Working ceased in 1858 when the output of East Wheal George amounted to 783 tons of ore which sold for £6,480 (figures compiled by Justin Brooke).

The principal copper mine of this district was **Wheal Franco** whose workings lay a short distance west of Horrabridge (OS 112 NW). The sett was a large one, extending along the south bank of the River Walkham, with an older portion on the western side of the Plymouth to Tavistock road. In this latter area, known as Old Wheal Franco, work had started by 1823 and in the course of the next twenty years the mine was developed to a depth of 160 fathoms. In 1838, 1,461 tons of ore were returned to the value of £5,078, 133 people were employed and there were six water-wheels varying in size from 14 to 32ft diameter.[52]

By 1843, when it had produced some £60,000 worth of ore, this part of the sett was thought to be exhausted and a new shaft was started on a rich course of ore to the east of the road, which henceforth became the active centre of the mine. In 1846, 140 tons of ore were being raised monthly and in the following years Engine Shaft was carried down vertically to 110 fathoms from surface, while six other shafts had been sunk on the property. With varying degrees of fortune, operations continued until 1862, by which date 10,333 tons of ore had been sold for £51,500.[53]

In 1870 Wheal Franco Consols was formed to acquire the properties formerly worked as Old and New Franco. Between these lay a piece of virgin ground containing three lodes of black and grey copper ore which had been intersected in a cutting of the Plymouth and Tavistock railway. To develop this ground, Sutton's Shaft was being

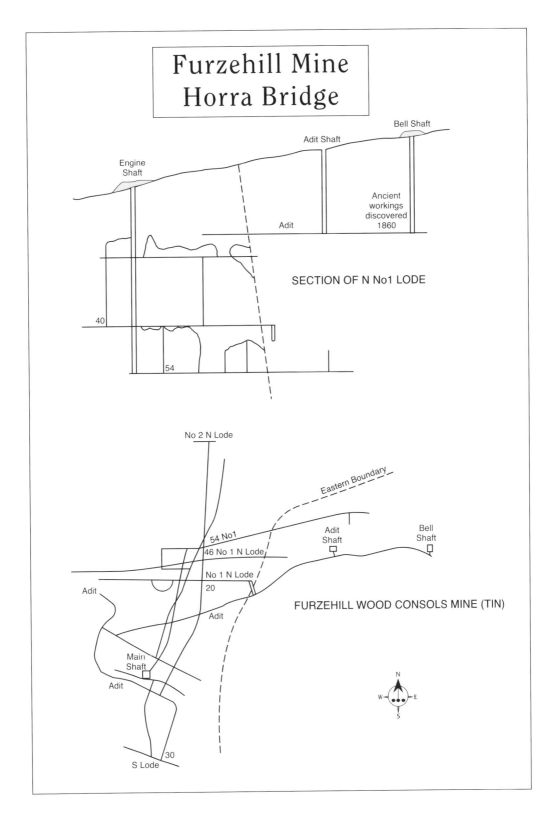

Furzehill Mine
Horra Bridge

Bell Shaft

Adit Shaft

Engine
Shaft

Ancient
workings
discovered
1860

Adit

SECTION OF N No1 LODE

40

54

No 2 N Lode

Eastern Boundary

54 No1

Adit
Shaft

Bell
Shaft

46 No 1 N Lode

No 1 N Lode

Adit

20

FURZEHILL WOOD CONSOLS MINE (TIN)

Adit

Main
Shaft

Adit

N

W E

S

30

S Lode

sunk in May 1870, while an adit, already driven 70 fathoms south from the Walkham River, was then within 22 fathoms of the shaft which it would drain to a depth of 23 fathoms. South of the shaft, the adit was expected to cut four other lodes and to give backs of over 64 fathoms. In the spring of 1871, 70 tons of ore were sold for £102, but soon after this transaction was effected the mine was abandoned.[54]

About half a mile south of Horrabridge, **Furzehill Mine** in Furzehill Wood (OS 112 NW) was reopened in 1860 on the strength of its erstwhile reputation for tin. Known to have been worked extensively in the eighteenth century and possibly far earlier, it had two adits; one 6 fathoms and the other 11 fathoms deep – the latter driven 500 fathoms across the strike of the lodes. A correspondent in the *Mining Journal* stated that these had not been worked to any extent:

'since the time of 'Bal Hatchett', the noted miner of bygone times but it seems to have been one of his favourites of several wrought at that period. The anti-quated mode of working then adopted – round shafts, shafts shammelled from the surface in steps to save tackies and ropes, immense open cuttings, and the many concave-sided stones for pulverising the tin – as also the trees now over-growing the whole workings – are all indicative of a remote age. It appears to have been the practice to under-let numerous small takings of ground to pares of men for a certain length on the lodes, to be worked from the surface as now in the Australian gold fields. By this great division of labour, coupled with the assistance of a crosscut adit driven more than half a mile in length, they coped with the water and drew the tin-stuff through some 30 shafts to surface and thereby sold at least £30,000 worth of tin despite the then low price of the metal and the three-fold cost of working in comparison with more modern methods'.[55]

Soon after its inception, the new company set about sinking an engine-shaft. At a shallow depth this passed through a lode estimated to be worth £25 per fathom, whilst four other lodes were expected to be reached by means of short cross-cuts. By 1867 the shaft had been sunk to 54 fathoms giving access to old men's levels in which the supporting pillars (arches) were valued at 44lb of black tin to the ton. From these, 21 tons of concentrate were sold for £1,053 in 1866.[56]

In a maze of irregular workings, exploratory work of this nature was not without danger, and in the following year seven men and a boy were drowned when the 40 fathom level unexpectedly holed into an old flooded gunnis. Due to the low price of tin, operations were suspended in 1868 when the machinery consisting of a 30ft wa-ter-wheel and a 24in rotary steam engine for pumping, winding and stamping was offered for sale.

Working was resumed at Furzehill Tin Mine in 1870 and the company was still on the active list in 1879 (although latterly it would seem to small advantage). But re-corded output from 1862-77 amounted only to 196 tons of black tin and 2 tons of arsenic (Dines p.700).

Today, the old 'coffan' or open-cast workings, with the numerous unfenced shafts of both latter days and more recent times appear but little changed – although more treacherously disguised than formerly by the dense bracken which has invaded the woodland.

CENTRAL DARTMOOR

On Yennadon Down, $1\frac{1}{2}$ miles east-north-east of Yelverton, a lode has been worked for iron ore in the **Yennadon Mine** (OS 112 NW). Advertised for sale in 1838, it was stated that the Plymouth and Dartmoor Tramway passed through the sett at two different levels and that in addition to iron-stone, manganese had been discovered, as had several copper and tin lodes which could be worked at a small outlay. By 1847 an adit had been driven upwards of 60 fathoms and was then approaching one of the lodes which it was expected to cut at 11 fathoms deep. The lode at surface was about 12ft wide and appeared to have been worked by the old men to a depth of 12ft where rocks of tin stuff had been found. Recent blasting of the ore body showed good leaders or branches of cassiterite running through it.[57]

To the east, tin has been worked in numerous small lodes traversing the high moorland area. The deposits, being situated in the heart of the granite country, constitute the bottom part of the tin-bearing zone – the 'roots' of lodes which had once extended upwards into the overlying killas before being swept away in the long process of denudation of the latter following post-Carboniferous times. Their outcrops, where exposed in the existing land surface, would have been clearly recognisable to the alluvial tinners as they roamed the moors, but the mines in which they were subsequently developed have necessarily proved to be as limited in depth as in productiveness.

In 1823 the lease was advertised of some 400 acres of land in the moorland parish of Sheepstor, together with underlying minerals consisting of tin, copper, manganese, cobalt, silver, lead and china clay.[58] To this list, gold might well have been added since it is recorded about this time that a miner called Wellington obtained £40 worth of the precious metal from an unspecified site in Sheepstor. This he sold to a Plymouth silversmith named Pearce – the discovery being claimed as the largest deposit of gold ever found on Dartmoor.[59]

Characteristic of other small lode workings of this area was the **Kit Tin Mine** which lay a few hundred yards south-east of Sheepstor church (OS 112 NE). No records have been found of the early history of the mine which was last tried in 1915 when the adit was reopened and a shaft sunk to 60ft. According to the Barclay MS the cassiterite occurred in quartz strings, in a country rock consisting of killas overlying the granite. The ore was treated by six heads of stamps which were still in existence (and photographed) in 1928. Only the wheel-pit now remains, together with two buddles and the former blacksmith's shop, these being situated near the Sheepstor Brook, a little to the west of Collyton.[60]

Half a mile east of the Rain Gauge shown on **Yellowmead Down** and immediately south of Outholme Wood the site of an old shaft is marked on the OS map 112 NE. An adit communicates with this shaft, with traces of a tram road extending from its mouth. The adit is said to have been driven about 1870 in search of china clay,[61] but probably served an earlier purpose as a tin trial, alluvial stream workings being visible throughout the length of the Narrator Brook which flows hardby.

By comparison with these small trials, **Eyelesborough** or Eylesbarrow (pronounced Ailsboro), some two miles north-east of Sheepstor, was a tin mine of some importance, but records of its output are lacking and there are no known plans of the underground workings. The mine was at work in 1823 when, along with Vitifer and

Whiteworks, it ranked among the few mines then active on Dartmoor. It had the further distinction of owning a smelting house where 100 blocks of tin metal were coined in the Michaelmas quarter of 1824.[62] Under the name of Dartmoor Consolidated, exploratory work was in progress from 1838 until 1844 when due to the low price of black tin (£40 per ton) and the difficulty of renewing the lease, operations were suspended after returns of over £30,000 had been made.

Work was resumed in 1847 consequent on a favourable report by Captain John Spargo of Stoke Climsland who recommended the deepening of Pryce Deacon's Shaft by 20 fathoms into more settled country. He also noted that small fibres of wolfram (known by the miners as cockle) were dropping towards the lode which, owing to water and the softness of the ground, had hitherto been scarcely worked below the adit level. About £3,000 was needed to reopen the mine on which there was a large 'mansion house', a dwelling for the captain, a smelting house, smith's shop and other buildings. In May 1847, Two Brothers' Adit was being cleared and the manager reported that the deep adit driven by the old adventurers had been cleared to Pryce Deacon's Shaft, which came down on the adit-end 600 fathoms from its mouth. Other shafts mentioned at this time included, from west to east, Whim, New Engine, Old Engine and Henry's, the whole of the workings being drained by a 50ft overshot wheel.[63] In 1848 it was decided to abandon the mine, which was largely controlled by shareholders living in Great Coggeshall, Essex, the expenses by this time having greatly exceeded the original estimate.

In 1849 working was renewed as Aylesborough. During that year it was reported that Henry's Shaft was down to 20 fathoms below adit, which was 10 fathoms deeper than any of the previous workings. In the last 10 fathoms of sinking, the shaft was producing 'good work for tin' and the men were then starting to drive on the lode. In the 10 fathom level, east, the lode was also producing good ore and appeared to be getting under the run of tin ground seen in the bottom of the ancient workings. The main bunch, however, from which the earlier company had made their returns, was still about 10 fathoms further east. In driving west, the lode was disordered by a slide, producing a little tin but not rich.[64] The mine at this date had six heads of stamp.

In April 1851 the company was refloated as Wheal Ruth Tin Mine. The prospectus tallied in nearly all respects with that of Eyelesborough, repeating earlier statements that thousands of pounds had been spent in sinking shafts, driving cross-cuts and bringing up adits, and that 600 fathoms had been driven on the course of the lodes which lay in decomposed granite. The ore was claimed to be superior in quality to any other in Devon, consisting of grain tin which had a market value of £15 per ton in excess of common tin. A report issued by Jehu Hitchins at this time states that principal operations had hitherto been confined to: (a) Michaelmas Shaft Lode, otherwise South Lode; (b) Aylesborough North Lode, and (c) Middle Lode, 'near to Wheal Kate'.

A new Engine Shaft, then sinking on the north of the property, had reached a depth of 13 fathoms under adit and in June 1851 the lode in the 12 fathom level, east, was 2½ft wide and worth £17 per fathom. Six months later the shaft was down to 24 fathoms below the 30 fathom deep adit. By the following May, however, operations had ceased and the sale was advertised of the whole of the machinery and materials consisting of the 50ft by 3ft water-wheel, 30 fathoms of whim-ropes, a 17ft wheel with six heads of stamps, and 70 fathoms of ladders.[65] No mention is made of the smelting house which may have continued in operation for some time after this, purchasing tin concentrates from other mines such as Vitifer and Bottle Hill.

The surface features of Eylesbarrow today consist of some fairly extensive open-cast workings on adjacent high ground and the ruins of an erstwhile farmhouse – no doubt the 'mansion' referred to in the 1847 report. From here, the dressing-floors of the mine can be traced down the eastern slope of Drizzlecombe, along with the sites of stamping mills, settling pools and the dry courses of the leats serving them. On the north side of the track approaching the mine from the west, may be seen a double row of short granite posts with grooves chiselled in their tops. The purpose of this alignment has sometimes been questioned but there is little doubt that it supported a series of rollers which eased the oscillatory movement of the rods, the grooves serving as bearings for the axles of the rollers. Traces of solidified animal grease, used as a lubricant, can still be seen on some of the granite posts.

The smelting works lay on the western side of the Drizzlecombe stream where it is marked on the OS map 112 NE as a blowing-house. Careful examination of the ruins by Hansford Worth showed that the internal dimensions of the building measured 60ft by 20ft, with a flue of over 70ft in length extending from the north wall. This layout differed materially from any of the forty known open-hearth blowing-houses situated elsewhere on the moor, whilst the Eylesbarrow slag was also of a different character due to lime having been used as a flux.[66] From existing evidence it thus seems clear that the smelting was carried out here in a reverberatory-type furnace which despite its introduction to Cornwall early in the 1700s was apparently unknown in Devon before the nineteenth century.

Approximately one mile north-east of Eylesbarrow lies the **Nun's Cross Mine** (OS 113 NW). A tin work adjacent to the 'cross of St Siward' (Nun's Cross) is referred to in a document of 1343,[67] but it is now impossible to say whether this related to an alluvial stream or an open-cast lode working. The mining sett granted during the last century was stated to contain three east-west tin lodes and two caunter lodes, all of which showed signs of having been extensively developed on the backs by the old men.

In 1862-4 exploratory work was carried out on these by a small cost-book company. Investigations revealed two long cross-cut adits driven at shallow depths, whilst on one of the caunter lodes a third adit, some 10 fathoms deeper, was found to carry fair values for tin. It was estimated that £500 would be needed to clear this adit and sink ventilation shafts. In June 1863 it was reported that a shaft then sinking from surface would shortly reach the adit level when driving would be resumed. A sum of £10 was also voted for exploring other lodes which it might seem advisable to work, more especially since a rich branch had recently been laid open in the Devonport leat tunnel which passed through the sett. About 30 fathoms remained to drive in the adit before reaching the Nun's or Main Lode where hopes were entertained of finding good values when it was intersected below the old bottoms.[68] Operations, however, appear to have ceased before the end of 1864 without recorded production.

Some two miles south-east of Princetown, the high moorland tract of **Foxtor Mires** comprises the source of the River Swincombe. Throughout the centuries the area had been worked for alluvial tin, in the course of which numerous small lodes were laid bare in the decomposed granite forming the bed-rock. By the late eighteenth century, if not earlier, underground development of these lodes had been started in the White Works Mine (OS 107 SW). Due to the topography of the area, the adits by which it was mainly exploited were rarely more than a few fathoms below surface, while the swampy nature of the ground, combined with the primitive pumping facilities of that time, prevented shaft-sinking to any significant depth. In 1808, the mine with its several 'workmen's cottages, capital water-engine, pumps, rods, and stamping mills' was advertised for sale,[69] having produced considerable, though unspecified, quantities of tin in its late working.

The mine is known to have been active again in 1820-6, and subsequently in 1848 when it operated for some years under the name of Wheal Industry. During this period, adits were further extended on several of the lodes and at least one new shaft was sunk. In February 1852 two-thirds of the mine was offered for sale by H. Bickford of Princetown, a principal partner in the concern. The sett at this time was stated to contain twenty-four lodes, from which the existing proprietors had divided over £500 worth of tin, and a prospective purchaser might expect to receive an income of £25 per cent per annum on his outlay.[70] It is not known whether the sale took place, but the mine itself continued in operation until 1863.

In 1868 the property reverted to its original name of White Works when a new company was formed and registered at Truro. Under the pursership of Moses Bawden of Tavistock, work started in April of the following year when preparations were being made for sinking and opening up the sett on a large scale. Two parcels of excellent-quality black tin were sold in January 1870, and by December 1871 over 29 tons had been returned for £2,234. In the early part of 1872 the mine was taken over by another company of similar name and in 1876, 96 tons of concentrate was said to have been sold. Although the plan of the workings as described by Dines shows no developments below adit, it was announced in 1877 that the mine had been sunk to 30 fathoms.[71] This was obviously deeper than all the known adits and probably represents the greatest depth attained by any of the fifteen or more shafts shown on the 1883-4 edition of the 6in map.

Bachelor's Hall Mine (OS 107 SW, NW), three-quarters of a mile east of Princetown, was started early in the 1790s following the discovery of a tin lode when cutting the Dock (i.e. Devonport) Leat. On this a shaft was sunk by Mr Gray, the owner of the estate, who subsequently erected a stamping mill and a smelting house on the banks of a small stream which empties into the Blackabrook. John Swete, who visited the mine shortly before 1797, states that it was then employing sixteen men 'two of whom worked the windlass over the shaft'.[72] Soon after this, misunderstandings arose with Sir Thomas Tyrwhitt of Tor Royal, in consequence of which operations were abandoned.

On the expiry of the original lease, Sir Thomas proposed to work the mine himself; but found difficulty in forking the water, 'the main rod of the engine was cut off just below the bob plat, leaving the pumps and pit-work standing in the shaft'. This small concern possessed a beam pumping engine, and this can only be explained by its altitude which rendered it impossible to obtain the water-power that was normally used in preference to steam in all save the largest mines of Devon.

For some time after the sett remained idle, but in 1845 a new company was formed with a twenty-one year lease from the Duchy. Its first task was to clear a deep adit which had earlier been started from the Blackabrook with the object of developing the mine 12 fathoms below the bottom of the Engine Shaft (33 fathoms from surface) where a large extent of tin ground was believed to be standing. The adit was 7ft high and 3ft wide, and by 1846 had been cleared for a length of 60 fathoms. At this point lack of funds, combined with 'disgraceful and almost unheard of mismanagement', brought the project to a close.

Two further attempts were subsequently made to reopen the property where the tin had the reputation of fetching a higher price than any other mine on the moor. In 1853 a report by J. Sims, of the Slimeford Office, Calstock, claimed with some exaggeration that Engine Shaft was then down to 50 fathoms and that the deep adit on completion would unwater the mine 30 fathoms below the existing bottom. There was also a second shaft on the property named Ann's, which had been sunk to the level of the shallow adit. In 1862 it was announced that only 120 fathoms remained to drive in the Deep Adit in order to bring it under the old workings. This could be achieved for a relatively small sum as the lode in the adit end was 2½ft wide and producing good tin stuff. The shallow adit had been driven on a parallel lode close alongside and this could be developed by short cross-cuts from the deep adit.[73] There is nothing to suggest that any of these proposals bore fruit and the plan of the mine, as described by Dines, shows Deep Adit as being stopped 200 fathoms short of its intended objective.

In 1797 it was noted by John Swete that tin ore had recently been found on the tenement of Brimpts adjoining the west bank of the East Dart River, about half a mile north of Dartmeet (OS 107 NE). Work started soon afterwards as evidenced in the following manifesto published in *Mining Journal*, 8 September 1849:

'I, Richard Tuckett of Dunnabridge, in the parish of Lydford do solemnly declare that I am now 79 years of age and that about 50 years since I was in the service of Mr Joseph Sanders of Brimpts and that whilst in his employ I was in the habit of drawing with a slide-but tin stuff from the shaft near to the stable, and also from a level in a field called the Potatoc Field, part of Brimpts estate, down to the stamps, and I continued drawing tin stuff from these places for two or three years. And I further declare that I remember the mine at Brimpts being worked by Joseph Sanders alone for 7 or 8 years and that the tin stuff when made marketable was taken to Tavistock, and I further declare that Joseph Sanders discontinued working the mine because he considered that the miners were imposing on him, and I recollect that the miners offered to work the mine at a low tribute but that Joseph Sanders refused their application.'

A report by Jehu Hitchins in July 1849 states that rich stones of ore were then to be found in the ancient open-workings, below which the old men had excavated the lode to a depth of 10 fathoms under the adit. He advised the immediate erection of a water-wheel and that the adit should be cleared and extended. Work started in September of that year, and by March 1850 the adit had been secured for 45 fathoms and was then within 3 fathoms of the Engine Shaft. Sales of tin nearly covered costs, as reported in August and November 1850, but this statement was subsequently denied at a stormy meeting of the adventurers.

In common with others on the moor, the Brimpts sett was extensive – two and three quarter miles on the course of the lodes and bounded on the south and east by the West and East Dart Rivers, and on the west by the Cherry Brook. Not content with this, the adventurers obtained additional ground in September 1851, extending north to Bellever Tor. At the same time a call was made to provide a new water-wheel with an additional twelve heads of stamps. The company was now in financial difficulties, and in May 1852 the materials including two water-wheels of 28 and 25ft diameter, 270 fathoms of flat-rods, two lifts of pumps, six heads of stamps and a horse-whim were offered for sale.

The sett and materials were acquired by a new company, the Duke of Cornwall Consolidated Tin Mines, which resumed operations in the same year. The property at this time consisted of two parts, known as the North and the South Mine.

The former lay on the summit of the hill where a lode underlying steeply south was developed by a vertical shaft 15 fathoms deep. This was drained by a 24ft wheel connected to the pumps by nearly 200 fathoms of flat-rods. South Mine on the side of the hill comprised three east-west lodes which had been intersected by a shallow cross-cut adit. The more important of these was South Lode on which a shaft was sunk to an eventual depth of 45 fathoms, the water being drawn by a 28ft diameter wheel operating 75 fathoms of flat-rods. Some 32 fathoms below the shallow adit, a deep adit had been started from the river but it appears that the latter was never driven far enough to connect with the South Lode workings.[74]

Owing to many of the shareholders failing to meet their calls, the Duke of Cornwall Mine survived for only one year, and in 1853 the sett was taken over by a company named Devon Tin Mines. Two hundred sacks of tin stuff were raised from a 5 fathom level during June of that year, and work was also proceeding in the 15 fathom level on North Mine. In November it was agreed to lease an area of ground from the Duchy on which to erect a residence for the manager and houses for the miners.

By January 1855 Engine Shaft on North Mine had been deepened to 26 fathoms, the last 15 fathoms being in good tin ground. Six heads of stamps were at work, and some 23cwt of black tin had been sold at the rate of £42 10s per ton. At a meeting held in July 1855 it was resolved to wind up the company. Justin Brooke has suggested that this decision was possibly due to the failure of its bankers, Strahan Paul & Co.[75] Collins records sales to the value of £1,363 during the final year of working, part of which may have come from the Arundell or Druid Mine near Ashburton which was under the same management.

About half a mile west of Hexworthy village (OS 107 SE) tin has been worked for centuries in the valley of the Swincombe River. Here, as elsewhere, development followed the usual pattern. The original streaming era is represented at **Gobbett** by a well-preserved blowing-house complete with a crazing-mill, moulds for casting the smelted ingots and a leat from the river to drive the wheel operating the bellows. Extending along the south side of the road from the village, an excavation 15 to 20yd wide and 15ft deep illustrates the next stage when a lode was worked open-cast, possibly with the addition of small shafts. Finally, the lodes were exploited solely by underground mining in Wheal Gobbett, Deby Hole and Wheal Compton (or Cumpston).

In the years 1836-40, when operating under the name of Dartmoor United Tin Mines, a shaft was sunk in the Gobbett section to a depth of 40 fathoms. From this levels extended on the course of the lodes yielded black tin to the value of £1,000. The machinery consisted of two 24ft diameter water-wheels, one being used for pumping and the other for driving stamps. Further development of the mines being hindered by disagreement among the adventurers, the property was offered for sale in 1840 and resumed work shortly afterwards as Dartmoor Consols. In the course of the next two years an adit was driven 150 fathoms on a lode which is said to have produced some 20 tons of concentrate.[76]

In the late 1860s, the sett was once more taken up when it was known for a time as Swincombe Vale. By 1874 the Engine Shaft had been cleared to a depth of 12 fathoms below adit (7 fathoms) and levels were being driven east and west with a view to finding new ore ground. The old water-wheel still standing on the mine was then in a 'feeble state' and a new wheel was about to be erected. Apart from this there was sufficient machinery on the sett to raise and dress 20 tons of ore a day. A grade of 1 per cent would render this viable, although considerably higher values were anticipated. The ore was said to be free from sulphides and $1^{1}/_{2}$ tons of concentrate were then ready for sale. It was intended in due course to sink the shaft to 10 or 12 fathoms below the existing bottoms.[77] Despite this favourable report it would appear that little more was done and no record of production has been found for this latest working.

The site of the Gobbett Mine is shown on the 6in map, but the whereabouts of Deby Hole and Wheal Compton are no longer identifiable, although the latter is thought to have been in the neighbourhood of Huccaby.

Hens Roost Mine as it is marked on the OS map 107 SE, is now more generally known as Hexworthy, a rather misleading title since it lies fully a mile south-east of that village on the borders of Holne Moor. The mine originated as a group of old men's outcrop workings, comprising Hens Roost on the north and Hooten Wheals to the south.

In 1854 it was reported that the lode in the former had been worked for 40 to 50 fathoms in length and to 30 fathoms in depth, partly as an open-cutting, and below this by back-stoping from an adit driven beneath. On the southern lodes the workings extended for three-quarters of a mile and were excavated in a similar fashion by the ancient miners to a depth of 20 fathoms. During 1852-5 exploratory work was carried out in the sett by a company which expended £4,000 in clearing adits and sinking a new shaft on which a 42in steam engine was erected. In one of the adits a small lode or branch was found, 5 to 6in wide, from which about 8cwt of black tin was sold in August 1854. The surface works included the construction of dressing-floors, erecting a 30ft wheel with eight heads of stamps and laying a tramway from the shaft to the floors. In July as a consequence of dissension among the shareholders, the mine and materials were advertised for sale, although it was considered 'by competent judges, that with a few months' spirited working they would pay costs and shortly after make profits'.[78]

A fresh start was made in 1891 when John Taylor & Sons, the well-known firm of mining engineers, were appointed to lay out the property. A report issued by the company towards the end of that year stresses the exceptional difficulties encountered in reopening the mine where due to its situation 'in a bleak and desolate region in the heart of Dartmoor', roads had to be cut for the transport of machinery and houses erected for the accommodation of the men.

Despite this, much had been accomplished. Taylor's Shaft had been sunk to 24 fathoms and an adit driven 170 fathoms. A 12 head battery of stamps was then at work, and two wheels of 21 and 30ft diameter had been erected for pumping and stamping – water for these being obtained from the O Brook which passed through the sett. No steam power had yet been required, but an engine had been placed near the stamps for use as an auxiliary in case of need. Production of black tin in 1891 amounted to 8 tons 7cwt, which sold at the rate of £60 per ton against an average price for that year of £50 15s.[79] Working continued until 1896 when tin (metal) reached an all-time low of £63 per ton. Output to this date had amounted to 135 tons of black tin which realised £7,525.

With the recovery in price to £143 per ton, operations were renewed in 1905 and from December 1907 to June 1909, 1,717 tons of ore were crushed and 54 tons of concentrate sold for £3,716 at a working cost of approximately £2,500. Owing to the coarse nature of the cassiterite, the treatment was very simple. The pulp from the stamps was passed through classifiers to Wilfley tables and the slimes to round frames and thence to buddles; final dressing was carried out by tossing and packing in kieves. During this period Californian stamps were employed and the mine was electrified, power being generated by a Pelton Wheel near Saddle Bridge, a mile downstream from the mill and a short distance from the confluence of the O Brook with the West Dart River.

Due to lack of capital and hand-to-mouth methods, the plant only worked for eight hours daily and in 1912 a Mr E. S. King, then consulting engineer to a number of mines in Cornwall, was called in to suggest improvements. He reported that there were three lodes in the mine. The most important of these was Low's Lode which was being worked at adit and in the 12 and 24 fathom levels. In the latter, the lode averaged 9$\frac{1}{2}$in wide over a length of 1,400ft, with a mean value of 37lb of black tin to the ton. In the following year, on Mr King's recommendation, the shaft was sunk a further 120ft, where the lode showed improvement both in size and value. The work was completed at the outbreak of World War I when further progress was prevented by the call-up of men for the services. The mine was then placed under care and maintenance and the last recorded production was 13$\frac{1}{2}$ tons of black tin in 1915-16.

During the winter of 1920, a rainstorm of exceptional violence destroyed the flume carrying water to the pumping wheel, and the mine became flooded. In 1925 proposals were made for a reopening, with the addition of a further ten heads of stamps in order to double output.[80] It would appear that nothing came of this suggestion, and the use of the site for combat practice by American forces during World War II destroyed most of the buildings which were left.

BIRCH TOR AND VITIFER

Near the fourteenth milestone from Tavistock, on the Moretonhampstead road, an area comprising some two square miles formerly constituted the largest tin-producing region of Dartmoor. Here can be seen the great gullies or open-cast workings excavated over the centuries by alluvial streamers; whilst all around stand traces of adits, shafts, leats and wheel-pits, together with ruined buildings formerly housing the stamps and treatment plant of a later period of mining. In contrast to its former activity, the area now lies silent and deserted amid the solitude of the moor, with heather and bracken regaining their old ascendancy over the work of man.

Chief among the mines of this locality were Birch Tor and Vitifer, the latter first described by Charles Hatchett, the eighteenth-century geologist and mineralogist, who visited the mine in 1796. He observed that the lode ran east to west, and had already been developed for over a quarter of a mile in length, as seen in the 'antient channels' cut down upon it in former times by streaming. The country rock consisted of pale-red decomposed granite or growan, in which the lode varied in width from one to twenty or more inches. The tin occurred in a matrix of quartz, often accompanied by black schorl, also with peach or chlorite of different tints of green. The cassiterite consisted of small prisms of pale-brown colour 'frequently coated with a brown earthy tin somewhat resembling Wood Tin'. Alongside the walls of the lode there generally ran a thin vein of Eisenglimmer (specular haematite). This iron ore was also found in larger quantities within the body of the lode, and was sold separately to a Mr Kingdon, the lessee of the sett, who had evidently found a market for the product. The tin concentrates were sent to Tavistock where there was a small smelting works owned by a Mr Lane. The mine at this time was employing forty men and had thirteen shafts. Engine Shaft was 21 fathoms deep with an over-shot wheel for pumping, whilst Western Shaft was in course of sinking to a 40 fathom level.[81]

In 1808, the Vitifer Mine was advertised for sale and during the 1820s was being worked in conjunction with Birch Tor by the Davey brothers of Redruth. With tin (metal) standing at little more than £70 per ton, the times were not propitious for mining. 'I never knew things so bad here,' wrote Stephen Davey to the manager in 1826. 'Gettings among the miners are very small, I should think under 50s per month, for which they are obliged to work *very hard* [Davey's emphasis]. Now seems to be the time to work Birch Tor to advantage and I think the reduced rate of labour will more than compensate the fall in the price of tin. I don't know the quality of the tin you have been sending to Ailsboro Smelting House.'[82]

Shortly after this time the Daveys appear to have taken into their partnership a distant relative named 'Quaker' John Palk. The latter had long been working part of Birch Tor on his own account, and was consequently better acquainted with the character of its lodes than the Daveys could have been. Having gradually worked his way into the position of manager, he continued to make call after call for money to carry on the mine and at length the patience of the Daveys became exhausted. Believing the property to be almost worthless, they offered it to Palk for a small sum. The latter equivocated. 'Friend,' he said, 'I am a poor man and cannot raise so much but by the blessing of the Lord I would like to try to earn a bit of bread from it to put into my mouth. Will thee not 'bate the price to the level of my means?' Eventually he became sole owner of the property as had been his aim all along. Although knowing full well where the best values lay, he had hitherto studiously avoided working anything but the poorest ore. Once the mine became his own its complexion showed a radical change, and he is reputed to have made an ultimate profit of £60,000 by his shrewd if unscrupulous deal.[83]

In 1838 Birch Tor was said to be the only mine of any magnitude then working on Dartmoor. Operated entirely by water-power, it had two 40ft wheels and one of 32ft and was employing 117 people, thirty of whom were women and children. The mine being situated at an altitude of 1,100 to 1,400ft above sea level, the leats supplying water for the wheels were commonly frozen up for several weeks at a time in winter. The miners consisted largely of men who had absconded from other districts on account of petty offences, and so scanty was the accommodation in the few and wretched hovels near the mine that the beds were always occupied – as one occupant left for work, he was succeeded by another returning from the mine.[84] Added to the ill effects of overcrowding, much hardship resulted from the nature of the work. This applied not only to those exposed to the weather on surface, but equally to those underground where due to the porous nature of the granite, the miners frequently laboured beneath streams of ice-cold water, a condition far more deleterious to health than the heat experienced in the close-grained rock of deeper mines.

Apparently the hardy native moormen withstood the conditions better. In 1864 it was recorded that a certain Joe Hamlyn had worked at Birch Tor for seventy-five years, and that another miner, Jacob German, had been there for sixty years. Men such as these usually had homes in one or other of the neighbouring moorland villages to which they periodically returned, bringing back food for the ensuing week and sleeping in sheds fitted with bunks provided by the mine. At the old Warren House Inn, where it is said that the peat fire never went out for 100 years, uproarious scenes were witnessed on pay days when those who could afford the dubious luxury of getting drunk indulged in countless brawls and horseplay.

In 1845 it was stated that the Vitifer Mine had been worked intermittently over a period of 150 years, and had been developed by the old men in open-cast excavations 100 to 200ft wide. A new company was formed at this time to amalgamate Vitifer and Birch Tor in a combined sett of over a mile in length. In 1846 Engine Shaft on the Birch Tor Lode was 84 fathoms deep from surface and some time later Hambly's Shaft reached a depth of 60 fathoms. During this period the mines were drained by two 45ft water-wheels, and Brunton frames were introduced for re-treating the halvans (discarded leavings). These were said to have proved effective in separating the iron ore from the tin. Generally speaking, however, the lodes were less rich than the company had been led to expect, more particularly in the deepest level (74 fathoms) where the drives extending east and west entered very poor ground.

Notwithstanding this, a fresh company was formed in 1859 entitled New Birch Tor and Vitifer Consols. In 1866, 95½ tons of black tin was sold for £4,739, 120 people were employed, and the mine was stated to be profitable and likely to continue so. The two water-wheels were then pumping from a depth of 70 fathoms from surface,[85] work being concentrated on three lodes: North, Graham's and Great South Lode. For some years the output enabled dividends to be paid, but by the 1870s the best tin ground was becoming exhausted. After 1880 no shaft sinking or driving was carried out, and in 1886 the sett was abandoned.

In 1923 a new lease was obtained from the Duchy and a considerable sum was expended on erecting machinery and improved dressing plant. A few shallow levels were reopened, but little tin was raised. Further trials carried out in 1938-9 were chiefly confined to the treatment of dumps and tailings. The outbreak of war caused this last working to be abandoned, and since that time the sett has remained idle.[86]

East Birch Tor Mine, as its name implies, lay east of Birch Tor and Vitifer Consols. The workings were situated in the valley between Headland Warren and Challacombe Warren, the main part of the mine being sited immediately south of Headland Warren farm (OS 100 NW). The mine was served by a cross-cut adit 287 fathoms in length which intersected six lodes. In 1848, levels driven 100 fathoms west and 150 fathoms east on South Lode were said to be yielding tin throughout. North Lode had been opened up at Shallow Adit for 100 fathoms east and 17 fathoms west from Engine Shaft which was then 12 fathoms below adit or 24 fathoms deep from surface. The bottom level extending 37 fathoms east and 52 west was producing more tin than at adit level. In 1856, twenty-seven heads of stamps were in use driven by two water-wheels. The pumps consisted of a bucket-lift operated by a 30ft wheel, the latter being connected to the shaft by three-quarters of a mile of flat rods.[87]

Due to financial difficulties, the mine was abandoned in 1851 but the company was soon reconstituted and the sett was amalgamated with **Devon Great Tin Croft**, which had started work some years earlier in adjoining ground on the east. The workings of the latter were originally confined to adit level, but during the next few years six shafts were sunk to a maximum depth of 24 fathoms. Despite the fact that some driving was done at this horizon, mainly by tributers, the results on the whole proved disappointing and in 1867 working ceased. In 1903 a fresh lease was acquired and operations continued intermittently and with diminishing success until 1926-7.[88]

Golden Dagger Mine (OS 99 NE), on the south of Birch Tor and Vitifer, lies close to the boundary of Manaton parish. The main workings were centered beneath the large open gunnises which extend across Soussons Down for a distance of over 1,000yd. Worked at intervals over a long period, the mine was noted for the very pure quality of its tin, and is said to have been actively developed in the period 1835-60.

In 1880 the sett was acquired by Moses Bawden, and in the course of the next four years £10,000 is claimed to have been spent in erecting machinery and treatment plant. Several new shafts were started at this time, among them Machine Shaft which was sunk to a depth of 40 fathoms. A long adit, to come in under the older workings, was also commenced in the lowest part of the valley.

In 1909 a new company was formed, and the Drainage Adit was extended to 1,250ft. The adit passed through 700-800ft of good tin ground from which one parcel of ore was sold at the rate of £131 per ton, then the best price for black tin for more than fifty years past. The mine was equipped at this time with a 6 head battery of Cornish stamps driven by a 22½ft by 9ft water-wheel, the pulp being concentrated on Wilflcy tables capable of treating 35 tons a day.[89] In 1924 a turbo-generator and magnetic separator were introduced, but the latter appears to have been unsuccessful. Operations continued on a decreasing scale until the late 1920s. The mine now lies in a forestry plantation.

On the western side of the Moretonhampstead road, some 14½ miles from Tavistock, a lease was obtained in 1850 of an area of ground adjacent to the **North Walla Brook**. From the side of this an adit was started to connect with a proposed Engine Shaft on the south-west. Through failure to obtain the necessary capital, the project was abandoned in 1852. In 1866 William Skewis, then agent at New Birch Tor and Vitifer Consols, renewed operations by sinking trial pits and trenches in the setts of Waterhill and Kings Oven.[90] Shortly after, Valley Shaft and Water Hill Shaft were started a short distance south of West Vitifer Mine (OS 99 NE).

In December 1869, the water being too quick to be kept by a horse-engine, it was proposed to bring in a leat from the North Walla Brook and to erect a pumping wheel. In the following year the property was acquired by a company formed in Bristol with a capital of £12,000. A 60ft wheel was erected at West Vitifer for stamping and pumping, and a number of promising lodes were opened up. In excavating the wheel-pit, old men's workings were revealed on the outcrop of the Black Pool Lode, samples of which showed values of up to £10 per fathom. In 1870 fourteen people were employed,[91] but three years later the authorised capital was exhausted. Although an additional £5,000 was raised, by 1875 this had also been spent and in that year the company was wound up, with no recorded production.[92]

Great Wheal Eleanor situated as shown on the OS map 90 SW about half a mile south-west of North Bovey village, was thought to lie on the most easterly extension of the Birch Tor and Vitifer run of lodes. The mine was restarted in 1875 by a local company when sampling showed fine-grained tin in payable quantities. On the strength of this a count-house and blacksmith's shop were erected, and soon after a 200hp engine with twenty-eight heads of stamps was purchased from Messrs Lanyon & Co of Truro. Water for dressing and other purposes was obtained from the boggy slopes of Easdon Down, and was fed into a pond immediately above the engine-shed.

The stamps were set to work in August 1876 when a commentator somewhat cautiously remarked, 'If they are able to keep all the buddies in full work (as from the enormous backs they have ready for stoping they seem likely to do) the returns of tin must be considerable.' In the following year the mine was inspected by Captain Josiah Thomas who reported that the lode in the 20 fathoms level contained 33 1b of black tin to the ton. Engine Shaft was later deepened to 30 fathoms and was served by a shallow and deep adit, below which the water was drawn by a 60ft wheel. New Shaft, 90yd west of Engine Shaft reached only to Deep Adit level, at this point 18 fathoms from surface. In 1880 the lode was said to be worth from 70 to 80lb of tin to the ton, and an additional eight heads of stamps were being prepared. In the following year, however, the mine was abandoned, the sole output of black tin recorded from 1876 amounting only to 20 tons.[93]

Little can be seen of the mine today other than a wheel-pit and, a short distance to the south-west, a fairly extensive opencast working which appears to have been excavated by the old men on the back of another lode.

CHAPTER 3

YELVERTON TO PLYMOUTH

About one mile west of Yelverton station, prospecting trials were being carried out in 1853 at **Devon Wheal Buller** (OS 112 SW), where stones of yellow and black copper ore, 'all but solid copper', had been obtained from a shaft less than 2 fathoms deep. To the north of this spot, at Stoke Hill, costeaning (trenching or pitting) had revealed an east-west lode 2½ft wide, carrying tin ore, while at Cumerew a search was being made for other lodes near the southern boundary of the sett. An adit had been driven about 8 fathoms[1] and later in the year a horse-whim was erected.

Up to this time the work appears to have been financed by Sir Anthony Buller as a private venture, but in 1854 the mine was taken over by a cost-book company. By May of that year Emma's Engine Shaft had been sunk to 20 fathoms, and from it cross-cuts were being driven northwards. A year later a 36in steam engine was put to work, Engine Shaft being then 34 fathoms deep. The 20 level had been driven 50 fathoms east and a like distance west. Western Shaft was down to 10 fathoms. Production in 1855 amounted to 86 tons of copper ore,[2] the lode being reported as 3ft wide and yielding 2 tons of ore per fathom. In January 1859 a new shaft was being sunk, presumably the one later referred to as Down's. In June 1862 a 50in pumping engine was set to work, the ceremony being performed by Miss Emma Buller, daughter of Sir Anthony, 'who baptized it "Emma's engine" amidst the cheers of the miners and visitors...' By January 1863 Down's Shaft had been sunk to 65 fathoms from surface. The lode in the 55 fathom level, west, was about 3ft wide, composed of capels and peach (chlorite), while in the same level, east, it showed traces of black copper ore.[3]

Four months later the whole of the machinery and materials were put up for sale, these comprising Emma's Engine, a 10in rotary-whim, boilers, a horse-whim and about 70 fathoms of pit work. Phillips and Darlington record an output of 276 tons of copper ore in the year 1855-6 whilst Dines gives a figure of 1,514 tons for the period 1855-61.

To the south of Yelverton, the area of **Roborough Down** is crossed by an estimated number of ten east–west lodes whose outcrop workings are visible today in the form of grass-grown entrenchments extending from Yeoland farm to the railway (OS 112 SW). Work was already in progress here in Elizabethan times, as appears from a letter by Sir Walter Raleigh to Sir Robert Cecil dated 15 November 1600:

'A gentleman, Mr Crymes, hath erected certain clash-mylls upon Roburghe Down to work the tynn which upon that place is gott with extreme labor and charge out of the ground. And because the townsmen of Plymouth seeke to procure all the commoditie thereabouts into their own hands, they allege that these mylls are prejudiciall to them and that the course of their water, which runneth through Plymouth, is diverted, contrary to a statute.'

In this conflict of interests, so familiar to mining companies of today, Sir Walter came down firmly on the side of the miners.

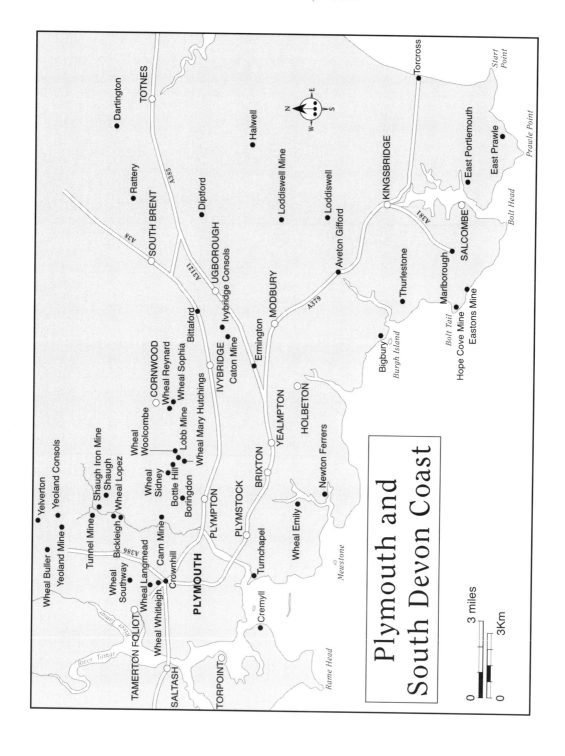

Plymouth and South Devon Coast

3 miles

3Km

'I took paines,' he continues, 'to view the river [Meavy] and mylls. I found that in my opinion they [Plymouth] could not disallow the using or the building of the same for that there are about 200 works which must be unwrought without the use of such clash-mylls and benefit of that river.'

The Plymouth townsfolk, however, were not willing to let the matter rest there:

'They have procured sub penas out of the Starre Chamber to call the matter in question – the matter being tryable and determinable in the Stannary Court where it now dependeth. But if this be suffered to proceed in the Starre Chamber it will not be available to speak of Her Majesty's... encrease of custom or to establish good lawes amongst the Tynners, when others who can by a great purse, or procuring extraordinary means, diminish... her Majesty's duties and the common benefytt of the people.'[5]

Although it is reasonable to suppose that the lodes were developed by adits and shafts at an early period, there are no known records to confirm this. An old but undated plan, referred to by Dines, shows a Shallow and a Deep Adit (the portal of the latter opening on the west bank of the Meavy, opposite Olderwood farm), whence it connected to the Engine Shaft of **Yeoland Consols** (marked on the OS map 2 SW as Yeoland Mine). In 1853 the depth of this mine was stated to be 64 fathoms from surface, with levels driven east and west at 30, 42, 54 and 64 fathoms, all of which had proved productive particularly the 42 and 54. The lode was of great size, '8 to 10 fathoms wide in places'. A new perpendicular shaft was then being sunk, which at 22 fathoms from surface would pass through the North Lode which was expected in depth to prove as productive as the Main Lode on which operations were then being conducted.[6]

By 1856 Engine Shaft had been sunk to 74 fathoms from surface on the course of the lode. There was a 36in steam engine driving twenty-four heads of stamps in addition to pumping, and a 22in engine served for hoisting. Since the commencement of operations in 1851, sales of black tin had realised £13,000, the latest quarterly returns amounting to 15 tons. Production was expected to increase as two new levels were then being opened out in good ground at 56 fathoms below adit. It was also intended to deepen the shaft,[7] but in March 1857 it was decided to abandon operations, and the mine and materials were put up for sale.

East Yeoland, which lay below the railway adjacent to the dressing-floors of Yeoland Consols, was by comparison only lightly developed, apart from a small winze there being no workings below the Deep Adit level. In 1853 the manager reported that a cross-cut had been driven 6 fathoms south from the adit intersecting a lode 9ft wide containing good work for tin.[8] There appears, however, to have been no production.

On Chubbtor Farm, a short distance south of East Yeoland, **Plymouth Wheal Yeoland** developed three lodes. A report on this property in 1848 by Charles Thomas, manager of Dolcoath Mine, states that on North Lode an adit had been driven for 100 fathoms, at a depth of 10 to 14 fathoms below surface. About £10 worth of tin had been raised from this level, but the appearances on the whole were 'exceedingly poor'. On South Lode, a shaft had been sunk 23 fathoms and an engine erected. The 2 fathom level extended 24 fathoms, and at one point had returned some tin; but the end of the lode was unproductive. The 24 fathom level passed beneath this tin ground, but was of value only for about 5 fathoms. New South Lode near the Engine Shaft had been worked for 10 or 12 fathoms, at a maximum depth of 5 fathoms from surface. Over a short length the lode was worth about £4 per fathom. In concluding his report the writer suggested sinking the shaft to 30 fathoms and driving on the South Lode at the 20 where it was about 2ft wide and not unpromising in character.[9]

In 1855 by which time the name of the mine had been changed to South Yeoland, a 32in engine and twelve heads of stamps had been erected and the shaft sunk vertically to 33 fathoms. Cross-cuts had been put out north and south to intersect parallel lodes. Some tin had been sold, but the workings at this time were principally for copper,'[10] of which Smith's Shop Lode had returned ore assaying 27 per cent metal from one bunch. Despite this, operations were abandoned shortly after, the sett and machinery being advertised for sale in August 1855 (Mining Journal).

It would appear from outcrop workings that the Yeoland lodes were formerly pursued for a considerable distance to the east. In 1886 Captain Joel Manley of Horrabridge stated in the Mining Journal (28 August) that at 'Elderwood [Olderwood as shown on the map] we are putting down a shaft through old men's workings and at a depth of about 7 fathoms are finding parts of the lode producing 200lbs of black tin to the ton of stuff'.

In 1881 a new company was formed, entitled Yeoland Consols, with a capital of £60,000–£20,000 of which was pocketed by the promoters. The project called forth an embittered letter from the former manager, Captain Richard Williams, whose opinion of the mine was summed up in his final words 'the lode is large, the ground bad and the average yield of black tin does not exceed 4lbs per ton. To say that the lode improved in depth is not true'. On the face of it, the fortunes of the company justified this condemnation. A first batch of concentrate, amounting only to 16cwt, was sent to the Redruth Tin Smelting Company in August 1883. It was stated at this time that 2,000 tons of tinstuff were ready for stamping, but no machinery had been erected nor had any arrangements been made for bringing in water to dress it.

In 1884, two years after operations had started, the mine was still without water or steam-power and no development had been carried out other than lengthening an adit by 20 fathoms and walling up the sides of a wheel-pit. Due to a prolonged drought, the mine was again short of water in 1886, although 36 tons of concentrate had been sold in the first seven months of that year. A promise had been made of additional capital for sinking a shaft, but in 1887 the directors reported that this had failed to materialise. Working at that time was still confined to above the adit level, and by the end of the year the funds of the company were virtually exhausted. A proposal to form a new company in 1888 came to nothing, and by 1890 the shares had ceased to be quoted.[11] It is clear that this last working was a costly failure, but whether primarily due to the incompetence of the directors in all matters relating to mining, or to poverty of the lodes it is impossible to say since the latter were never seen in depth.

THE BICKLEIGH
AND PLYMPTON NEIGHBOURHOOD

About 1858 a copper lode was discovered in the parish of Bickleigh when the Leebeer Tunnel (OS 112 SW) on the Plymouth to Tavistock Railway was being driven. In the roof of the tunnel, about 66ft below surface, the lode was fully 4ft wide showing 'stones of rich horseflesh copper ore and green carbonate, the north part of the lode for a foot wide being almost as green as a leek'. Near the floor of the tunnel, however, the lode contracted to one foot 'very hard, no ore and but little greens to be seen'. The enclosing rock was an exceedingly hard granite. In 1859 a prospectus was issued under the heading of the **Tunnel Mine**, a name which was altered in the following year to Bickleigh Vale Phoenix. The copper lode was stated at this time to be 12ft wide where it had been opened at surface, while a tin lode 4 to 6ft in width had recently been found near the tunnel's mouth. Abundant water was available from the river which ran close by, and a good road passed through the property to the 'copper quay'. Despite these attractions, it appears that the company failed to interest the investing public, and beyond driving a short adit, little work was done and in 1862 operations were suspended.[12]

In Vicarage Wood and Hele Bottom (OS 118 NW), some three-quarters of a mile north-west of Bickleigh Church, two lodes carrying copper, blende (zinc ore) and small amounts of tin strike east–west across a north–south valley. These were exploited in a mine called **Wheal Lopes** (or Lopez), a lease for which is said to have been granted by the Lopes family in 1760. However, the earliest working of which any particulars are known took place in the second decade of the nineteenth century. By 1821 the Main Lode had been explored for 120 fathoms west and 60 fathoms east by an adit. Below this, the 10 fathom level extended 5 fathoms east and 20 fathoms west; and the 14 fathom level extended 15 fathoms east and 65 fathoms west. In this last, the lode yielded 140 tons of good copper ore. The bottom level (24 fathoms below adit), was driven 7 and 50 fathoms east and west respectively, and also contained ore of 'superior quality'. South Lode (40 fathoms south of Main Lode) returned a few tons of yellow copper ore at the Adit Level (here about 7 fathoms below surface).

As shown on the OS map, water to drive the machinery was brought to the mine by a long leat from the Plym, an expensive undertaking which involved tunnelling through 500 feet of hard granite at the intake from the river. In 1823 the sett and materials were put up for sale, the latter comprising a 30ft water-wheel, horse-whims and a stamping mill. The mine was described as being near Jump (now known as Roborough), within four miles of Lophill (Lopwell) Quay, and five from Plymouth Dock (Devonport).[13] Subsequent to its closure, 26 tons of copper ore were sold in 1825.

About 1840 the sett was acquired by the Plymouth and Dartmoor Mining Company, and two 40ft water-wheels were installed, together with a new drawing machine. During the spring of 1844 work was proceeding in the 30, 50 and 60 fathom levels, and returns were averaging 20 tons per month. In May of that year the *Mining Journal* reported that the mine was also producing copper precipitate at the rate of several hundredweight a month, and that the copper ore raised during this working had totalled 552 tons which realised £2,666. Most of the ore had come from the western part of the mine. The main shaft was then down to 82 and another shaft to 62 fathoms below adit. Owing to the fall in the standard of copper from £107 to £90, working ceased at the end of 1846, the materials being auctioned in March 1846. The sett was taken up again in January 1856 when the standard had risen to £130. In addition, a great quantity of blende, which had been laid open in the previous working when that mineral was almost valueless, was now worth £3 a ton, so that profits were anticipated. A new 40ft wheel, 8 feet in the breast, was erected together with other machinery, but owing to mismanagement and various financial difficulties the lower levels were never forked (pumped out).[14]

In 1860 the plant was still standing on the property and ready to work again 'at a week's notice'. An attempt to sell the mine in 1862 failed to obtain a purchaser, but at length in 1865 a company was formed, under dubious auspices, and as Devon Wheal Lopes working was resumed. In the course of the next two years the leat and adit were cleared, the 40ft wheel rehabilitated, and the Engine Shaft forked to the 62 fathom level. But the shareholders were not happy, and complaints were frequent regarding the misappropriation of capital and the unscrupulous character of some of the directors. Operations continued for a short time longer, but by 1868 the mine had closed and the company was being wound up.[15]

Until the early 1960s, the shaft in Vicarage Wood was open to the adit, and on the eastern bank of the stream the wheel-pit, with ruined buildings adjoining, was still visible. However, the area had already been planted with young conifers, and these have since obscured the last traces of its mining past.

Near the east bank of the Plym, south of Shaugh Bridge, a vertical north-south iron lode has been worked in a sheer-sided open-cut in Square's Wood (OS 118 NW). The excavation was drained by an adit, with a communicating shaft, brought up from the west, and in the four years prior to 1838 operations were carried on by Messrs Langdon & Paddon of Stonehouse. The ore was said to be intermixed with plumbago (black lead), and there were 'indications' of a copper vein crossing the iron lode, the former supposed to be an extension of one of the Wheal Lopes lodes. By 1840 a leat had been brought in from the River Cad,[16] and a water-wheel erected with flat-rods and pumps. Parallel with the Square's Wood Lode, about 50yd to the east, a long narrow quarry is shown on the map adjacent to the road to Shaugh Prior. Iron stone has also been found here.[17]

In 1859 the **Shaugh Iron Mine** was advertised for sale; numerous enquiries were received, but there were no takers owing to the exorbitant dues of 2s 6d a ton demanded by the mineral lord, Sir Massey Lopes. The mine was subsequently worked during the short-lived iron boom of the 1870s, when an output of 4,670 tons was recorded.[18] Some further examination of the deposit was carried out by a Mr Ward in 1938, but the ore was found to be too much contaminated by arsenic to justify working.

A short distance north of Plym Bridge (OS 118 SW), the small **Cann Mine** was worked about 1824-5 by Messrs Petherick of St Blazey, Cornwall. The lode was originally cut when excavating the canal which served the Cann Slate Quarry, and for this reason the venture was otherwise known as the Canal Mine. In 1829 the sett was regranted to Joseph Thomas Austen, the well-known Cornish industrialist who later assumed the name of Treffry. A surface plan prepared in that year[19] shows three shafts, one on the west bank of the canal adjoining the river, the others just east of the canal. The mine is said to have been drained by a branch of the Boringdon Mine adit, and was later developed by a steam engine 'the remains of which and the old burrows can now be seen', as a correspondent of *Mining Journal* pointed out in December 1859. More remarkably, traces of the little engine-house still remained in 1956, having just escaped obliteration by the embankment of the Plymouth–Tavistock Railway, at the foot of which it stands. Nothing else is known of this virtually forgotten mine which receives no mention by Collins or Dines.

East of Plym Bridge, **Boringdon Park Mine** (OS 118 SW) has been worked on at least three occasions. About 1820 a certain Captain Remfry started operations on a lead lode exposed on the edge of the wood, some three-quarters of a mile west-north-west of Boringdon Manor. From here an adit was driven 200 fathoms on the course of the lode, but owing to the flatness of the ground was nowhere more than 12 fathoms below surface. Working continued until 1824 when the sett and materials, including a 23ft water-wheel, were advertised for sale.[20] Ten years later the mine was taken up by a Captain Bray, soon after which a company was formed. In the autumn of 1836 a 30in steam engine, designed by William West, was ordered from the Hayle Foundry in Cornwall, its shipment to the mine being considerably delayed by the storminess of the weather. Some rich parcels of silver-lead ore and a quantity of black jack (zinc ore) were returned during this working which ended in 1839, mainly through lack of power in the engine to cope with the water when the shaft reached a depth of 50 fathoms from surface.[21]

About 700ft to the east, **East Boringdon Mine** developed an extension of the same lode. To unwater this, the Boringdon Park adit was extended to a total length of nearly three-quarters of a mile, entering East Boringdon Shaft at a depth of 32 fathoms from surface. Meanwhile, work had restarted at **Boringdon Park Mine**, and in 1852 the two setts were united and became known as Boringdon Consols. A new 40in cylinder pumping engine was erected on the Boringdon Shaft, whence by means of flat-rods it also drew the water from East Boringdon. In the course of the next few years, Murchison's or Engine Shaft was sunk to 40 fathoms, Hitchin's to 35 fathoms, and Annie's Engine Shaft was deepened to 72 fathoms from the surface. The East Mine was eventually developed to a 48 fathom level below adit, and in the Old Mine there were levels below adit at 15, 30 and 40 fathoms.[22]

Records of output from 1852-7 comprised 400 tons of lead ore, 10 tons of blende, about 8,000oz of silver (Dines, p.686), and an unspecified amount of copper ore. The final sale of the materials took place in February 1857 and included the engine, a 38ft diameter water-wheel for crushing and several horse-whims. Summing up its history in December 1859, the *Mining Journal* remarked that the stoppage of the mine resulted more from financial embarrassment than impoverishment of the lodes and that there was a probability of its being worked again.

Adjoining Boringdon Consols on the north, and separated only 'by the drive through Boringdon Wood called the Forty Foot Ride', **Wheal Harriet Sophia** was said to lie on a westward continuation of the Wheal Sidney lodes. The sett had been only slightly worked, but in 1859 'the Sidney party were said to be taking it up as their levels were approaching the boundary'.[23]

Through Fernhill Wood a line of old surface workings coursing east-west marks the outcrop of the lodes of **Wheal Sidney** (OS 118 SE), its name derived from the mineral owner, Sidney Strode of Newnham Park. The sett extends from the Tory Brook on the east to a point just west of the road running north from Plympton to Cadover Bridge, and contains three lodes yielding tin and arsenic. When reopened in 1850, the mine was said to have been 'supposedly worked over 300 years since'. Although little is known of its early history beyond the fact that it was active in 1795,[24] the outcrop workings are probably far older than this and might indeed be almost of any age. At the time of its restarting, the shaft was already down to 90 fathoms on the underlie and was served by a Shallow Adit brought up by the old men from the Elfordleigh valley on the south-west, the adit entering the shaft at some 12 fathoms below surface.[25] Deep Adit is driven into the sett from the Tory Brook Valley, and near its mouth lay the dressing-floors which were connected to the shafts by a tramway through the wood. In 1854 there were twenty-four heads of stamps in operation, and 100 tons of black tin had been sold in the two previous years at prices varying from £65 to £82 per ton. By 1855 the mine had about broken even, the value of sales to that date having amounted to £8,459 on a called-up capital of £8,832.[26]

Some time before 1860 a new shaft was started 100 fathoms north of the old mine with a view to taking the lode in its northerly dip. The workings were drained by a 45ft water-wheel situated on the west bank of the Tory Brook and connected to the pumps by wooden flat-rods over a quarter of a mile in length. On reaching a depth of 65 fathoms, a stream of water was cut in the shaft bottom, which drowned the pumps and inundated the mine. However, this setback was soon overcome. Within a few months the shaft was re-equipped with 15 and 16in plungers, and the old flat-rods, which had been subject to constant breakages, were replaced by new 2½in rods with hammered-iron joints – enabling the shaft to be sunk to its ultimate depth of 100 fathoms. By means of cross-cuts, a large amount of tin ground was opened up, although the mine still laboured under the disadvantages of being worked solely by underhand stopes and having only a crab winch for hoisting the ore.[27] Between 1854 and 1864 sales of 412 tons of black tin were recorded, part of which may have come from Wheal Julian, which stands about 300yd north of Wheal Sidney and developed parallel lodes.

In 1855 the Wheal Julian sett was acquired by Messrs H. D. Skewis of Beer Alston and John Sims of Calstock, who initiated trials in the old men's workings. A gunnis 3 to 4 fathoms wide was opened up in which oak trees believed to be over 200 years old were standing – proof that nothing had been done there since the work of the ancients'. Tin worth £65 to £70 a ton was found in some of the old pillars (arches), and numerous veins were also visible on the northern side of the gunnis. Near this a small shaft was sunk to take the lode at a depth of 20 fathoms. In the south part of the gunnis, some 70 fathoms east of the shaft, the lode was 3ft wide and worth 'at least' £100 per fathom.[28]

After a lapse of two or three years, occasioned by the exorbitant terms and unreasonable restrictions imposed by the mineral owner, Mr Julian of Laira House, Plymouth, working was renewed on a somewhat larger scale. At the bottom of the trial shaft a cross-cut was put out to the South Lode and on this a level producing rich stones of tin was driven 8 or 10 fathoms. A 22in steam engine was installed in 1857, and in the following year South Lode was reported to be 7 to 8ft wide in the 8 fathom level and carrying tin, peach (chlorite) and gossan worth £30 to £40 per fathom. However, due to the lack of water for dressing and other purposes and the difficulty of acquiring rights over certain adjoining fields, the materials were offered for sale in April 1859 and in the following January the sett was advertised to let with immediate possession. Working was resumed in that year, the water being drawn out by a small 18in 'double-engine' acquired from North Tamar Mine.[29] According to the plan, Engine Shaft was eventually sunk to 60 fathoms, where a cross-cut south from the bottom intersected the Main Lode at a distance of 58 fathoms. Although worked until 1860 as separate mines, Wheal Julian was subsequently amalgamated with Wheal Sidney, and in 1865 the machinery of the combined sett consisted of a 56in pumping engine and a 18in winding engine, together with two 45ft water-wheels. Operations appear to have continued into the 1880s, a section of the Main Lode accompanying the plan being dated 1882.[30]

Eastward of Wheal Sidney a number of mines, mostly small, have been worked along the course of the Smallhanger Brook. The more southerly of these was **Hemerdon**

Consols (OS 118 SE),[31] which included the Lobb Mine on the farm of that name. About 1820 an adit had been driven there on a promising tin lode, but since it adjoined Mr Strode's game preserves no grant could be obtained and the trial was abandoned. The southern portion of Hemerdon Consols was started or restarted in 1851 when a shaft was sunk to 40 fathoms by means of a 32in William West rotary engine which served for pumping, hoisting and stamping. The upper levels showed good values, but the productiveness of the lodes is said to have diminished in depth where they entered the hard granite. Some thousands of pounds were spent, and about £1,200 worth of black tin recovered prior to the mine being abandoned in 1856.[32]

Ten years later, working was resumed in the western part of the same sett under the name of Wheal Mary Hutchings. By October 1868 more than £5,000 worth of tin had been returned from a depth of only 20 fathoms, and 'hundreds of fathoms of tin ground had been laid open'. During the same month a new pumping wheel 50ft in diameter, 6ft breast, was set to work, being christened 'Medlycott' by Mrs Strode, wife of the mineral owner. Water from this was carried on to a second wheel, 45ft in diameter, which drove twenty-four heads of stamps. In the year ended November 1868, sales of 53 tons of black tin were recorded, and in 1873 the mine was 52 fathoms deep from surface and employed 105 people. Between 1866 and 1880 sales amounted to 426 tons of black tin, 221 tons of mispickel, and 230 tons of arsenic.[33]

Near the 500ft contour between the valleys of the Smallhanger Brook and the Tory Brook, the stack of **Bottle Hill Mine** (OS 118 SE) forms a conspicuous feature of the landscape. Among the most extensively developed of all the mines in this area, it also possesses one of the longest recorded histories. On 24 June 1715, a new lease of the sett was granted by Sidney Strode of Newnham to John Long of Tavistock, bookseller, and James Mager, tinner, of Plympton St Mary. The latter, it was stated, 'on making an essay to dig delve and search for tin within the tin work or mine known by the name of Bottle Hill, situate... in the Bowling Green there', had discovered a copper lode adjoining the tin lode. Liberty was afforded to work this for 40 fathoms in length and 5 fathoms in breadth on the course of the lode 'that is to say fifteen fathoms in length to the westward of the west shaft that is now on the said work and 25 fathoms to the east of the said shaft'. The 'dish' or royalty was fixed at one-ninth; the division of ore to be made once a month 'or as often as twenty tons shall be raised and made merchantable'.[34] This appears to be the earliest instance of copper being found at Bottle Hill, but it is clear from the reference to existing shafts that the tin lodes had been developed by underground mining long before 1715.

In a later working from 1811 to 1846, the sett was described as a mile long on the course of the lodes, of which there were four. A deep adit brought up from the Tory Brook unwatered these to 60 fathoms in the higher ground, where the Engine Shaft was sunk 110 fathoms from surface. Tin and copper ores to the value of £100,000 were raised during this working, which was abandoned when good returns were still being made. The water-wheel, however, had broken down and most of the machinery being in a bad state, the adventurers were unwilling to put up the money for replacements in the then depressed state of the tin market.

In 1850 a new company was formed and in June of that year the committee reported that the lode in the 12 fathom level, west, was 5 to 6ft wide and worth £100 per fathom. In the 24 level the lode was of similar width, carrying tin and copper ores. Eight shafts had been sunk, of which five extended to the 40 fathom level and three to the 110. A 50in cylinder engine was erected at this time, together with five water-wheels, and thirty-six heads of stamps were in operation. However, in April 1853 the manager reported that he was unable to develop the property in a miner-like way through lack of funds, and two years later the sett was abandoned and the machinery advertised for sale.[35] Working was resumed in 1860, and the mine continued in operation until 1882 when the Engine Shaft reached a depth of 130 fathoms from surface, or 70 fathoms below adit. Subsequently, however, little or no work was done below that level, and it would seem that future prospects for the mine must lie in deeper development of the ore shoots above or within the underlying granite.[36]

At Drakeland on the eastern side of the Smallhanger Brook (OS 118 SE), **Wheal Woolcombe**, or East Bottle Hill, lay near the granite-killas contact at the northen foot of Hemerdon Ball. The sett contained the Bucking House and New South Lodes of old Bottle Hill, but did not include the Main or the New North Lodes of the latter mine. Under the title of East Bottle Hill, operations commenced in 1862 when an adit was driven into the rising ground, intersecting first a copper and then a tin lode. The outcrop of the latter had been extensively worked by the old men and was cut in the adit at 30 fathoms from surface. A shaft was also sunk on this lode, which was said to be rich. In 1867 a 60ft diameter water-wheel was erected for driving the stamps, and also to serve for pumping and winding. Spargo (1868) gives the depths of the workings as 24 fathoms, adding that although no sales had been recorded 'hopes were entertained of future profit'. Sixteen people were employed in 1870, and the mine was still on the active list in 1873.[37]

North of Bottle Hill Mine, on Crownhill Down, a shaft with a number of old entrenchments mark the site of a mine known locally as **Whiteworks**. Here the backs of at least two lodes had been worked by the old men in bygone days, both by streaming and mining. In 1846, under the name of Wheal Albert, the sett was taken up by a group of working miners. 'In resuming the work of the ancients', several rich branches of pure-grain tin were discovered at a depth of 11 fathoms, underlying north. On one of these a shaft was sunk to a depth of 26 fathoms, the water being drawn by a 20ft wheel, whilst a 12ft wheel drove three heads of stamps. The ore required only the lightest possible crushing, 'Indeed,' as the captain reported, 'most of it may be washed without stamping at all, the ground being a soft decomposed granite and china clay.' About two tons of tin concentrates were prepared for sale, but on driving the 25 fathom level they holed into old men's workings. This proved so discouraging that the sett was abandoned after a trial of eighteen months. In 1859 the property was acquired by another party and entitled Wheal Florence, the name which appears on the OS map (118 SE). In December of that year the sett was being 'only slightly worked'.[38]

Near **Baccamore Pits** (OS 118 SE), one mile east of Hemerdon Ball, work was in progress in 1846 at a little mine called Wheal Reynard (or Renard), where a shallow adit driven north about 70 fathoms intersected a copper and a tin lode. The latter was said to be 2ft wide and yielded fair values, although only 60ft below surface. At this depth a level was extended for 20 fathoms and the lode thought worthy of further trial, but the owner of the adjoining land refused to permit the work and it was abandoned.[39]

Further to the east a 10ft wide lode composed of gossan, peach (chlorite), mundic and spots of copper ore was opened up in 1853 in a pit sunk at **Wheal Sophia**. In the hope of attracting investors, specimens of the ore were displayed at Cornwood Station which lay within the sett.[40] Apparently they failed to do so. Near the station a promising copper lode was reported to lie beneath the lawn of Blatchford House on the Yealm. Sir John Rogers, the owner of the estate, allowed some trials to be made, but permission was subsequently withdrawn by his widow.

LEAD, SILVER AND IRON AROUND PLYMOUTH

In 1849 during excavations for a new road northward from Crownhill to join the Tamerton Foliot road, a north-south lead lode was discovered about half a mile east of Whitleigh Hall (OS 117 SE). Under the name of **Wheal Gennys**, a shaft was started on 9 January 1850, the ceremony of cutting the first sod being performed by Mrs Gennys, wife of the owner of the Whitleigh estate. Six months later the shaft was down to 19 fathoms and on reaching the depth of 25 fathoms it was intended to cross-cut to the lode. The amount of water at this time was trifling and was bailed by a horse-whim, but a 36in cylinder steam engine had been erected for use when needed. The engine-house was of unusual design with a flat roof 'from the top of which is a delightful view of the Hamoaze'. At the 32 fathom level, 26 fathoms south from the shaft, the stopes yielded 6cwt of ore per fathom. In the 42 fathom level similar values obtained, the lode being 5ft wide in places. Sinking was continued to a depth of 52 fathoms, soon after which the shaft 'fell together' and in a mood of panic the mine was abandoned.'[41]

A year or two later, working was resumed as Wheal Whitleigh, and in 1854, 45 tons of argentiferous lead ore was sold for £870. By the end of that year the shaft had been made secure and deepened to 72 fathoms. In the 62 fathom level a rich course of silver-lead was encountered, 30 fathoms in length. This was intersected again by a cross-cut at the 72 where it showed an improvement on the level above. Driving was then in progress north and south at that horizon, and by May 1855 Engine Shaft reached its ultimate depth of 82 fathoms where another cross-cut was started to the lode. Soon after this, for what reason it is not clear, the mine was stopped and the 36in engine with the rest of the materials was offered for sale – leaving two engine-houses standing on the property. Output during this last working is recorded as 62 tons of lead ore and 1,436oz of silver.[42] In 1958 traces of the mine were still visible at Zoar Cottages (OS 117 SE provisional edition), on the fringe of one of the new housing estates of post-war Plymouth. These remains consisted of two small dumps in the gardens adjoining the road-cutting, 1,000yd north-west of the Crownhill junction. The cottages themselves (since demolished) had the appearance of having formerly been the mine count-house. When the Tamerton Foliot road was widened in 1973, traces of the lead lode in soft clay were exposed in a side-cutting which has since been walled in.

In September 1859 readers of the *Mining Journal* were informed that:

'Near Knackersknowle village [now Crownhill] a little mine is working called the Devonshire Silver-Lead Mine from which some splendid specimens of silver-lead ore have been produced. The sett extends north and south of the turnpike road and the southern part was worked as Wheal Gennys and was abandoned some years since... Operations are now being conducted on the north part of the sett and include a cross-cut adit driven 60 fathoms, with a trial shaft 5 fathoms deep.'

In the following year the adit intersected an east-west lode consisting of white iron, with a leader of argentiferous ore assaying 337 oz of silver to the ton. However, the captain stated that in continuing the adit north the ground was becoming harder and the lode had split. By November 1859 about 97 fathoms of development, including 50 fathoms of cross-cuts, had been carried out at a depth of a little more than 4 fathoms. A further 16 fathoms had been tested by surface shoding. All work appears to have ceased by July 1860[43] with no recorded production.

The discoveries originally made at Wheal Whitleigh gave rise to a number of other trials in the same area. On 27 March 1850 work was started at **Wheal Langmaid** where there were said to be two lodes lying immediately north of the Whitleigh sett. An open cutting was brought up on one of these, where the back of the lode was over 5ft wide and showing traces of lead ore impregnated with silver. On this a shaft was sunk to 26 fathoms and a cross-cut put out to the lodes which were believed to form a junction at that depth. A level was then driven north through ground consisting of flookan (soft clay) in which cubes of lead were visible. The venture was claimed by its promoters to be a 'model mine', and it certainly boasted one strange innovation. As a shareholder of the concern wrote to the *Mining Journal* in June 1851, 'If any of your readers had been travelling on the Tamerton–Plymouth road in February last, they would have feasted their eyes with a new spectacle – namely a water-wheel turned by human power or treadmill fashion which as one of the "convicts" told me, made him sore all over at the end of the day.'

During the same month a Captain Lean was asked to report on the property. In this he stated that the bottom level had a slate-coloured flookan 1ft wide running north-south and dipping west 2ft in a fathom. Twenty-nine fathoms had been driven north and the flookan presented the same character throughout: 'a few specks of lead but not a lead lode'. In the level above, the same results attended the driving. Captain Lean's conclusion was that a cross-cut should be put out west 'and if nothing better is discovered than what you have been driving on, the sooner you wind up the concern the better, for to go on thus is nothing but a wilful waste of money which you will never see back if you wait till Doomsday' [sic].[44] In the face of these disparaging remarks it was decided to abandon the mine, the 20ft wheel or 'treadmill' being sold soon after.

Some years earlier two east-west lodes had been prospected by an adit in an adjoining sett named **Wheal Looseleigh**. In driving north a branch of copper ore 4ft wide was intersected at 38 fathoms from the mouth of the adit, which was continued to an ultimate length of 64 fathoms. Here it cut into a large 'dropper' believed to be part of the North Lode. The latter had a steep underlay and was thought to unite with the South Lode in depth. In addition to copper, the lodes carried small amounts of lead, black jack (zinc ore) and fluorspar.[45] Although little else has been recorded of this mine, traces of a shaft were still visible in 1958 on the housing estate due north of Looseleigh, and a second shaft was formerly to be seen near the altitude figure 364 in Southway Lane, east of Tamerton Foliot (OS 117 SE). It is impossible to say whether these shafts were sunk by the Looseleigh adventurers or by a company called Wheal Southway which was formed in 1857,[46] since no particulars of the latter are known.

There can be no doubt that mineral deposits exist beneath the streets of Plymouth. Within recent years, iron ore has been found on an industrial site in George Street, Stonehouse, and about 1958 traces of copper were discovered near Eldad Hill. The name Copper Place is commonly thought to commemorate a deposit of ore, but may equally refer to a former copper regulus works in this neighbourhood. In 1850, when the foundations for the new prison (now the Plymouth Police Headquarters) were being excavated, a copper lode was revealed crossing the old Tavistock turnpike road at North Hill.'[47] There is no evidence of any of these mineral finds being worked.

In contrast to this, limestone was extensively developed and there is little doubt that the now 'lost' caves of Stonehouse were subterranean quarries which were active in the eighteenth century and possibly very much earlier.[48]

During the last century at least two mines were in existence on the shores of the Cattewater. The earlier of these was the **Wheal Morley Iron Ore and Clay Works** which was started in 1839. In 1841 it was stated that about 600 tons of good quality iron ore was then standing on the quays. The clay was taken out in 'open heads' and proved equally suitable for potting and brickmaking. Several thousand tons of this clay were awaiting sale on the premises.[49]

In 1877 the sale was advertised of the **Turnchapel Iron Mine** on the Cattewater. Here a shaft had been sunk about 7 fathoms deep, 100yd from the quay, and opening up a lode 7ft in width from which 40 to 50 tons had been 'brought to grass' (surface). The ore consisted of a brown haematite yielding 57 per cent of metallic iron, with an almost complete absence of phosphorus. The plant comprised a 14hp steam engine, 8 ton Cornish boiler, together with the necessary drying sheds.[50]

THE YEALM AND ERME VALLEYS, AND THE SOUTH HAMS

East of Plymouth a number of widely scattered ore deposits have been worked or prospected in the coastal belt between the A38 road and the sea. On the Courtgate estate in Plymstock, work was restarted in 1857 at **Pollexfen Consols**, under a grant from the Bastard family of Kitley House. In December of that year an adit capable of giving 20 fathoms of backs was being driven into a hill towards a promising copper lode. At a depth of only 8ft from surface the lode was 5ft in width and composed of yellow ore and pyrite. A shaft was then sinking through old men's workings which extended to a depth of 32ft. Below this a level was driven south for 5 fathoms, but here the lode was only 8in wide. In the following year a north-south lead-course was encountered assaying 60 per cent lead and 25 to 40oz of silver to the ton. Soon afterwards the lack of pumping facilities prevented further exploration.[51] The mine derived its name from the Pollexfens who were resident at Kitley in the reign of Henry VIII. In 1710 the property passed by marriage to the Bastard family in whose possession it still remains (W. G. Hoskins, *Devon*, 1972 ed, p.520).

On the west bank of the River Yealm, just south of its junction with Coffiete Creek, **Wheal Emily** (OS 130 NE) was notable for the presence of antimony in association with silver-lead. Following an earlier working, the mine was reopened in 1849 when the development consisted of sinking a vertical shaft and driving two adits. The shaft is situated in a piece of rough ground bordering the south side of Wembury Wood, about 200ft above river level. Shallow Adit lies in the steep wooded slopes below and was driven 35 fathoms southwest where it meets the lode which it then follows 5 fathoms southeast and 20 fathoms northwest, passing the shaft on the northeast side. Some small heaps of ore near the mouth of this adit were examined by the late Sir Arthur Russell, Bt, in 1949 and yielded jamesonite with pyrite and quartz, together with a small quantity of bournonite and galena.[52] Deep Adit's portal adjoins the letter W of HWMO Tides as shown on the 6in map and was driven 355 fathoms (2,130ft), no small achievement prior to the introduction of the compressed-air rockdrill.

In 1849 assays of the ore in the 12 fathom level gave a produce of 45, 80 and 110oz of silver to the ton. A winze sunk below this level showed a branch of solid lead ore 1ft wide which was opened up for a length of 24 fathoms. In this the assay value of the silver was said to have been as high as 375oz. Five assays made in the following year by Captain W. Knott of Wheal Langford, gave a more conservative view of the silver values, the produce of these being 14, 16, 24, 30 and 53oz per ton. A single stone of antimony selected from the dressing-floors yielded 19oz to the ton. The shaft at this time was only 17 fathoms deep and the intention was to continue it down to the 35 fathom or Deep Adit level 'at the mouth of which a vessel of 200 tons burden may anchor with perfect safety'[53] In fact, this communication was not made since according to plan, the Deep Adit level passes south-west of the shaft.[54] A new manager was appointed in April 1850 when further rich silver ores were discovered and the deep adit was cleared. Working ceased before 1852, as a consequence, it is said, of quarrelling and litigation among the adventurers.

In contrast to many equally small mines, Wheal Emily has passed almost unnoticed in the mining literature of the last 100 years, and today its existence is largely unknown even to local people. That this is so can only be explained by its isolated position and the concealment of the workings in the precipitous wooded countryside in which they lie.

Wheal Francis, in the valley of the Erme near Ivybridge, was a small silver-lead mine, the sole knowledge of which is derived from a prospectus,[55] undated but by the watermark of the paper judged to be c.1820. The mine was stated to have been worked 102 years earlier than this when, despite the lack of any machinery, it had given large returns from a shallow depth. At the time when the prospectus was issued, an adit was being driven into the hillside on the opposite side of the river from the older working and due to the steepness of the ground the adit end was already 17 fathoms below surface. The lode at that point was 20in wide and becoming richer as the work advanced. Eight or ten tons of ore had already been recovered, giving assay values of 14 in 20 of lead and 40oz of silver to the ton.

Below the adit a copper lode had been found, showing rich stones of green ore (malachite). It was intended to explore this to a depth of 12 fathoms. The expense of bringing the little mine into production was described as 'trifling', being no more than £385 inclusive of the cost of a water engine and the erection of stamps. Whether the promoter, Mr F. Bullin of 89 Fore Street, Plymouth Dock, succeeded in obtaining this modest capital is not known.

In 1859 the discovery was reported of a rich bed of alluvial tin about a mile above **Ivybridge Viaduct**. The deposit was said to be 4 to 5ft in thickness with a superficial area of nearly four acres. A proposal for working it came to nothing owing to fear of its fouling the water which supplied the paper mills of Ivybridge.[56]

One mile south-east of Ivybridge, **Fillham Silver-Lead Mine** (OS 125 NE), better known as **Ivybridge Consols**, was the most important mine of this region. Started before 1838, under grant from the provost and fellows of Eton College, working continued at intervals over a period of twenty years, during which time appreciable amounts of argentiferous lead ore were returned. Operations were suspended in December 1840 when the machinery, including a 12in condensing engine, was advertised for sale. Three years later the mine was reopened under the same management, and in October 1843 output was averaging 20 tons of ore per month, the shaft was down to 60 fathoms and preparations were in hand for further sinking. Working on this occasion lasted until March 1845 by which time sales had amounted to £4,500. The materials consisting of two water-wheels (the larger one 24ft in diameter by 10ft breast), together with 190 fathoms of flat-rods, a horse-whim, and drawing machine with crusher, are said to have realised £1,000, the sale being attended by miners from almost every part of Cornwall.[57]

Very considerable development had been carried out on the property before its closure. The shaft had been sunk to over 70 fathoms, 30 fathoms vertically and the remainder on the underlie of the lode, whilst levels extended north and south at depths of 11, 30, 43, 48, 58 and 68 fathoms, the two last for 50 and 55 fathoms northward, respectively. The south-driven levels while being more productive were short, this being due to the very restricted size of the sett. Thus in several places where good bunches of ore existed, the boundary was no more than 2 fathoms from the shaft, beyond which the ore body passed beneath the land of an adjoining owner who refused to grant. It was due to this cause more than any other that working was suspended.

Subsequently, the mine remained idle until 1852 when a new company was formed with an enlarged sett. By the summer of 1854 a 24in steam engine had been installed and the old shaft unwatered to the 30 fathom level. Meanwhile, a new vertical shaft, named Beresford's,[58] had been started and on this a 50in engine was erected in 1855 – the 24in engine being then converted for hoisting and crushing. Each of these engines did double duty, pumping and winding from both shafts respectively. By 1856 the shafts reached their maximum depths – 78 fathoms at the old shaft and 68 fathoms at Beresford's. During 1855 and 1856, lead and silver ores were returned to the value of £3,446,[59] the price of lead being then in the region of £30 a ton. Because many of the shareholders failed to meet their 'calls', it was resolved in July 1856 to abandon the cost-book system and to place the company under the Joint Stock Companies Act with a view to raising additional capital. However, due to legal difficulties this was never achieved, and in the following year the machinery and materials were put up for auction and the mine was finally abandoned.

The new Ivybridge by-pass now runs little more than half a mile north of the mine which was recently visited by Mr Frank Booker who contributes the following notes on its present-day appearance:

'The engine house, built of slate rock probably quarried on the sett, still stands adjoining Beresford's shaft, but minus its roof and stack. The brick arches of the window openings, however, still retain traces of ornamental mouldings. Beresford's shaft, open and nearly filled with water a few years ago, is now blocked with rubbish. The older 70 fathom shaft in line with it, about 80yd due west, is apparent only from a marked depression, although the shaft is said to be capped. There are now no surface traces of the buildings housing the crushing plant which were prominent enough in the 1920s for C. F. Barclay to sketch. South-west of the 70 fathom shaft and at approximately the distance covered by the 190 fathoms of flat-rods is a large, partly filled water-wheel pit, big enough to take the 10ft breast overshot water-wheel sold in 1845. The leat, much narrower than the wheel it powered, was split into two sections above the mouth of the wheel-pit, thus allowing the water to fall more or less evenly across the full width of the wheel. Although now dry, the two leat courses are still plainly visible after the passage of more than 130 years.

The dumps of the mine, particularly around Beresford's shaft, are much overgrown and hidden by trees, whilst the slatey rock [shale] of which they are composed appears to have rotted into a fine, black, gritty substance, superficially resembling coal dust. [Since this was written these dumps have been removed.]

On the Ivybridge–Ermington road near the southern end of Wadland Wood, which adjoins the Fillham sett, is a house, now empty but shown on OS 125 NE as Caton Lodge. Tradition asserts this was used by the Fillham miners as a chapel and until recent years it still had a small wooden cross let into the gable end of the roof.'

About 1 1/4 miles south-west of Ivybridge Consols, work was in progress during 1854 at the **Caton Copper and Silver-Lead Mine** on the banks of the River Erme. Here an adit driven 41 fathoms on a cross-course intersected two lodes of silver-lead ore, with three others containing stones of yellow copper. On one of these, Adam's Shaft was sunk 10 fathoms below the adit, from which depth an unspecified quantity of ore was raised.[60] The property was favourably reported on by Captain John Clemo of Devon Great Consols, but no further record of its working is known.

Near the prehistoric encampment on Black Down Hill 5 miles north of Kingsbridge (OS 126 SW), some grassy dumps and traces of shafts indicate the site of the **Loddiswell Mine**. In August 1847 the main shaft was 14 fathoms deep and in course of further sinking. Thirteen tons of ore, valued at £30 a ton, had already been sold and a further 3 tons were then being prepared at surface. The lodes were said to be large and kindly and likely to form a junction in depth. The ores consisted of barytes, white quartz, galena and grey copper, the two last in association with silver, some assays showing as much as 400oz to the ton. Although described as a copper mine,[61] lead appears to have been the predominant mineral. Working continued until October 1849 when the materials, comprising an x 8ft by 12ft water-wheel, 350 fathoms of wood and 300 of iron-rods, 70 fathoms of whim rope and a similar length of chain, were advertised for sale. In his brief description of the mine, Dines refers to the remains of an engine-house. No trace of this is visible today, but his statement suggests a later working in which steam-power was employed.

In the cliff-lands extending from **Bigbury Bay to Prawle Point**, trials have been made in a number of places both for iron ore and copper. Shafts are, or were, recently to be seen on Thurlestone Golf Links. East of this in Hope Cove an iron mine was formerly opened in the cliffs beneath the Greystone adjacent to the village. The values, however, proved insufficient to pay the cost of working, and access to the mine was so dangerous for shipping that after one vessel had been wrecked with its cargo of ore on board, the project was abandoned.

A like fate attended the copper trial known as **Easton's Mine** near Bolt Tail which was started by a John Easton of Dodbrook in the year 1770. The excavations lay at the foot of an almost inaccessible cliff near the western end of Bolberry Down, adjoining Ralph's Hole.[62] The adventure did not last long, the spangled ore proving when assayed to be merely iron pyrites. The promoter gained nothing from his enterprise, 'save the empty honour of leaving the shaft his name'.[63]

Portlemouth Consols was a more pretentious affair, being the name of a full-blown company formed in 1859. The sett lay at East Portlemouth, across the river from Salcombe, and was said to contain five lodes of silver-lead in a 'highly mineralised laminated killas' extending 600 fathoms into a hill which rose to a height of 500ft. In addition, there was a champion copper lode of 'immense width similar in character to that of North Dolcoath'. By the end of 1859 a cross-cut adit had been started just above high-water mark and was calculated to give 80 fathoms of backs as it entered the hill. In the following May a correspondent wrote that the mine was being worked solely for plumbago (black lead). Contracts for the sale of this had been agreed and works were being prepared for its treatment in Lancashire and Yorkshire. 'By admeasurement they have over half a million tons discovered and containing a fair percentage of the precious metals, mica schists being their native home...' Apart from the possibility of finding silver and gold, the plumbago was worth £2 per ton and on this alone the mine was expected to pay dividends.[64] After this 'puff' little more was heard of the company and its shares had ceased to be quoted by August 1861.

In the early part of 1857 reports were circulated that a mine had recently been started near **Prawle Point** where iron lodes, 9ft to 20ft wide, were visible in the 200ft cliff. Pits sunk on the backs of these lodes for a quarter of a mile inland showed continuous mineralisation and, despite the values being erratic so near surface, the lodes appeared to be making together downwards and likely to produce 'great bodies of ore and of richer quality' in depth. Whilst the existence of iron ore in these cliffs must have long been recognised, it would seem that no attempt had previously been made to exploit them and the opening up of East Prawle Mine excited considerable interest in this quite new locality.

In 1858 a correspondent of the *Mining Journal* described a visit to the workings by a 'dubious path' down the cliff. Here the ore was being blasted in adits and open-cuttings and then wheeled out to dressing-floors where the richer portions were handpicked, whilst the refuse was thrown into the sea. It was intended to keep a stockpile of 5,000 to 6,000 tons ready at all times for shipment, and for this purpose a railway was being laid to a projecting rock in the bay, alongside which vessels of 300 tons burden could safely anchor, provided the wind was not in the south-east or south-west. It was later proposed to establish a depot at Salcombe to which the ore would be carried in the company's own barges and thence freighted to Wales. This could be done at small expense since the colliers which frequented that port would readily take it as ballast. The average run of ore contained from 35 to 40 per cent iron, worth 13s to 15s per ton delivered at Cardiff or Newport.

A short distance west of the iron workings, several caunter lodes were visible in the cliff. These were thought to contain copper ore, but being almost inaccessible they could only be seen by looking up the gullies 'which in St Just would be called zawns or "wragals".[65] Collins (p559) records a sale of 300 tons of iron ore for £142 in 1858. After that year no further reports appear to have been issued, and it is probable that the mine was abandoned during the depression of the iron trade in 1859–60.

No description of the mines in this coastal area is given by Dines, nor in the *Geological Memoir*,[66] an omission excused by the *Memoir* on the curious grounds that they were the 'result of private speculation'. Through what other agency, it might be asked, was any mine started?

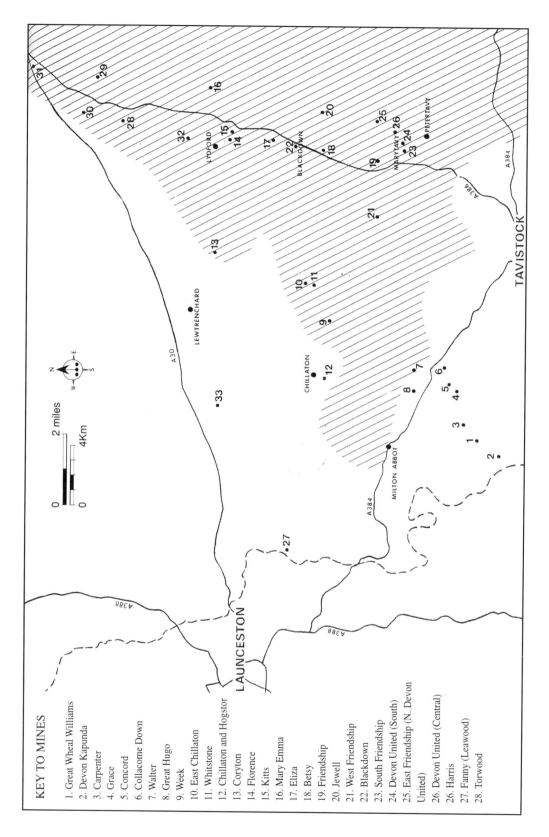

KEY TO MINES

1. Great Wheal Williams
2. Devon Kapunda
3. Carpenter
4. Grace
5. Concord
6. Collacome Down
7. Walter
8. Great Hugo
9. Week
10. East Chillaton
11. Whitstone
12. Chillaton and Hogstor
13. Coryton
14. Florence
15. Kitts
16. Mary Emma
17. Eliza
18. Betsy
19. Friendship
20. Jewell
21. West Friendship
22. Blackdown
23. South Friendship
24. Devon United (South)
25. East Friendship (N. Devon United)
26. Devon United (Central)
26. Harris
27. Fanny (Leawood)
28. Torwood

LAUNCESTON

TAVISTOCK

LEWTRENCHARD

CHILLATON

MILTON ABBOT

PETERTAVY

LYDFORD

BLACKDOWN

MARYTAVY

A30

A386

A384

A388

0 2 miles

0 4Km

N
E
S
W

CHAPTER 4

SYDENHAM DAMEREL TO COLLACOMBE DOWN

In the Culm Measures to the north of the copper and arsenic complex of Devon Great Consols, the mineralisation consists for the most part of blende associated with silver-bearing galena. These have been worked in a number of small, shallow mines extending from the Tamar and thence throughout the parish of Sydenham Damerel to a point some 2 miles NE of that village. (OS 105 NW)

During the years 1845-7 trials were carried out in this area by a company entitled 'Great Wheal Williams'. The sett appears to have had no clearly defined limits but was stated to comprise the mines of Wheal Grace and Wheal Carpenter on the north, Combe Vale on the south and south-east, Wheal Maria & Fortescue to the south-west, with the River Tamar forming its western boundary.

Among the various lodes prospected the majority had an E-W strike although others were encountered trending N-S. The work carried out by this company was chiefly confined to the area adjacent to Sydenham Damerel village. In 1846 Lomer's Shaft, a short distance north of the church, was sunk to a depth of 10fm on a 7ft wide lode, principally composed of quartz and gossan. The water being 'very quick and trouble-some' an adit was started to drive towards the lode which it was expected to drain to 20fm. References were also made to driving an adit in Hartwell Wood with a view to unwatering Cross Park Shaft which was then full of water. Near this, yet another adit was extended to a length of 68fm on a N-S lead lode. Trial shafts were also sunk at various other sites no longer identifiable. None of these small-scale operations appear to have revealed any mineral of economic consequence and in April 1847 the sett was abandoned.[1]

Shortly before this time work had been started or renewed at **Combe Vale Consols** immediately adjacent to Combe farm house. (OS 105 NW). By 1845 costeaning (surface pitting) had revealed four E-W copper lodes varying from 18in to 6ft wide, together with a silver-lead lode 7ft in width – the latter claimed to be 'a direct continuation of the lead-bearing cross-course of the Wheal Maria section of Devon Great Consols'. Assays of this last at only 7fm deep showed values of 64, 66 and 92 ounces of silver to the ton. (MJ 21 June 1845)

In December of the same year it was reported that the adit had been driven 58fm and an engine shaft sunk to 30fm from surface (21fm below adit). The 12fm level was extended 51fm on one of the E-W lodes and on this a prospecting shaft had been commenced. During May 1847 a cross-cut from the 36fm level intersected a N-S lode on which drives were put out 23fm south and 15fm north, the lode being 18in wide and carrying a small leader of silver-lead. Two winzes were then being sunk below the 36 level.[2] In April 1848, however, it was decided to lease the working and the materials, consisting of a 22in rotary engine and a 36ft diameter water-wheel with 90fm of flat rods, were offered for sale in the *Mining Journal*.

Three years later operations were resumed under the name of Devon Consols North. The prospectus of this company stated that the former engine shaft was then in perfect order and was 40fm deep from surface. An unlimited supply of water was available to drive a 50ft wheel capable of draining the mine to 100fm below adit. The sett at this time comprised the farms of Middle and Lower Woodley (OS 105 NW), the property of a Mr Doidge and his sons. At Lower Woodley a copper lode had been traced for nearly 900 fathoms by means of **shode pits**, whilst northward at Middle Woodley two other copper lodes had been cut in the adit. To the eastward these lodes appeared to unite, forming a single gossany lode, 12ft in width. During the next few months two, if not three, new shafts were started on the course of the lodes. In June 1851 Morris' Shaft was down to 12 fathoms on North Lode and on South Lode an unnamed shaft had been sunk five fathoms. Two years later the (new) engine shaft reached a depth of 24 fathoms.[3]

By this time, the adventurers were clearly losing faith in the property and in July 1854 the machinery comprising a 22in steam engine and a horse whim was advertised for auction. Despite the fairly extensive development carried out, no mention of this mine is made by Collins or Dines under either of its alternative names.

About half a mile SW of Sydenham Damerel Church, **Devon Kapunda** (OS 105 NW) derived its name from a formerly celebrated mine in South Australia. From 1852-58 the property was managed by the firm of John Taylor & Son who drove an adit 300 fathoms from the side of the Tamar on an E-W lode and sank at least four shafts. In 1853 a 40in engine was erected and a number of levels were opened up, although the existing plans show no stoping. In all six lodes were said to have been discovered – one of these being 14ft in width and acclaimed as the 'largest copper gossan ever seen since the discovery of the Wheal Maria lode' of Devon Great Consols. During 1856 a 3ft wide lode was cut in the 34fm level, valued at £15 to £25 per fathom (copper ore was then selling at an average price of £6.10.6 per ton). Despite this it was soon after decided to abandon the mine on which some £15,000 had been expended, with no recorded return other than a small quantity of lead ore in 1853. The materials, including the engine and a 25ft water-wheel, were offered for sale in April 1858 but failed to obtain a purchaser.

In 1859 it was proposed to form a new company. According to the prospectus among the lodes discovered by the earlier company two had been worked to 50fm below adit. On North Lode drives had been extended for 33fm and on South Lode 42fm. Their average width was 2½-3ft and consisted of quartz, chlorite 'mundic in immense quantities' and occasional stones of rich copper ore. Many tons of lead ore were said to have been raised in the upper levels but in depth the lode content appeared to be changing to copper. Of the three principal shafts Engine Shaft was 34fm deep, Whim Shaft 50fm (on the underlie) and Trial Shaft 20fm. These figures related in each case to depths below adit.[4] Whether this proposed re-working actually took place is uncertain.

Wheal Carpenter situated half a mile NE of Sydenham Damerel (OS 105 NW) was started in 1845 on a lode striking a little N of E and believed to be a westward extension of one of the lodes then being worked in the adjoining mine, Wheal Grace. By September 1851 a new shaft had been started drained by a water-wheel, the latter being soon afterwards replaced by a 36in engine. Ten tons of rich copper ore were sold in November of that year and in 1853 John Taylor & Sons were appointed managers at an annual fee of fifty guineas. In July 1854 Bridgman's Engine Shaft was sinking below the 52 fathom level and £1,815 worth of ore had been sold. Nineteen men and three boys were employed underground at this time and a quantity of lead ore was also being raised. By January 1855 the mine reached a depth of 62 fathoms.

Six months later the property was offered for sale and was shortly after acquired by 'a Tavistock party' who renamed it West Collacombe.[5] On 22 September 1855 the

Mining Journal announced that the shaft was cleared to the 67 fathom or bottom level and the mine was making regular monthly returns, £2,600 worth of copper and lead ores having been sold in the preceding four months. Several tribute pitches were being worked in the 40 and 52fm levels. Operations ceased in 1857 when the machinery and materials including the 36in engine, a horse whim and a small water-wheel were put up for sale. Although considerable quantities of copper and lead ores had been sold it is impossible, as Mr Justin Brooke has pointed out, to ascertain the exact output of the mine, the figures quoted by Collins and Dines having been confused with those of the better-known Wheal Carpenter in the West Cornwall parish of Gwinear.

About 1 ¼ miles NE of Wheal Carpenter the ground gradually rises to the elevated tract of Collacombe Down (OS 105 NW). In this area a number of lodes coursing a few degrees north of east have been exploited over a length of 500fm in at least three mines. Of these **Wheal Grace** stands at the western end, **Wheal Concord** (or Conquer) occupies the central part, whilst **Devon Mine** forms the most easterly of the group. The boundaries of these setts were subject to frequent changes during the period of over fifty years in which they were, intermittently, worked.

Wheal Grace was started or perhaps restarted in 1845. At a depth of only five fathoms a lead lode 2ft wide was cut in the shaft from which 30 tons of galena were returned. This discovery was made near the western boundary of Wheal Concord into which the lode was dipping and was consequently regarded as a good omen for the latter mine. In September 1846 the Wheal Grace adventurers decided to erect a 22in rotary steam engine with drawing apparatus attached, preparatory to deepening the shaft to take the lode at 60 fathoms. A year later there is reference to a lode being found in the 18fm level after which the mine appears to have languished, and in December 1848 the sett and materials including the small Hocking & Loam engine were advertised for sale.[6]

In 1836 the Imperial British Mining Company was formed to work mines in Cornwall and Devon, among them being **Wheal Concord** and **West Wheal Friendship** on Collacombe Down. A report issued at that time showed that considerable work had already been done on both these properties. At Wheal Concord an adit had been driven 20 fathoms and an engine-shaft sunk to that level where the two south lodes of West Friendship formed a junction. In cutting these lodes near surface stones of copper and lead ore had been raised. At West Wheal Friendship, immediately adjoining Wheal Concord on the east, three 'champion and three smaller lodes had been seen in the adit 18fm from surface and had been opened up for a length of 70fm. The Engine Shaft, sunk to 19fm below adit, was drained by a 50ft water-wheel.[7]

Although the Imperial British Mining Company did not long survive, activity continued at the mines. In 1843 a sale advertisement of West Wonwood (on the western side of Collacombe Down) stated that the property 'comprised the valuable and lately worked mine called Wheal Concord [where] a very rich course of lead ore was discovered from which upwards of £10,000 was realised. The mine was abandoned about two years ago in consequence of disputes between the adventurers of the two companies'.[8]

In 1845 a fresh group was formed, the new sett including West Wonwood, Colford Park and Meadow, together with two fields known as Shortaburn Parks. Soon after, a lead lode being discovered 100 fathoms west of the existing engine-shaft and it was decided to sink a new shaft and to erect a 30in engine. Two years later, in April 1847, Henry English reporting on a visit to the mine, stated that 26 tons of copper ore had

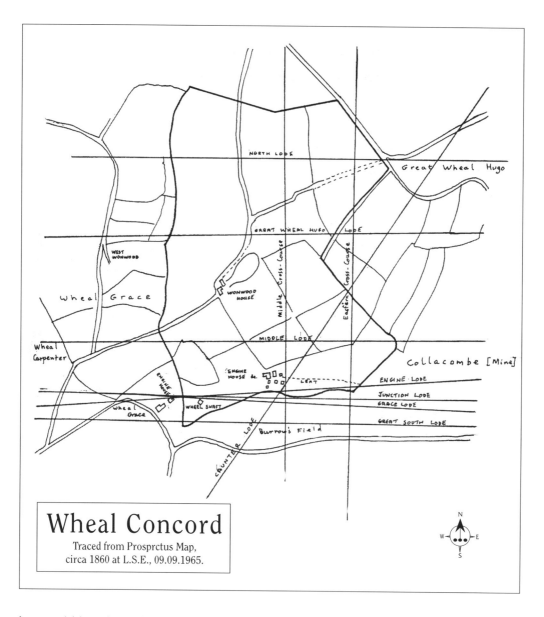

Wheal Concord

Traced from Prosprctus Map,
circa 1860 at L.S.E., 09.09.1965.

been sold but through failure to set aside any money for development there was then scarcely half a ton left in sight. Instead of raising fresh capital and opening up reserves as he had advocated, the underground labour force was reduced to six, although the manager advised that 40 men ought to have been employed.

About this time the company became involved in litigation, the cost of which exhausted such capital as remained and brought the adventure to a stop. Shortly before the winding up, a report on the property was made by a Captain Lean which in the absence of any known plans of the mine, merits attention – the ten fathom level had been driven 100fm E and W of the (old) Engine Shaft; the 20 level 54fm E and 65fm W; the 28 level 53fm E and 64fm W; the 38 level 21fm E and 60fm W and the 50 level 14fm in an unstated direction. The lode had a steep northerly underlay and became narrower and poorer in depth, the greater part of the ore having been produced between the 28fm level and surface.[9]

In 1854 work was restarted as Collacombe Down Consols 'formerly West Wheal Friendship' where a lode cut in the 50 fathom level was estimated to be worth £70 per fathom. By 1856 Engine Shaft had been sunk to 60 fathoms and was drained by a 36in engine, whilst a 22in engine served for hoisting and crushing. In the previous year 200 tons of ore had been sold averaging 10% copper. In 1860 the mine was reported to be paying dividends: but the principal copper lode then being worked lay only 20 fathoms from the boundary of Wheal Concord and was underlaying northward into that sett.[10] During the spring of 1861 a marked improvement was noted in the Collacombe lode whilst sinking below the 96fm level, and on the strength of this a 60ft water-wheel was erected and speedily put to work.

Two years later the adjoining mine was resuscitated as New Concord. Summarising its history, the prospectus stated that it had formerly been worked on one lode only and to a maximum depth of 50 fathoms. About 1,700 tons of lead ore had been returned containing 80 per cent lead and 15 ounces of silver to the ton, in addition to some 1,400 tons of copper ore. Subsequent litigation between the company and the freeholder resulted in the ruin of both parties. In 1863 a small quantity of lead ore was being raised from the 12 fathom level, the water being drawn by a 35ft wheel which was replaced in 1864 by a 40in engine. In the following year the mine was forked to the bottom and the 28 and 38fm levels were being cleared. After this little appears to have been done and by 1866 working had ceased, with no recorded production.[11]

In the early part of 1880 the Devon Copper and Blende Company was formed with a capital of £50,000 to acquire the sett 'lately known as Collacombe Down Copper Mine'. The latter, it was said, had been stopped some eighteen years earlier through the bursting of a boiler, coupled with disputes among the adventurers, after selling ores to the value of £45,000. In the first week of October the shareholders gathered to witness the start of an engine, somewhat ominously named 'The Call' – after Lady Call the mineral owner. As the engine made its first stroke the chairman picked up a bottle of sherry to cast into the shaft, but falling short of its aim this christening token was caught in mid-air by a nimble onlooker who bore it off to be 'cracked' elsewhere at leisure. After this slight contretemps, the party adjourned to the Blacksmith's Arms at Lamerton where an 'excellent spread was provided by Host Howard'.[12]

The **Devon Mine**, as it was known for short, is the only one in this district of which plans of the underground workings have survived. These show two shafts, Morris's and Western, both sunk to a depth of 96 fathoms on the underlie. From the adit downwards the shafts are connected at all levels to the 96; the 40, 50 and 60fm levels opening up the lode for some 50fm east of Morris's Shaft. The deeper levels eastward from that shaft are short. At Western Shaft stoping is extensive between the adit and 62fm level. Below this two winzes were sunk, blocking out a small piece of ground to an ultimate depth of 105fm. Output is recorded as 8,900 tons of copper ore in the years 1855-69 and 1884-5, together with 18 tons of pyrite and 480 tons of blende in the earlier period.[13] The massive 'bob' wall of an engine house is still (1973) standing on the property.

About half a mile north of the north-eastern corner of Collacombe Down (OS 97 SW), on the banks of a streamlet flowing southward from Foghanger, traces of a shaft and adit mark the site of **Wheal Walter**, a name derived in all probability from Walter

Week the lessor of the sett whose family were long resident at Willestrew nearby. Working commenced in December 1845 and by the following June London Shaft had been sunk 10½fm on a lode consisting of sugary spar, with specks of copper ore in a matrix of black slippery killas. Shortly after a 12hp portable engine was acquired from Messrs. Beale of Greenwich and in October 1846 the shaft reached a depth of 30 fathoms (24fm below adit). At the 20fm level 'C' Lode was 4ft wide, narrowing to 2ft in the 30. In neither level did the lode contain ore of saleable value.

In April 1847, the adventurers were furnished with a report of the work done to date. The adit had been driven 150 fathoms and the 20fm level on 'C' Lode for 16fm E and 12fm W of the shaft. The 30 level extended 4fm west and 7fm east. On 'B' Lode another adit was driven 40 fathoms 'home against the cross-course'. During the previous six months the engine had been standing idle and it is clear that working had virtually ceased by this time. The sale of the materials, including the engine, 21 fathoms of 6in pumps and a horse whim took place in the following August.[14]

At Tuelldown, half a mile to the westward, on a tenement shown as Palkshouse on the OS map 97 SW (Edition 1906) lies the shaft dump of another small mine to which the misleading title of **'Great' Wheal Hugo** was given. The sett was reputed to contain two E-W copper lodes traversed by a N-S lead course. In October 1853 a shaft had been sunk 14½ fathoms where it was temporarily stopped by an increase of water. During the next twelve months a 40ft wheel was erected and in October 1854 a cross-cut at the 20fm level intersected the N-S lode. This was composed of flookan, cann (fluorspar) and quartz 'full of small cubes and particles of lead... similar to that of the Concord Mine, adjoining'. The North and South copper lodes had also been opened up on surface where the backs were 8 to 10ft wide. In 1856 application was made for a mining grant to replace the existing lease. Negotiations, however, with the mineral lord proved unsuccessful and in September of that year the water-wheel, pumps, a 10in rotary condensing engine and a horse whim were offered for sale by auction.[15]

THE MANGANESE DISTRICT
NORTH OF TAVISTOCK

To the north and eastward of these last mines, the parishes of Milton Abbot, Marystow, Coryton and Brent Tor were chiefly notable for their small and irregular deposits of manganese. According to Lysons the mineral was first discovered in this part of Devon about 1815 and by 1821 the output of the mines, (excluding Chillaton and Hogstor) had risen to 1,440 tons a year. The ore in many cases 'made' almost to surface where it was revealed by ploughing and draining farm land. Few of the deposits extended to any great depth and as De la Beche remarked in 1839 'We are not aware of any in which more than a horse whim is employed for raising the ore. Common hand-winzes [windlasses] are often sufficient and are most frequently employed'.[16] The resulting yield was proportionately small being estimated by Dines as averaging little more than 100 tons per mine.

Among the earliest known workings of this type was at Cholwell on the borders of Marystow. In 1819 the sett was granted to John Hawkes and John Williams of Cornwall, with liberty to sink shafts, drive adits, divert water for leats and bring the ore 'to grass', paying a rent of £1.15s.3d per ton. In 1838 application was made for a new lease by Jonathan Pallam of Okehampton. The capital on this occasion was only £60 which was shared in equal parts by ten members of the Prout family of Tavistock. Dues were fixed at 20/- a ton of cleaned ore 'should any manganese worth pursuing be found'.[17]

It would be superfluous to enumerate all the sites in this area where manganese has been worked or prospected and a selection only of those which are least well known or of special interest will be touched on here. Among these was the **Week Mine**, about one mile south east of Chillaton, where nearly a dozen old shafts are shown on the OS map 97 NE in the fields adjacent to Week farmhouse. Although mentioned in none of the standard works, the mine is an old one, a specimen of its ores being formerly in the possession of Edmund Pearse, surgeon of Tavistock, whose mineral collection was formed in the early years of the last century.

In 1944 the site was examined by the late Sir Arthur Russell Bt, doyen of British mineralogists, in company with Mr Arthur Kingsbury of Oxford now also deceased. In their published account of the minerals observed the most outstanding was rhodonite (a manganese silicate) large blocks of which, weighing 80lb or more and coated with pyrolusite (manganese dioxide), were found lying loose in the fields or built into the field hedges. 'From these intensely hard masses' wrote Sir Arthur, 'magnificent specimens may be obtained. The rhodonite has a beautiful uniform rose-pink colour... and when polished has a decidedly wavy appearance with alternating bands of pale and dark pink'.[18]

One mile NNW of Brent Tor Church, two distinct but closely adjoining mines have been worked for manganese on Bowden Down (OS 97 NE). At **Bowden Hill or Bowden Common Mine** the deposit was exploited by four shafts which were evidently sunk to some depth since the sale of materials in 1847 included a 21in pumping and grinding engine, together with 'a gig adapted for shaft work'.[19] At a later date between 1875-77 when it was known as East Chillaton the mine returned 132 tons of ore; whilst Whitstone Mine its immediate neighbour on the south sold 161 tons in 1882-84 and, in 1899, 154 tons of ochre. This last mine was reopened in 1942 when it operated briefly under the war-time name of Whitstone Ochre Works (Dines p.716).

Among the many mines of this district Chillaton & Hogstor surpassed all others in depth and productiveness. Worked extensively from 1858 to 1907 the group returned over 46,000 tons, a yield equivalent to 90 per cent of the sum total of the area, and the greatest output recorded by any manganese mine in Devon or Cornwall. During the period 1860-80 when under the management of the Sims brothers of Calstock, purchases were also made from the smaller neighbouring mines, including those of Lifton, Allerford, Lewtrenchard, Coryton, Sydenham and Lee Wood.

As shown on the OS map 97 NW the workings lay on the steep western bank of the stream flowing northward through Chillaton and Marystow. Development was carried out by shafts sunk on the high ground and adits opening into the valley below. Two of the deeper adits known as Hogstor Middle Level and Hogstor Deep Level penetrated the hill at depths respectively of 34 and 50fm from surface, whilst the Chillaton Deep Adit was 90fm below shaft collar. To the west of these workings lie a number of old shafts including those of the **Harris and Narracot Mines** of which relatively little is known.[20] The ore after being washed and hand-picked was conveyed in wagons to Slimeford near Calstock on the Cornish bank of the Tamar where the Sims partnership had a treatment and distributing yard, some remains of which are still visible.[21]

From 1815 onwards manganese was also being sent in increasing quantities to Morwellham on the Tamar. Here it was ground in a water-powered mill situated near the quays, packed in 4cwt casks and shipped from a special dock to avoid contamination of the copper and arsenic ores which constituted the chief trade of the port. As early as 1819 1,335 tons of manganese was despatched down river to Plymouth and by 1821 shipments had increased to 2,212 tons.[22]

Near the eastern end of the West Devon manganese belt, the mineralisation shows a gradual change in character giving place to small impregnations of copper. At Burcombe farm in Brent Tor parish (OS 97 NE) a cross-cut adit was started in 1846 under the name of **Wheal Thomasine**. On driving 30fm a lode was encountered which yielded some rich stones of malleable or native copper. In extending the adit some 17fm a second lode was cut on which a level was driven 13fm. Still further north a third lode was intersected 3ft in width. This was opened up for a few fathoms east and west where it resembled the others in containing small quantities of metallic copper. It was proposed to sink a shaft and erect a 30ft pumping-wheel in order to examine all three lodes at a depth of 40fm.[23] Nothing more is heard of this hitherto unrecorded venture whose site is uncertain but is said to have lain between the Langstone and Bowden Hill manganese mines.

Not far from this more extensive trials were carried out in the wooded country adjoining the River Lyd. On its northern bank **Augusta Consols**, earlier known as the Longham Mine, was restarted in 1852 when, as shown on the OS map 87 SE, adits were driven and a number of shafts sunk close to the margin of the river. Three copper and two lead lodes were found, the principal copper lode said to be 8ft wide. In July 1852, 20 tons of ore were returned from the latter on which a shaft had been put down to a depth of 10fm. An adit already driven 60fm was then within 36ft of this lode which it was expected to cut at 30fm from surface. Meanwhile a second adit 80fm in length, was being extended on a cross-course with a view to intersecting all the lodes at approximately the same horizon. Due, however, to dissensions between the adventurers and the agents (captains) working ceased in December 1854. The sale of materials which followed soon after included a 40ft wheel, 60fm of flat rods and a quantity of pumps.[24]

Some years before this, trials were in progress in two other small mines, **Wheal Broadbridge and Wheal Susan**, situated on the south side of the Lyd. The Broadbridge lease comprising the area of Broadbridge Wood and Cole's Wood (OS 97 NE) was granted in February 1845 to Richard Sleeman, surgeon, and Joseph Edgcumbe, druggist, both of Tavistock, with rights to extend a deep adit through the same but 'no drives to be made within five fathoms of the neighbouring owners' ground'. This proviso clearly referred to the Wheal Susan adventurers whose sett embracing the farm of Woodmans Well, immediately to the east, had been granted in the same year. On 22 August 1846 Wheal Susan reported that 12$\frac{1}{2}$ tons of 12 per cent copper ore was then ready for sale and that four lodes had been discovered. North Lode had been intersected at the 15 fathom level by a cross-cut from the shaft and on it a drive had been extended 40 fathoms east and west. The shaft was then down to 26 fathoms, whilst 100 fathoms to the south a second shaft had been sunk 14 fathoms on another lode. About 15 men were employed at this time and a sum of £5,700 had been spent in developing the property.[25]

At this point it was thought advisable to form a merger with Wheal Broadbridge and to erect a steam engine. No agreement, however, was reached between the two companies and as a consequence both mines were abandoned in December 1846. In 1851 an attempt was made to float Wheal Susan as Woodmans Well and Broadbridge Consolidated Mines, and in 1852 as Devon United Copper Mines but in neither case with any success.

On 28 August 1852, acting on instructions from the Miners' Speculating Company of Union Street, Barnstaple, John Harper reported on a visit to a mine named **Wheal Wastor**. The shaft had then been recently cleared to about 10 fathoms and at that depth it was found that a level had been driven a short distance on a 5ft wide lode 'strongly impregnated with manganese of the richest description', several tons of which had been raised and dressed by a former party. The level was also stained with 'greens' (malachite) from a copper lode which lay alongside.

On the day following his arrival the writer procured picks, gads, borers and candles and two pitches were set on tribute, 'a singular thing in the annals of mining' as he complacently remarked, that work should have been started 'even before the shaft was secured'. By the following month, the shaft had been timbered and the tribute pitches were said to be good although the air was bad: ventilating pipes would shortly be needed.[26] Nothing further is known of this forgotten little mine whose site is uncertain but probably lay in Wastor Wood due north of Woodmans Well. (OS 87 SE, 97 NE).

AROUND LYDFORD

Near the village of Lydford, the River Lyd flowing westward from the Moor bends to the south before entering the deep and narrow Lydford Gorge. On either side of this ravine a number of lead lodes strike N-S through the slates of the metamorphic aureole. These have been opened up in some half a dozen small mines, the sites of which in the absence of any mining map are now virtually unidentifiable, despite numerous reports of their activities which appeared in the *Mining Journal*.

From the mineralogical point of view **Wheal Florence** was probably the most worthy of remembrance. Started or restarted in 1848 it worked for about five years and was then abandoned on account of the poverty of the lead lode. In 1858 operations were resumed by a Captain William Knott, formerly manager of the Langford and Wheal Brothers silver mines in Calstock, who in clearing the adit found native and ruby silver in the lode. Selected stones of these sent to Johnson, Matthey, the assayers of Hatton Garden, London, gave the remarkable produce of 1,086 and 4,532 ounces of silver to the ton, the latter believed to be the highest silver value ever recorded in a British mine.

Engine Shaft at this time was down to 20fm (10fm below adit) at which depth levels had been driven by the former company. It was proposed to unwater these and then sink deeper. In the meantime the old adits were cleared on the Lake and Indies Lodes, the latter standing parallel with Lake Lode about 50fm to the west. In May 1858 7½ tons of ore were raised, 4 tons of which gave a yield of 109 ounces and the remainder 415 ounces of silver to the ton.[27] Working continued for some months after this but had apparently ceased by the end of that year.

Lydford Consols was the name of a company formed about 1846 to consolidate a number of small mines including Wheal Mary, Wheal Mary Ann, Wheal Adventure, Wheal Castle and the Kitt's Mine. The sett was a large one, approximately a mile long on the course of the lodes. Wheal Mary lay to the north in the area of Fernworthy Down and may perhaps be identifiable with the Battishill Down Mine shown on the OS map 88 SW.

Wheal Mary Ann developed a copper and lead lode in Raddon Wood on the western side of the Lydford Gorge. In a winze sunk below the adit the lode was 15 to 18 inches wide containing particles of galena. In July 1852 a 16 x 5ft water-wheel and a horse-whim were erected and the shaft was sunk to 25fm from surface. The results appear to have been discouraging and after an expenditure of £4,000, the machinery and materials were advertised for sale in August 1853.[28]

At the southern end of the Lydford Gorge the river emerges into a steep-sided valley clothed with woodland where it is joined by a tributary stream near the 90ft high White Lady Waterfall. Adjacent to this lay the **Cascade Mine** which claimed to posses six lodes standing to the north of the Brent Tor road. To develop these a cross-cut adit was started 'capable of giving backs of 60fm on being continued into the hill'. In October 1849 it was reported that six feet had been driven east and west on one lode but apparently with so little success that shortly after the mine was brought to an abrupt end.[29]

In 1845 operations began at **Wheal Castle** on a lead lode stated to be 2 to 3ft wide showing good stones of ore. By November of that year 60fm had been driven on its course and a shaft was being sunk to test it below the adit. In a later working from 1851-4 a 40ft wheel was installed for pumping, water to drive it being obtained from the lake [sic] and also from the Lyd 'the lake water alone not being sufficient in the dry season'. In the spring of 1854 a horse-whim was put up and the shaft reached a depth of 21fm from surface. The lode, however, was small, chiefly composed of pyrite and carrying only spots of galena.[30]

Kitts Mine on OS map 88 SW, lay $1/2$ mile east of Lydford village. Earlier known as Wheal Reform it developed a lead lode striking N-S across the river. On this an adit was driven and three shafts were sunk, the most northerly being shown on the Lydford Consols plan as 40fm deep. The exact date of this working is not known nor are there any records of output.[31]

Wheal Mary already mentioned as forming part of Lydford Consols, included the lode of Wheal Adventure. In October 1851 Engine Shaft was 20fm below adit and was drained by a 40ft water-wheel operating 90fm of flat-rods. In July 1852 it was decided to 'hive off' Wheal Mary from the parent company and to work it as a separate mine. During September of that year a cross-cut was being driven eastward and it was reported that the shaft had been drained to a depth of 70 fathoms. The principal lode averaged $2^1/2$ft in width and contained quartz, barytes, mundic (pyrite) and, in places, good quality lead ore of which some 20 tons were sold assaying 66 per cent lead and 10 or 11 ounces of silver to the ton. Operations were suspended in 1856 and in the following January the mine and machinery were offered for sale by auction. There were no bids.

In February 1857 a somewhat similarly worded advertisement announced the sale of Lydford Consols. Although reported to be 40 fathoms deep, the eastern of its two N-S lodes had been developed only by a shallow (10fm) adit and the western one to the 13fm level below adit.[32] Recorded output is given by Dines as 15 tons of 54 per cent lead ore in 1848, 1849 and 1879, the last date implying a late reworking.

About $1^1/2$ miles NE of Lydford village, the sett of **Wheal Mary Emma** on the west bank of the Lyd comprised the moorland tract of High Down (OS 88 SW). Situated near the margin of the granite, the area had been worked from time immemorial for alluvial tin and in several places had been developed by the old men in pits and open-cast excavations drained by a shallow adit.

In 1849 when working was resumed by a mining company, two lodes were found standing 40fm apart and thought likely to form a junction about 160fm to the west. In a 'sink' put down to a depth of 5ft below the old men's adit, one of the lodes was 20 inches wide and yielded some exceedingly rich ore containing 'cubes' or crystals of cassiterite $^1/_4$ to $^1/_2$ inch in size. Payable values being also found in a lead-bearing cross-course, a deeper adit was started to test the ore bodies 10fm beneath the old men's workings. As the surface of the ground rose steeply on the west it was estimated that by driving 60fm the level would gain backs of nearly 30fm. Two old shafts shown on the map on the west bank of the Lyd were probably sunk in connection with this adit. In April 1850 a 40ft wheel was erected to drive eight heads of stamps and in the following August the mine was stated to be just paying cost. Two tons of concentrate were sold in that year, realising £100. Work was still in progress in 1862 when the mine was 12fm deep and employing 10 people.[33] Little remains on the site today other than scattered dumps of much-weathered rock. How far these belong to the streaming era or the later period of mining it is impossible to say.

Immediately north of the 6th milestone from Tavistock on the road to Okehampton, an old shaft situated on the edge of a plantation marks the site of **Wheal Eliza**. The sett comprised the tenements of Hall and Henscott (OS 98 NW) and contained two lodes of copper and one of lead, the latter thought to constitute the northernmost extremity of the Wheal Betsy cross-course. Investigations carried out in 1845 showed that an adit had been driven some 20fm by former workers. In a winze sunk 5 fathoms below the adit, the lode was of considerable width and contained stones of galena. In 1846 it was decided to purchase a water-wheel and to cross-cut in search of further lodes. No subsequent reports having been found it seems that any work which may have been done ceased by the end of that year. In February 1856 it was rumoured that Henscott Consols and Wheal Fanny were about to be restarted but evidently nothing came of this since in October of the same year the mine was stated to be idle.[34]

MARY TAVY – BETSY, FRIENDSHIP AND JEWELL

On the eastern side of the Okehampton road, a short distance north of Mary Tavy, the engine house of **Wheal Betsy** stands strikingly situated against the background of the Moor (OS 98 NW). The mine is an old one, reputedly started in 1740 although possibly very much earlier. The principal lode or mineralised cross-course runs N-S and was developed for three-quarters of a mile along the strike, yielding lead and zinc with considerable quantities of silver. The ores at one period were smelted on the mine by means of peat fuel, gangs of 24 men being commonly employed in cutting this in the surrounding wastes. The silver was afterwards refined by the old process of cupellation. A snuff box 'Made of silver, the produce of Wheal Betsy in the parish of Mary Tavy, Devon, 1820' was formerly in the Plymouth Museum. Weighing 3$^1/_2$ ounces it bore the initials R.E. and E.B. i.e. Rebecca Emes and Edward Barnard, London silversmiths of the period.[35]

After an interval of idleness, the mine was restarted in 1806 and from 1816 (if not earlier) was worked in conjunction with Wheal Friendship, both mines being under the management of John Taylor. Taylor's reports, contained in two surviving minute books,[36] provide a detailed account of the fortunes of Wheal Betsy during the next twenty years. In November 1821 the mine was looking well, with good courses of ore opening up in the 24, 45 and 57fm levels driving north. Stocks were larger than at the end of the previous year and the current output was more than the smelting furnaces were able to convert to metal. The lead was rich in silver and 4,202 ounces had been returned in the preceding quarter.

By 1822 production of ore had risen to 100 tons per month and although work was impeded by the amount of water in the deeper levels a new engine-wheel then being erected would, it was hoped, relieve the situation. In December 1823 six levels were being driven beneath the rising ground to the north. The deepest was 70 fathoms below adit, and there was a prospect of this part of the mine yielding large returns. Prior to that time only the best ore had been smelted on site, the poorer grades being sold as ore. Due, however, to the adoption of a new method of smelting by blast furnaces, the whole output was then being smelted on the mine, to the general benefit of the company.

From 1821-30 sales were recorded of 52,302 ounces of silver, 4,000 tons of pig lead, 1,195 tons of lead ore and 77 tons of litharge, realising an overall figure of £102,661.[37] During 1828-9 the price of lead fell from £25 to £13.10.0 per ton and the mine was working at a loss, whilst in the winter of 1830-31 the increasing amount of water was again causing difficulties. To remedy this the agents, supported by John Taylor, recommended driving the Wheal Friendship adit into Wheal Betsy which it would drain to a depth of 40 fathoms from surface. It was estimated that this would cost £5,000 and take about three years to complete. Owing to objections raised by one of the mineral lords of Wheal Friendship the start was delayed by nearly four years and it was not until 1835 that Taylor was able to report that driving was in progress N and S from several shafts and that the adit had attained a length of 143 fathoms. Two years later, however, 600fm of the total length of 860fm still remained to be driven.

From 1830-34 some 1,540 tons of pig lead was sold at an average price of £12.15.0 per ton. This resulted in a loss of £1,430, occasioned equally by the low price of lead and heavy pumping charges.

By 1836, however, lead had risen to £25 a ton and Taylor was hopeful that the mine would shortly be showing a profit 'as we know that the deeper part of the mine was never better than when we left it'. In 1837 it was agreed to terminate the connection with Wheal Friendship and to form a separate company for Wheal Betsy. In 1842 the latter was equipped with four overshot water-wheels of 40ft and 44ft diameter which served for pumping, hoisting and ore crushing.[38] The quantity of ore, however, raised at this time proved barely sufficient to cover costs and with the machinery in bad condition and the flat-rods subject to constant breakages, it was decided in 1846 to abandon working and sell off the materials.

In 1863 a new company was formed in Glasgow under the name of Prince Arthur Consols. In the course of the next few years, two 50ft wheels were erected for pumping, with two others of lesser size for hoisting and crushing. On 25 May 1864 a huge capstan rope 220fm in length, 14$\frac{1}{2}$in circumference, was delivered on the mine from the rope works of John Cox of Tavistock,[39] and by 1865 the two-mile long deep adit had been cleared and a 12in steam engine erected. In 1866 about 210 tons of lead ore was sold for £2,882 but the outlay to that date had far exceeded the returns.[40] During the early part of 1868 the mine was employing 128 people and in the following year was sold to another company under which it reverted to its original name Wheal Betsy. Working continued on a reduced scale until 1877 when the mine finally ended its long and chequered career.

Among the many mines which have been worked on the perimeter of Dartmoor, **Wheal Friendship** otherwise known as Devon Friendship, long held pride of place. The mine exploited two principal lodes – Sprague's or Main Lode on the north and Bennett's Lode to the south – with numerous side lodes and stringers forming an interlaced pattern between. The workings extended for nearly a mile westward from the Tavy, passing beneath the Tavistock-Okehampton road ¼ mile north of Mary Tavy village. (OS 98 SW)

In 1798 when John Taylor, a civil engineer from Norfolk then only nineteen years of age, was appointed manager, the mine had already been worked on several previous occasions. Evidence of this appears in an advertisement of 1790 when the sett with a water-engine, was offered for sale with the comment – 'the present adventurers having not even drawn the water from the deep bottoms'.[41] Operations were resumed by a new company in the following year and Charles Hatchett who visited the mine in 1796 records that it had started to make a profit 'within the last year and a ½'. Some 40 to 50 men were employed underground at this time, with numbers of women and boys preparing the ore at surface. The sett had two shafts, the deeper being 28fm from surface. From this the water was drawn by a 26ft overshot wheel operating bucket lifts. The known length of the lode was then about 60fm. Striking E-W it underlay north about 5ft in the fathom, in a country rock of greenish or blue-grey killas. The ore consisted of yellow 'pyritical' copper, accompanied in places with galena and blende. Returns averaged some 40 tons per month worth, after dressing, £13 a ton. It was sent to Cornwall for sale and thence to South Wales for smelting.[42]

In 1825 it was announced that 'rare mineral Tungstate of Lime [scheelite], rarely if ever before met with in England' had been found in a tin lode at Wheal Friendship. The ore had been analysed by a 'gentleman of the neighbourhood' and was described as having a bright yellow colour.[43] At a later period in the mine's history, well-formed crystals of scheelite up to 1½ inches long were found in association with cassiterite at the 112fm level (Dines p.706, quoting Collins *Mineralogy of Cornwall & Devon*). Between 1821-30 sales of 26,650 tons of copper ore, 124 tons of lead ore and 795cwt of white (i.e. smelted) tin realised £273,240.[44]

In 1838 the mine was employing 453 people and was equipped with seven waterwheels. The largest was 51ft in diameter, 10ft in the breast, and worked at a speed of five revolutions per minute. By the following decade Wheal Friendship and Wheal Betsy, together, possessed a total of seventeen wheels. Eight of these were employed in pumping from a depth of nearly 200fm; four others served for hoisting – the remainder being used for crushing and grinding.[45] Water to drive this remarkable assemblage was supplied by two leats. The longer one had its intake at the foot of Ger Tor near Tavy Cleave and was brought over the moors first to Wheal Jewell, then to Wheal Betsy and thence southward to Wheal Friendship. A shorter leat, taken off the river at Hill Bridge, flowed direct to the eastern part of the Friendship sett.[46]

As a safeguard against the failure of the leats in periods of drought or severe frost, Wheal Friendship was provided with an 80in cylinder beam engine whose steel work 'as bright as any drawing-room grate, is for ever raising and depressing its heavy arms, one being a ponderous weight of stones [the balance box] and the other drawing from below the superfluous water' as a lady writer described it in 1845. During that year the mine was visited by 'many of the literati who attended the British Association at Plymouth. They came (270 in number) in vehicles of all descriptions, making Tavistock quite gay in their brilliant transit. Good cheer was amply provided for them by the active Secretary of the Association and the enlightened director of the principal mines in the West of England, John Taylor Esq'.[47]

Among the eleven shafts on the Friendship Main Lode, Taylor's was the deepest, being sunk vertically to 90fm below adit and thence on the underlie to the 220fm level. In addition there were two inclined planes. The first to be constructed was about 500yds in length and reached a vertical depth of 600ft from surface. The second or New Plane was 650yds long, meeting Taylor's Shaft between the 190 and 200fm levels. Each of these planes was equipped with a single tramway over which four-wheeled tipping wagons, holding from 20 to 25cwt, were drawn up by chains operated by a 40ft water-wheel. By 1863 the mine had raised 133,937 tons of copper ore, 141 tons of black tin, 2,950 tons of arsenical pyrites and 996 tons of lead ore. Sales to this date had realised £1,335,366 giving a net profit from the year 1800 of £294,441.[48]

Collins' (p.485) quoting figures of output down to 1885 gives totals of the various classes of ore considerably in excess of the above. It is clear, however, that after 1870 the production of copper ore showed a rapid decline and by 1875 had been almost wholly supplanted by arsenic and pyrite for which the mine continued to be worked intermittently until 1924. By 1912 the old water-wheels had been abandoned in favour of Pelton wheels and in that year the property was taken over by a company known as the Wheal Jewell and Marytavy Mines. In this latest period work was concentrated on treating the tin ore of Wheal Jewell, activity at Wheal Friendship being confined to picking over the dumps for tin and arsenic.

The main lode of **Wheal Jewell** lies approximately one mile north of Friendship, its course being marked by a line of old shafts extending across Horndon and Kingsett Downs, from the west bank of the Tavy to the boundary of Wheal Betsy. (OS 98 NW). The mine is an old one and was principally productive of tin. Charles Hatchett who visited the property on 7th May 1796 noted that the strike and dip of the lode resembled that of Wheal Friendship and that it was worked to a depth of 50 fathoms by means of two shafts, drained by a water-engine. About 40 men were employed underground at this time, with the usual complement of surface workers. The lode consisted of 'vitreous tin' in small particles, mixed with a blackish-brown caple. The ore was roasted in a burning house using pit-coal, the floor of the calciner being constructed of brick with stonework under it. The burning operation was sometimes only done once, never more than twice. The concentrate was afterwards sent to a small smelting house in Tavistock owned by a Mr Lane.

For Hatchett and his companion Mr Savaresi it had been an arduous day and it was doubtless with a sense of relief that they turned their backs on the mines and repaired for the night to the Bedford Arms in Tavistock where, however, they were treated to a 'very bad dinner of fish and tough beef steaks'.[49]

Wheal Jewell is said to have been abandoned in 1797 but was subsequently reworked on a number of occasions. Of the three lodes developed Middle Lode was the most important, the deepest shaft on this, 820yds WSW of Willsworthy Bridge, being vertical to 17fm and thence on the underlie to 70fm from surface. Below the 40 fathom adit levels were extended at 48, 56 and 70fm, opening up ground for 60fm west and 75fm east of the shaft. The lode carried cassiterite and mispickel and varied in width from 2 to 20ft. In 1912 bulk samples from various parts of the mine showed an average of 301lb of black tin to the ton, together with some arsenic. About 6,000 tons of ore were estimated to be then standing above the 70fm level. Records of output are unknown since from 1916-24 when the mine was last worked, the ore was treated at Wheal Friendship by the company referred to above as Wheal Jewell and Marytavy Mines.[50]

MINOR FRIENDSHIPS

At the time when Wheal Friendship was at the height of its fame, a number of mines were started or restarted in the surrounding area, each embodying the parental name. Among the more extensively developed of these was **West Wheal Friendship** about 1^1/$_2$ miles WNW of Mary Tavy. The workings adjoined the now disused Launceston branch railway and included three E-W lodes claimed as extensions of those of Wheal Friendship – the sett being under grant from the Batten family of Brinsabatch farm (OS 97 SE) in whose occupation it had been since 1559.[51]

Work started in 1845 and in the following year a 34 x 4ft water-wheel was erected. By November 1846 Engine Shaft was 33fm deep from surface – or 13fm below the 20fm adit – and drives were being extended on North Lode which was from 6 to 12ft wide and said to be yielding rich yellow copper ore. Two years later the shaft was sinking below the 43fm level but the water being quick, a dam had been put in at the 33. In the summer of 1850 additional pumping facilities were provided as the lode in the 50fm level was letting out more water than had been anticipated. Despite this the mine was drowned out for a short period in January 1851 but by dint of minor altera- tions to the pumps was in fork again within a week. About this time it was decided to sink a new shaft with a view to developing the lode in the 43fm level.[52]

In July 1851 the company was reorganised. Reviewing progress to that date the prospectus stated that the mine had been worked for the past five years during which time £5,000 had been spent in clearing the old adit and erecting a pumping-wheel and horse whim. Engine Shaft had been sunk to 53 fathoms and the 33fm level had been extended 20fm west and 6fm east. In the 43 level the lode had merely been cut, the water issuing from it being more than the 'machine' could cope with. A cross-cut from the bottom of the shaft was then within 6 or 8ft of this lode but through lack of steam-power it had not been possible to drive any levels below the 33. The new pro- prietors were willing to sell half their interest in the mine in order to raise funds for purchasing an engine.[53]

Although this proposal came to nothing, working continued in a desultory way for some time after, 177 tons of copper ore (9 tons metal) sold in 1856 realising £843.[54] Two years later operations were suspended and in June 1858 the materials including the water-wheel, bobs, flat-rods, pulleys, launders and pumps were advertised for sale. In 1863 a further attempt was made to resuscitate the mine. Of the three princi- pal lodes which had been explored, Middle and Great South Gossan were expected to unite a little below the bottom of the engine shaft and it was accordingly resolved to advertise for a 45 or 50in engine and to raise fresh capital. It would seem, however, these suggestions awakened no response from the investing public and by April 1866 a liquidator had been appointed and the embryo company was being wound up.[55]

Some 5½ miles north of Tavistock, west of the road to Okehampton, an 'old shaft' adjacent to BM 1033 marks the site of the **Black Down Mine** (OS 98 NW). Although generally regarded as a late trial, the working is shown on a surface plan of June 1791 (now in the County Record Office, Truro). In September 1848 operations were re-started as North Wheal Friendship when two 'very kindly' lodes were revealed at a depth of 8-10 fathoms. In December of that year the sett was acquired by Sir Anthony Buller and others and it was reported that the 'greatest activity and bustle prevailed'. In February 1850 four 'pares of tributers' were at work in and above the adit and by August of the same year Buller's engine shaft had been sunk to the 40fm level. Re-turns for 1850 included 34½ tons of lead ore which realised £371. 13s 6d.[56] Working is believed to have continued for some time after this but with little ultimate success.

Near the confluence of the Gurgie stream with the Tavy, a quarter of a mile south of Mary Tavy village, **South Friendship** (OS 98 SW) was started in 1824 when a small shaft was sunk from which a level was driven about 50fm east and west. Eastward the lode was 'obstructed' by the Wheal Friendship cross-course and was similarly cut off by another cross-course on the west. After raising 7 tons of good quality copper ore between the cross-courses operations were abandoned.

In 1845 a company named **Wheal Anne** acquired a sett on the east bank of the Tavy opposite South Friendship. Here the lode was intersected beyond the eastern cross-course and a shaft was started with a view to exploiting it at a depth of 30fm. Soon after this the Wheal Anne Adventurers obtained a grant of the former South Friend-ship ground where the lode was similarly found to the west of the western cross-course. In 1846 a 40ft wheel was erected, 10ft breast, and preparations were made to develop the full extent of the lode, utilising for this purpose the original South Friend-ship shaft together with the shaft of Wheal Anne.[57]

By October 1852 the 26fm level had been driven some distance east and from it a winze was put down a further 6¼ fm. At that depth the lode was 2ft wide and con-sisted of 'beautiful' copper ore. Nine months later a local correspondent stated that the mine as a whole was still unproductive although values were thought likely to improve in the western part of the sett. In 1854, however, after an expenditure of between £30,000 and £40,000 work was stopped, the lode being considered unwor-thy of further trial. Recorded production from 1847-54 amounted only to 5 tons of copper ore and 12 tons of black tin.[58]

Despite this, operations were resumed at a later date when, as the South Mine of **Devon United**, Engine Shaft was sunk on the underlie to the 52fm level and Mill Shaft to 28fm. From the latter a drive was extended 55fm east and 60 west, this being the longest level in the mine. The lode averaged 3ft in width and is said to have contained about 30lb of black tin to the ton. During the last period of activity which terminated in 1922 the output was included in that of Devon United and not separately recorded.[59]

On the west bank of the Tavy adjacent to Hill Bridge (OS 98 NW) a little mine called **Wheal Saturday** is known to have been worked – and abandoned prior to 1809.[60] In 1847 further trials were made on the same site by a company entitled North Wheal Friendship, very confusingly since there were then two mines of that name in Mary Tavy parish. The North Wheal Friendship on Tavy-side was said to contain three lodes. On one of these a 'shaft' was sunk a mere 3fm deep where on driving west stones of tin ore were encountered of 40 to 50lb in weight. The lode was reported to be 3ft wide and in addition to cassiterite showed traces of copper, with wolfram and fluor spar.[61] Nothing further is known of this mine; the sale recorded by Collins (p.486) of

319 tons of lead ore in 1854-57 being clearly referable to the North Wheal Friendship on Black Down.

East Wheal Friendship developed an extension of one of the northern lodes of Wheal Friendship and was a mine of some importance. Work had started here before 1835[62] and in 1846 the property was taken over by a London company. The sett consisted of two parts. The major portion, 600fm in length on the course of the lode, lay east of the river in the parish of Peter Tavy: the smaller section, 50fm long west of the river being in Mary Tavy parish. Shortly after this time East Friendship was incorporated in the sett of Devon United, a group comprising three mines, North, Central and South situated on the eastern bank of the Tavy (OS 98 SW). East Friendship lode was developed in North Mine, 600yd N of Cudlipptown, and in 1846-56 returned 14,277 tons of copper ore which realised £120,010.[63] The workings consisted of an adit and two shafts, the lode in the former averaging 10ft in width. In July 1853 the mine was employing fifty people and a 60ft water-wheel was in course of erection. At Central Mine, 600yd SW of Cudlipptown, a shaft was sunk near the river to 26 fathoms below adit, the 10fm extending 140fm and the 26 level 90fm east of the shaft. The lode consisted mainly of mispickel (arsenical pyrites) with small amounts of cassiterite and occasional bunches of copper. The developments on South Mine (formerly South Friendship) have already been described.

With the expansion of the chemical industry during the eighties and in the following decade the demand for arsenic increased rapidly. In 1902, however, a slump took place and the price falling to under £10 per ton, the majority of mines in this area were forced to close down. The mining industry in general remained in a depressed state until 1904 when a boom in tin led to a similar revival in arsenic. South Mine of Devon United was reopened in that year mainly for tin and Central Mine in 1909 principally for arsenic. The outbreak of war in 1914 gave a further impetus to arsenic production and the price soared to over £100 per ton. The conclusion of hostilities was followed by a widespread depression in trade which lasted until 1923. In the ensuing period arsenic gradually rose to £70 per ton, the product being largely used at that time for combating attacks of boll-weevil in the American cotton fields.[64]

By 1925 the market had once more relapsed and apart from a period of activity during World War II the price remained generally unremunerative. The old processes of 'burning' and refining arsenic continued at South Crofty Mine in Cornwall until 1950 but since that time 'flotation' has replaced calcining as a means of eliminating the sulphides associated with tin ores. This has resulted in big changes in the mining scene where the calciners with their labyrinth of flues and tall stacks have either been demolished or fallen into ruin.

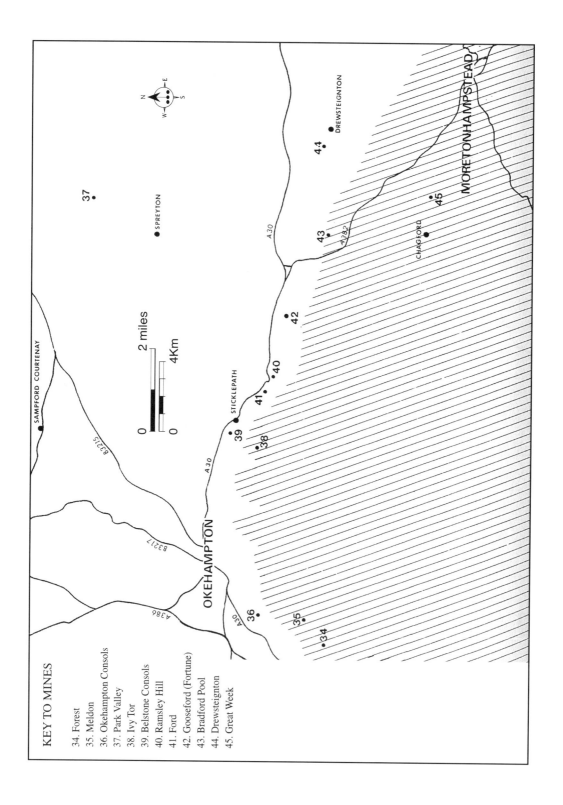

KEY TO MINES

34. Forest
35. Meldon
36. Okehampton Consols
37. Park Valley
38. Ivy Tor
39. Belstone Consols
40. Ramsley Hill
41. Ford
42. Gooseford (Fortune)
43. Bradford Pool
44. Drewsteignton
45. Great Week

CHAPTER 5

LIFTON – BRIDESTOW – SOURTON

A short distance south of the village of Lifton, on the A30 road from Launceston to Okehampton, the OS map 96 NE shows a number of shafts on Gatherley farm. In 1850 three lodes were discovered here, yielding at a depth of only 10ft stones of galena producing 60 per cent lead and 52 ounces of silver to the ton of ore. On the strength of this a shallow adit was brought up and a shaft sunk to 27fm. At 13fm from surface a large N-S lode was intersected, underlaying east. From the shaft bottom a cross-cut put out SW intersected an E-W lode on which a level was driven 15fm. In places the lode was 20 inches wide and composed of quartz and mundic, with spots of copper ore and good stones of lead. The mine was known as **Wheal Harris**, taking its name from the Harris family of Hayne of whose estate it formed part. Working continued for less than two years by which time it was thought to have had a sufficient trial.

In 1860, however, it was reported that a copper lode had been found in some adjoining ground and that this lode was underlying into the Wheal Harris sett where it was likely to prove a valuable adjunct to the lead lode. As a consequence a fresh company was formed and the old mine unwatered. Samples of newly discovered caunter lode assaying 12 in 20 for lead and 40 ounces of silver to the ton were sent to the London office but apparently no copper was present and after another brief trial the mine was finally abandoned.[1]

Although of no economic importance, the mine had a mineralogical interest. In 1948 the late Sir Arthur Russell on examining a dump directly adjoining the farm house noted, in addition to fine-grained galena, a quantity of jamesonite in association with much pyrite and a little blende. Elsewhere in digging on the presumed site of the old dressing floors, a small pile of solid jamesonite was found, a discovery of some importance since no antimony minerals had previously been recorded in this area.[2]

On the north side of the A30 road in the parish of Bridestowe work was started in 1850 at a mine called **Wheal Hamlyn**. The sett was a large one extending 1½ miles on a champion lode and comprising Great Close, Burley Wood, Water Gates, Combebowe and Comebowe Downs. The workings are said to have lain in an abandoned limestone quarry on the side of a hill sloping south-west but as there are a number of quarries in the area answering to this description, it does little to clarify the position of the mine which Collins merely describes as 'in Devon' and Dines does not mention at all.

Despite this, the mine was regarded with great interest in its day and the nature of the lode and its geological features are described at length in contemporary reports. In August 1850 a correspondent ventured to suggest that the lode was the largest in the Kingdom, being 30ft wide and composed of native copper, 'greens' (malachite), sugar spar, gossan, prian and mundic. An adit had been driven for 100fm into the hill and a shaft which was then being sunk on the lode was expected to hole to this level at a depth of 17fm. Droppers or feeders rich in yellow copper ore had been passed through in the adit, near the mouth of which there was a powerful waterwheel for working machinery. Operations had also been commenced about a quarter of a mile to the west where the lode was exposed in the side of a high hill.[3]

After a period of inactivity the mine was restarted in 1856. A reporter who inspected the workings at this time noted that the adit had been driven north from the upper part of the quarry and on proceeding into the level he was struck by the remarkable increase in temperature which rose by as much as 12°F within a few feet. Before communication had been made with the shaft the quantity of carbonic acid gas in the level was so great at times as to extinguish a candle, whilst the men engaged in sinking the shaft were generally unable to work there for more than half an hour at a stretch. On thrusting a knife or iron tool into any part of the soil where there was moisture it became coated with metallic copper in a few seconds. In the lode itself fragments of sulphate of iron and copper were of frequent occurrence, their bright colours contrasting with deep black of the matrix. Metallic copper of a peculiar granular texture could also be picked out from the carbonaceous rock. The water finding its way down through this had a strong acid reaction and in the adit – hanging from the roof, lining its sides and also underfoot – was a substance varying in colour from white to bright orange, whilst here and there 'delicate brushes of hair salt' stretched in web-like formation from stone to stone. These stalactites consisted of iron-alum mixed with a small proportion of copper ore.[4]

A further account of the mine was provided a few years later by John Simmons, mineral agent to the Duchy. He describes the country rock as slatey, with patches of limestone and a considerable quantity of black shale having the appearance of lignite. The darkest layers consisted of soft decomposed matter impregnated with black oxide of copper; the lighter coloured seams were harder and contained native copper and allophane (silicate of alumina), stained with copper carbonate. Attracted by the extensive copper staining, operations had been started by the 'late company' under the management of a Cornish mine captain. A considerable quantity of stuff was raised and bulk sampling gave a produce of about $2^1/_2$ per cent copper (metal). As this was insufficient to pay for working, attempts were made to wash and dress it but the application of water caused the copper to be carried away in solution and the ore which remained was entirely worthless. After lying idle for some time another party started a deep adit at the foot of the quarry where the copper stains appeared strongest. In driving this level a 6ft wide lode was intersected but although promising was never opened up since shortly afterwards the mine was again abandoned 'and is still idle to this day' (December 1861). Had the deep level been continued it would shortly have cut through the two large E-W lodes 10fm deeper than where they had been seen in the shallow adit at 7fm only from surface.[5] It is tantalising to think that this mine with its many unusual features will probably never be seen again through want of information as to its exact site.

Wheal Fanny and Tor Wood Mines originally formed one sett, although their workings lie more than a mile apart. The site of Wheal Fanny is shown on the OS map 88 NW adjoining the road near Cranford farm, three-quarters of a mile SE of Bridestowe village. The mine is said to have been originally opened for copper about 1822 and some five years later a lead lode was discovered. Working continued intermittently until 1836 by which time the engine shaft was 30fm deep from surface. The portal of the adit lies west of the road which crosses the Crandford Brook at Dam Ford. Ventilated by six or more air shafts, it extends in a south-westerly direction for approximately 300fm where it connected with Engine Shaft and, subsequently, by means of a cross-cut with Hitchin's Shaft.[6]

After a period of idleness, the mine was reopened in 1851. By May of that year Hitchin's Shaft had been sunk 10fm and 115fm of the adit had been cleared. Pumping was effected by a 40 x 4ft waterwheel but when this proved insufficient to cope with the water a 36in steam engine was erected in September 1852. A year later the manager reported that new buckets and clacks (pump valves) with stronger timbering had been installed in the shaft but meanwhile operations had been suspended due to the 'pecuniary difficulties' of one of the largest shareholders. In July 1854 the sett and materials were advertised for sale by auction.[7] Three years later a letter by George Henwood calling attention to the mine stated that it had never had a fair trial – 'all that mass of gossan which has never been sunk through is not there without something else being beneath'. He considered that it ought to be reopened with the aid of a 70in engine 'the lode being large and the water quick'.[8]

Although this letter had no immediate effect, in April 1864 working was resumed as the Leawood Mine, taking its name from the nearby seat of Mr Calmady Hamlyn, the mineral owner. During the next eight months the adit was cleared for 200fm, the shaft timbered, and an engine-house erected in which a 60in engine from Harvey's of Hayle was installed. After forking the water to 19fm a crush took place in the shaft, causing it to run together from the 15 fathom level downward. Repairs were speedily carried out and a few years later 28 people were employed and the shaft was in commission to 30fm below adit, a total depth of 45fm from surface. The prospects at this time were said to be very encouraging both for copper and lead but despite this the mine was abandoned in 1868 with no recorded production. The chimney stack was felled c.1900 but part of the ruined walls of the engine-house yet remains.[9]

Tor Wood Mine is marked on the OS map 88 NW by an old shaft about 400yd NE of the Lake railway viaduct and is presumed to lie on an extension of the mineralised bed which has been tested in the Forest and Homerton mines to the eastward.[10] Little is known of Tor Wood's history other than the fact that it was being worked in the 1820s when an adit was driven upwards of 70 fathoms on a lead lode averaging 2ft in width. In 1828 the sett and materials were advertised for sale, the latter including a 30ft waterwheel, horse whim and a four-armed capstan with oak axle.[11] Of its subsequent working, no record has been found. On the western edge of the now abandoned Sourton limestone quarry the OS map 88 NW marks the site of an old shaft which is believed to have been sunk on an E-W copper lode. Referred to by Dines as Sourton Quarry, for want of a better name, the dump contains chlorite and quartz with specks of pyrite, whilst specimens of chalcopyrite have also been found. Nothing else is known of this working which appears to have been only a prospecting trial.

On 15th March 1851 the *Mining Journal* records that near the border of the parishes of Bridestowe and Sourton, **New Copper Bottom Mine** lay in the 'heart of a vast basin' where an adit had been driven 110 fathoms, at 27 fathoms from surface, and that 'in driving a further 50 fathoms it would cut the Great Sourton lode.' Nothing further is related of this mine and its whereabouts is uncertain – any attempt to identify it with the Sourton Down Mine lies over a mile away to the north-east.

About 100yd south of the 4th milestone from Okehampton on the A30 road and a short distance from its junction with the road from Tavistock, may be seen the engine-house stack of **Sourton Down Consols** (OS 76 SW). Work was started here by a Plymouth company in the autumn of 1845 when a shaft was commenced on Rendle's Lode which trended a little north of west and was said to contain quartz, mundic and spots of yellow copper ore. In November of that year the shaft passed through the lode and a cross-cut was being driven towards it at the 10fm level. Two years later the shaft reached a depth of 18fm and a 40 x 2½ft wheel with flat-rods had been erected, together with a horse whim. Although there was sufficiency of water in the sett to drive the wheel at most times of the year, by clearing an existing leat additional supplies could be obtained from the West Okement River at the modest charge of 1/6d per day.

Due, however, to debts incurred by 'improper management' an auction of the mine and materials was arranged to take place in March 1849 and later in that month the property was acquired by a London company and re-floated under the same name. During the next few years another shaft was sunk to a depth of 10fm and in 1852 a 30in steam engine was purchased with a view to deepening the original shaft and developing Rendle's Lode at the 35fm level. Although the prospects were reported on favourably by Jehu Hitchins and others it would appear that little more was done and in the summer of 1854 the sett and materials were advertised for sale.[12] The dumps which had long been very overgrown have been levelled in recent years and the area now forms part of Minehouse farm.

Adjoining the western boundary of Sourton Down Consols lay a sett named **Wheal Sarah** where in 1850 an adit driven 110fm north from the foot of a hill intersected a number of E-W lodes and caunters. The first lode encountered at 35fm from the adit's mouth was 1½ft wide and productive of native copper. Nineteen fathoms north of this a branch 7ft in width yielded yellow copper ore, intermixed with malachite, chlorite and pyrite. A few fathoms beyond this point two other lodes were intersected with estimated widths of 9 and 21ft and containing stones of grey and yellow copper ore. In a number of cases these lodes were crossed by the 'N-S silver-lead course of Wheal Calmady'.[13] In April 1853 it was announced that the adit had passed through the western extension of the Sourton Down Consols Lode and had also intersected two further lodes beyond. 'We are glad' wrote the *Mining Journal* 'that this young mine has such good prospects which will doubtless be made more apparent when the steam engine at Sourton Consols goes to work which is expected immediately.[14] Soon after this, however, the abandonment of that mine appears to have brought its neighbour to a halt.

No mention of Wheal Sarah is found in any of the standard works on mining nor are any traces of its existence visible on surface today. This is not wholly surprising seeing that it was worked solely by an adit. In view, however, of the number of lodes revealed the area would seem worthy of further investigation. This should not be an expensive matter since the depths at which the lodes were encountered nowhere exceeded 30 fathoms.

AROUND OKEHAMPTON

Although the aureole skirting the northern margin of the Dartmoor granite has not proved very productive of mineral, considerable mining activity was formerly witnessed in and around Okehampton. Early records of the individual mines, however, are scanty. Polwhele in his *History of Devonshire* refers to an unnamed copper mine in this neighbourhood as having been worked for some years but by 1798 had long since been abandoned, whilst Lysons (1822) briefly states that a certain **Wheal Oak** which lay near the town had ceased working before 1808. De la Beche in his *Report on the*

Geology of Cornwall, Devon & West Somerset (1839) confined his observations chiefly to the granite area and to the 'tin lodes' crossing Longstone Hill between the Red-a-ven Brook and the West Okement River. Although regarded today as a sulphide-rich bed rather than true lodes, the ore has been worked in several places, notably in the **Forest Mine** on the West Okement River, and in Meldon Mine (OS 76 SE) where the bed exposed on the side of the Red-a-ven Brook, carries arsenopyrite and small quantities of chalcopyrite.[15]

In 1852 the Forest Mine was restarted under the name of Okement Consols. The sett was claimed at this time to have five copper lodes and a lead lode and to have been earlier developed by water-power to a depth of 30 fathoms. Working was abandoned in 1853 but was subsequently renewed under its original name in 1870.[16]

In 1863 a new sett was taken up on the eastern side of the West Okement River. Known as the **Devon Copper Mine** its position was described as about $2^{1}/_{2}$ miles SW of Okehampton and half a mile south of the road thence from Tavistock. Josiah Hugo Hitchins who inspected the property in 1864 noted that it had formerly been named Okehampton Wheal Maria and that the lode in places was 20ft wide with a gossan back. Beneath this it yielded black and yellow copper ore, native copper and large quantities of mundic. Captain Charles Thomas reporting on the mine a week later said that it contained three lodes. On one of these an adit had been driven 25fm eastward from the N-S valley and a shaft sunk 14fm (7fm) below adit). The lode appeared to be improving in depth and where opened at surface some 15fm beyond the adit-end was 18ft in width. The workings were drained by a 29 x 4ft waterwheel.

In September 1864 a hauling machine was attached to the wheel and the shaft was down to 12fm below adit. A few months later the men were engaged in cutting through the Great Lode at 18fm under the adit and hopes were entertained that the levels about to be started east and west would substantiate the values shown at adit level. Apparently this was not the case and a year later the machinery and materials were put up for auction.[17] No sales of ore were recorded and despite what has been said above, the location of the mine remains uncertain.

In the killas country north of the railway and south of the road to Okehampton from the west, trials were formerly carried out in **Okehampton Consols**. The sett extended from Meldon Lane, two miles west of the town, and thence for $1^{1}/_{2}$ miles eastward. In this area comprising the lands of Fowley, Wigney and Estrayer Park a number of old shafts are shown on the OS map 76 NE midway between Wigney and Minehouse. On its eastern boundary the sett is traversed by a N-S cross-course carrying small amounts of silver-lead which have been developed in old workings in the direction of Okehampton Castle.

In 1854 a fresh lease was acquired from the Rev. John Luxmore, the principal mineral owner. A report issued at this time states that earlier workers had driven an adit 40fm in length on a 10ft wide lead lode which had been traced through the property for over 1,200fm. Near the tail of the adit there was an immense quantity of mundic, quartz and fine gossan, the last showing traces of gold. Adjacent to this an engine shaft was sunk to 21fm below adit. In May 1856 a capstan, shears and other materials were purchased from (Old) Wheal Robert and a 40 x 8ft wheel was erected, driven by the water of the West Okement River which flowed hard by. Despite extravagant claims that the property was likely to become 'one of the greatest lead mines in Devonshire', by 1857 the company was heavily in debt and was shortly after forced into liquidation.

Working was renewed in 1862 and some five years later 15 men were employed and Engine Shaft had been sunk to a 50fm level. At this depth a cross-cut had been put out to the lode which was 15ft wide and composed of gossan, quartz and mundic. Despite this no saleable ore had been raised, a fact which caused little surprise to a Cornish critic who remarked 'more ill-spent money I never saw. I would as soon think of cutting a shoal of fish as a course of copper there'. By May 1868 all work had ceased and the sale of materials followed soon after. These included the 40ft waterwheel with balance and shaft bobs, all in good condition 'the mine having been worked but a very short time'.[18]

A few years before this a new mine had been started on a lode crossing the Okement River a little below Okehampton Bridge. Dubbed with the indistinctive name of the **Okehampton Mine**, it formed one of the properties of the Mid Devon Copper Mining Association, a company owning extensive mining rights in the area between Okehampton and Sticklepath. The first sod of the engine shaft was cut on August 11th 1864 in the presence of a large crowd. 'Upon the first barrowful of earth being dug out by Captain Waye, the agent, three hearty cheers were given, two barrels of beer broached and healths were drunk of the proprietors and of Squire Holly, the lord of the manor. A band was in attendance, and sports and games followed'.[19] In January 1865 the shaft was reported to have reached the 15fm level where a cross-cut was being started towards the lode which was claimed to be 5 to 7ft wide and to have been traced by shoding and outcrop workings for more than two miles to the eastward. Later in the same year the sett was acquired by the Okehampton Mining Company and preparations were being made to deepen the shaft to 30fm.[20] How much longer the mine survived is not known.

In Halstock or Holestock Wood on the west bank of the East Okement River, the Old Series one-inch Geological Map, sheet 25, shows two E-W copper lodes crossed by a N-S lead-bearing vein. These were developed by two adits near which some small dumps may yet be seen. Due to their proximity to the prehistoric encampment marked on the OS map 77 NW the mine bore the name of **Wheal Castle**. The date when it was worked and the extent to which the lodes were exploited is not recorded.

About 8 miles ENE of Okehampton and far outside the zone of metamorphism of the granite, lead ore was found in about 1848 whilst quarrying stone on the estate of a Mr James Bartlett. The site adjoined the boundary of the parishes of Spreyton and Bow, being just within the former and $1^1/_2$ miles NE of Spreyton village. Following the discovery, a number of farmers clubbed together to work the lode, the mine being marked on the OS map 66 SW as **Wheal Maria**, although more generally known as the **Park Valley Mine**. John Bibbings, the schoolmaster at Bow, was appointed secretary and purser of the concern and a practical miner with a small staff of men were engaged. Within a few months 10 tons of good quality ore was raised from the adit which was driven on lode at a depth of only 5fm. About this time, however, it was found that the ore, although increasing in value, dipped into an adjoining property whose owner, Mr Roach, persistently refused leave to work it. As a consequence the project, to the disgust of its farming adventurers, had to be abandoned. The mine captain was presented with the ore which had been raised as recompense for his services, and shortly afterwards left the country to take up an appointment at a copper mine in South America.

During the next thirty years nothing was done, the adit and air shaft collapsed and the existence of the mine might have faded from memory had it not been for its former manager. In his letters home to mining friends he constantly stressed his faith in the property and urged that it should be taken up again if the opportunity ever arose. At length in 1878 this came to the notice of a Captain Hosking of Newton Abbot, then manager of Great Wheal Eleanor. In conjunction with an Exeter business man a fresh approach was made to Squire Roach, He had grown more amenable with age and consented to grant a lease for 21 years. A small syndicate was thereupon formed and by March 1878 the adit had been cleared and the shaft repaired. After driving a few fathoms a small leader of lead was found crossing the back of the adit and from this 2 tons of rich ore were brought out.

Four months later the mine was visited by a Mr Rutter who gave a pleasing description of the homely little concern with its 'commodious engine-shed, steam engine, pumping and winding gear and the happy and contented mien of the men, all as busy as bees'. Lighting a candle he then proceeded unattended through the workings 'examining every hole and corner' and noting with admiration the rich solid veins of lead ore many inches wide. In the level he found a pile of at least 4 tons waiting to be brought to surface. The shaft was then about 10fm deep and near it was a convenient space for dressing-floors with an ample supply of water. From conversation with the men Mr Rutter learnt that peat was to be used for firing the boiler, thus effecting a considerable saving on the cost of coal. In the same issue of the *Mining Journal* a commendatory letter appeared from Mr Bibbings, then 76 years of age and still resident in the district. His knowledge of the mine gained from experience of its first working was said to have proved most helpful to the new partners.[21]

For the subsequent history of the Park Valley Silver Lead Mine we are dependent on an unorientated and undated transverse section, now in the Devon Record Office. This shows two parallel lodes about 3fm apart underlying east and crossed at an estimated depth of 30 to 40fm below surface, by another lode with a flatter underlie. The workings consisted of two shafts 12fm deep, connected by cross-cuts at adit level (5fm) and at the bottom. The adit extended 35fm, the shaft nearest to its portal being sunk close to the outcrop of the two lodes. A proposed development of the lodes to a depth of 60fm is also indicated. Dines (p.685) whose reading of the plan is thus quoted, suggests that the mine lay on the Cornish bank of the Tamar, 250yd NW of Cargreen, having failed to notice that Park Valley was an alternative name for Wheal Maria which (on p.754) he correctly states as being in the parish of Spreyton. When the present writer visited the site in 1959 the two shafts were still visible in the wood about 200yd north-westward of Park farm. Near these lay some small dumps showing traces of calcite and galena. In the corner of a field a little to the north a modern-type windmill was standing on what may have been another shaft.

BELSTONE – RAMSLEY

On the south bank of the River Taw where it flows through the gorge of Belstone Cleave (OS 77 NW) trials were started in the 1840s at the **Ivy Tor Mine** when an adit driven into the steeply-rising ground intersected a number of mineral deposits containing mispickel (arsenical iron pyrites), bismuth and copper ore. To develop these a shaft was sunk in 1845 near which a few years later a 30 x 4ft wheel was erected for pumping. Operations were conducted in a desultory fashion with frequent stops and starts. By 1851 the adit cross-cut had been extended 27fm where a level was driven

12fm east and west on one of the lodes. Below this a winze was sunk in one place to a depth of 21ft. In February 1854 it was reported that the men had cut into a chamber of crystals 'as varied for beauty as the scenes in the late Crystal Palace'. Three years later a solid leader of bismuth ore was encountered in a caunter lode but apparently the quantity was not sufficient to render it saleable. Adjacent to this there was a copper lode 14 inches wide. In April 1858 it was announced that the Ivy Tor Mine 'where such hopes were entertained a few years since' was about to be worked again. Six people were employed in 1862, the mine being then 30fm deep from surface. By 1865 the shaft reached a depth of 42fm and a cross-cut was being put out to a north lode.[22]

Up to this time no sales of ore had been recorded and in 1866 the mine was incorporated in the sett of **Belstone Consols**. The latter comprised the farm of Greenhill, immediately south of the 3rd milestone from Okehampton on the Exeter road (OS 77 NW). Under the name of Sticklepath Hill Mine work was originally started here in 1829 when a local company consisting chiefly of farmers, drove an adit which at a depth of 14fm from surface intersected several lodes showing favourable indications for copper. From levels extended a short distance east and west, 38 tons of ore were returned and a winze was put down 5fm below the adit. Here the lode was richer than at any previous point but the water being quick and the company having no capital to purchase machinery the project was abandoned.[23]

At a later date the sett was renamed Copper Hill and by 1865 four mineralised beds, locally termed lodes, were being developed. The ore body consisted of garnet rock disseminated with chalcopyrite, mispickel and pyrite, yielding in places from 11 to 14 per cent copper. In 1874 the main lode or bed was reported to be over 100ft wide (or thick) and on this an inclined shaft had been sunk to 54fm, with levels driven at depths of 30, 40 and 47fm. At the 30 and 40, values were bunchy but below this more regularly-defined branches of yellow copper ore were met with. Meanwhile a vertical shaft had been put down to 73½fm and was expected in a few months time to reach the depth of 80fm where it was anticipated that a cross-cut would intersect the principal lode 200ft below the existing workings.[24] By 1876 Main (or Copper Hill) Shaft was 88fm deep and a cross-cut had been driven 9½fm towards the Great Lode. A large deposit of rich ore had also been found in the 40 fathom level from which 40 tons were returned at an actual working profit of 400 per cent [sic]. The ore at this level proved on assay to contain cobalt.[25]

In the spring of 1878 a serious breakdown occurred in the pumping machinery and the Belstone adventurers having insufficient capital to repair the damage, the property was transferred to the Mid Devon Mining company by which name it is shown on the 1906 edition of the OS map. Shortly afterwards a Captain W Phillips was appointed to inspect the mine, with a letter from the Company's secretary giving a broad hint as to the expected tenor of his report. The letter goes on to say 'The new company will drop all the old names and the Belstone Mine will be called the Great Copper Hill Mine. The Taw River Mine (? Ivy Tor) will be called the Prince of Wales Mine. Please use these names in your report'.[26] About this time a huge waterwheel operating 2,000ft of 2½ inch Swedish iron flat-rods was erected to drain the mine, the pit in which the wheel turned being still visible just below Higher Sticklepath. Measuring 70ft in diameter,[27] it is thought to have been the largest ever erected on the mainland of Britain, being only exceeded by the Lady Isabella wheel of the Laxey mine in the Isle of Man which is 72½ft in diameter.

To drive the Belstone wheel water was taken off the river at a point near Birchy Lake, a quarter of a mile south-east of Belstone church. From here it was carried in a leat whose course is plainly shown on the 1883 edition of the OS map 77 NW and is still traceable in part. Following the 900ft contour north of the Taw it flowed in an easterly direction to Skaigh House beyond which it was deflected northward, to within 150 yards of the mine, and thence turned abruptly south-east. Here it was carried by an aqueduct to a small building which probably contained the compressor with a hearth for tempering the drills. From this point the water descended through a deep valley or ravine, at the lower end of which it was conveyed by another aqueduct over the Skaigh-Sticklepath road and thence on to the great wheel. It is recorded that the latter was painted bright red and was an object of such terror to horses that it was almost impossible to ride or drive them past it.

Under the pseudonym of 'Viator' a correspondent of the *Mining Journal* in 1886 gives the following description of the mine where on arrival he and his companion were hospitably received by Mr Neill, the Manager, 'who had just come up from underground to his dinner'. Operations as he relates were conducted solely by water-power. 'The first thing we saw was the hauling machinery with its endless wire rope bring up 12 or 14 sacks (an archaic unit defined as 9 to 18 gallons beer measure) of magnificent black copper ore (melaconite) from the 50 fathom level, as well as debris from the 62 level where it is intended to cut the lode which runs in an oblique direction through the sett'. The perpendicular of 'A' shaft had then been sunk to the depth of 99 fathoms and at 98 fathoms a cross-cut had been driven 24 fathoms. From this it was expected shortly to cut the great lode 'which is now yielding 6 to 7 tons of ore per week at the 50 fathom level. My friend who is younger and more active than I am, descended the mine and spent more than an hour exploring it, finally returning with some specimens of ore containing axinite. We subsequently inspected the various water wheels and finally came to the great wheel, being nearly the largest in the Kingdom. Near it is one of the smaller wheels working the air compressor to drive the rock drills' (MJ 31 July 1886). Operations continued until 1891 when the vertical shaft was still 99 fathoms deep from surface and the inclined Shaft had reached a depth of 61 fathoms. Output of copper ore from 1867-91 is recorded as 2,934 tons which realised £14,583. After the closure of the mine the great wheel gradually fell into decay and was finally broken up for scrap in Finch's foundry at Sticklepath during the First World War.

In 1905-14 the Copper Hill main lode was explored eastward of the Okehampton-Exeter road in a sett called Belstone Extension where a shallow adit, ventilated by five shafts, was driven for an overall length of 1,500ft along the strike.[29] The outcome of this trial is not recorded.

A short distance east of Sticklepath the A30 road is bordered on one side by a cutting designed to improve the gradient of the hill. Before the construction of the present retaining wall the cutting afforded a cross-section of the country rock in which lodes and branches were visible of ferruginous quartz, fluorspar, mispickel and pyrite, with traces of copper ore. To test these an exploratory adit was started by a local syndicate in 1851, with rights extending over the whole of **Ramsley Hill**. (OS 77 NE). The adit revealed three mineralised beds akin to those of Belstone Consols in dipping at so high an angle as to resemble and hence be termed lodes. On one of these a shaft was sunk some 10 or 12fm drained by a small waterwheel. A year or so later the adventurers having lost heart, sold their lease to a London company who started another adit in a different part of the sett. Here the lodes were intersected at 25fm from surface and some hundreds of tons of ore sold.[30] In 1854 it was reported that in addition to the copper a north-south lead lode had been found, 30ft wide, 18ft of which was payable and yielding an average of 15 ounces of silver to the ton.[31]

Shortly after this the mine became involved in a succession of Chancery suits but in 1858 working was resumed under the name of Ramsley Hill Mine. In that year 211 tons of copper ore were returned from above the adit level. Being gossany and very light at this depth it proved difficult to dress, the first few batches which were tried resulting in complete failure due to over-crushing and washing.[32] These teething troubles resulted in a temporary suspension of underground operations. Work, however, was renewed during 1859 by the Fursdon Mining Company and in the following February a large crowd assembled to witness the starting of a new 50 x 4ft wheel. The ceremony was performed by Mr George Fursdon, lord of the manor, who as the water was turned on for the first time named the shaft Ellen [sic]. Throughout the remainder of the day the proceedings were enlivened by the music of the South Tawton band, the evening concluding with a dinner at the Oxenham Arms when the usual toasts were drunk.[33]

In 1862 the mine was 45fm deep from surface, with 45 people employed. Production, however, was still on a small scale, and in 1866 returns amounted only to 159 tons. By 1868 the main shaft reached a depth of 55 fathoms (31fm below adit) and a second wheel of 35ft diameter had been installed for crushing. In the same year, due to further law suits, the company was under a winding-up order in the Stannary Court.[34]

Throughout the 1870s the mine appears to have languished and any work which may have been done was on a very reduced scale. Mr M E Jobling, however, retained his position as manager, as did also two of the agents, one of whom was resident on the mine.[35]

In 1881 the sett was taken over by a company entitled the Emily Copper Mines otherwise **Wheal Emily**. At the first annual general meeting held in December 1882 the Chairman stated that the two over-shot wheels had been erected on the property before the present company came into existence and that large sums of money had been spent on the mine both by the present managing director (Mr Jobling) and his relatives and friends before him'. A 72fm level was then being driven east of the shaft and the lode in the end was yielding 4 tons of rich ore per fathom over a width of 4ft. In the same level west the values averaged about 3 tons per fathom. Engine Shaft at this time was being sunk to an 82fm level and the turbine, air compressor and rock drills were said to be working satisfactorily. From 1883 to 1887 966 tons of ore were returned for £3,543[36] – these figures being additional to the output recorded by Collins of 6,036 tons in the years 1861-80. The mine was still active in 1891 but no information regarding its progress has been found for the remainder of that decade.

In January 1900 when the property was acquired by the Ramsley Exploration Company it was stated that 'the Emily Mines, formerly known as the Fursdon, are being worked by this syndicate'. [sic][37] During the next eight years the mine was extensively developed. Engine or Lambert's Shaft on North Lode, adjoining the Exeter road, was sunk to the 170fm level below adit, whilst Western or Jobling's Shaft, 140yd W by S of Engine Shaft, was 73fm deep and connected with the former on the 21 and 41fm levels. In addition Middle and South Lodes were developed down to the 60fm level, with stopes extending for almost the whole length of the drives. Production from the various parts of the mine is said to have totalled 10,000 tons of ore grading about 10 per cent copper.[38]

During this last working Engine Shaft was equipped with a double skip-road and although the machinery was mainly operated by water-power, a steam engine with Cornish pit-work was installed for pumping in dry seasons. At such times the water was delivered to surface where it turned the wheels which drove the crushing and treatment plant. From the latter the water was carried in a launder across the Throwleigh road to the Ford Arsenic and Copper Works, a subsidiary of the company situated on the western side of the valley.

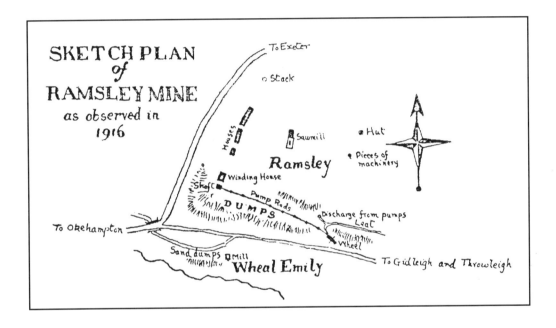

When operations were finally abandoned in 1909 the Ramsley Mine was said to have been the last in England to be worked exclusively for copper. Little is to be seen in the way of surface features today other than extensive dumps and a lone stack. The dressing floors have been levelled on the plea that the stonework had become dangerous to children who found it a happy playground.

Immediately west of the Ramsley Mine, an adit started about 1844 on Ford farm intersected a bed of garnet rock 30ft thick containing veinlets of chalcopyrite, mispickel, pyrite and some blende. On these a shaft was sunk about 14fm and some good stones of copper ore were raised. The work was carried out by a small local company and through lack of capital was soon afterwards abandoned.

Further trials were made here between 1900 and 1909 and again in 1920 when arsenic was much in demand as a pesticide. No plans of the mine are known to exist and its only visible remains consist of an old shaft in the woodland 150yd SW of the farm house and near it a small dump which is thought to mark the entrance of the shallow adit.[39]

On Gooseford (pronounced Gooseyford) farm in the parish of South Tawton (OS 77 SE), 450yd S by E of the 6th milestone from Okehampton on the Exeter road, traces of two shafts standing in the fields indicate the site of the once vaunted **Wheal Fortune.** Started in 1851 by a company boasting nine directors the sett was proclaimed as a 'vast metalliferous field, containing 20 to 25 lodes rich in copper, tin and lead, all within 5fm of surface'.[40] By the latter part of that year a shallow adit had been driven 10 or 12fm on a lode said to be 12ft wide and containing white mundic (mispickel). Twenty people were employed in the spring of 1852 and on 7th July 'being Old Midsummer Day', the directors together with the miners, neighbouring farmers and their wives, assembled to christen the mine. A flag was hoisted and toasts drunk, 'the gentlemen being supplied with wine and brandy and the men with a cask of beer.' Preceded by a band the company, 38 in number, then adjourned to 'a good hot dinner with plenteous drink at the hotel'.

Shortly afterwards a shaft was sunk about 100ft on which an engine was erected. A second copper lode was found in 1853; specimens of which were said to give a produce of 25 per cent copper (metal) and one ounce 4cwt of silver to the ton. Among the adventurers, however, there was a growing dissatisfaction with the management and in 1854 it was questioned whether the company possessed a clean title to the property. At a meeting held at this time the chairman admitted that looking at the past history of the mine it was clear that 'gross deception had been practised upon the public by the original promoters – not least by the reports put forward by a man supposed to be a professor of mineralogy'. It was accordingly decided to stop work and wind up the company, the steam-engine, horse-whim and 11fm of 7 inch pumps being advertised for sale in July 1854.[41]

As a correspondent remarked some four years later, such was the ill-repute of this adventure that it 'well-nigh ruined confidence in the locality'. Notwithstanding this, working was renewed about 1908 for arsenic, the sett being then known as Gooseford Mine. The resulting output is not recorded. For some unaccountable reason, Dines gives brief descriptions of the property under two headings viz. Gooseford and Throwleigh. There is no doubt, however, that both refer to the same mine.

DREWSTEIGNTON AND CHAGFORD

The parish of Drewsteignton is notable for its limestone deposits rather than mineral. Tin, however, has been found in several places where it has been worked both alluvially and by mining, whilst impregnations of manganese have also been recorded. The latter so far as they have been tried have shown little success.

Of the cassiterite occurrences the most noteworthy was Bradford (or Bradmere) Pool 1 1/4 miles SE of the road junction at Whiddon Down and south of the by-road leading to Drewsteignton village (OS 78 SW). covering upwards of four acres the site originated as a stream-work for alluvial gravels. Stannary records show that dues were being paid here in 1539 and similarly in 1583 at Parford Wood nearby[42] where other, smaller, excavations still remain.

In 1789 the Rev. John Swete described the Bradford site as a 'vast hollow excavated through a succession of ages by miners'. The work had previously lain idle for a considerable time due to collapse of the drainage adit as a result of which an accumulation of water had overwhelmed the bottoms.[43] In 1783, however, the old adit driven beneath the hill on which the prehistoric dolmen known as the Spinsters' Rock stands, was cleared[44] and at the time of Swete's visit the excavation was again dry.

On working down to the shelf or bed rock the streamers had revealed the backs of a number of lodes. To develop these a mining sett was granted at the northern end of the Pool sometime before 1841. Two prospecting shafts were sunk to a depth of 40ft and short drives extended on three lodes carrying tin, together with small branches assaying 2 to 13 per cent copper.

In 1846 working was recommenced by a Bristol company who named the sett **Wheal St Ann**. By 1848 the principal shaft was 34fm deep and an 18-inch cylinder rotary steam engine had been erected, with a horse-whim for hoisting. The lodes at this depth were said to contain some 'excellent copper ore as well as tin, with a mixture of silver'.[45] It would seem, however, that little development was carried out and in March 1849 the sett and materials were advertised for sale. At some time prior to 1848 the adit referred to by Swete had again become choked and Rowe who visited Bradford in that year found it once more a pool[46] – as it still remains.

About half a mile to the east, trial was formerly made for manganese near **Stone Cross** (OS 78 SW) but other than this bare statement by Ormerod[47] nothing is known. On the northern side of Drewsteignton village (OS 78 SW) limestone has been worked in a series of quarries covering a large area and to an estimated depth of 200ft. These were unwatered by a shallow and deep adit originally started about 1830. In driving the latter several E-W lodes were intersected showing traces of copper and fluorspar and crossed by a N-S silver-lead lode. The presence of manganese was also noted.

In 1853 the **Drewsteignton Copper, Silver-Lead, Tin and Limestone Mining Company** was formed for the purpose of developing the various minerals which appear to have been neglected by the earlier quarry owners. Work began by clearing and enlarging the existing adits and in August 1853 it was reported that one of the copper lodes had been opened up at about 30fm from the mouth of the shallow adit where it was 8ft wide and producing good specimens of black and yellow ore. A 3ft wide lead lode had also been encountered. During April 1854 the south or deep adit was similarly being extended and was expected in due course to come in 27fm below the quarry floor. By the early part of 1855 a deep adit had been driven between 80 and 100fm and 30 tons of gossan were being tested by one of the new-fangled gold-separating machines then much in vogue. The result gave an equivalent of $^1/_2$ ounce of gold per ton, silver values varying from 5 to 1,270 ounces and 8 per cent lead (metal).

Two further lodes were subsequently met with standing about 50ft apart. One of these was 26 inches in width and consisted of prian (white clay), quartz and gossan but showed little mineral other than a few specks of copper. The second lode had a width of $2^1/_2$ft and was thought might prove productive of lead on being further developed. The limestone being capable of yielding an annual profit of between £5,000 and £6,000 it was decided to work it in conjunction with the lodes, whilst at the same time prospecting elsewhere in the sett.[48] It would seem that this programme was only carried out in part and although the limestone quarries continued in operation for many subsequent years, little more was heard of their supposed mineral potential.

About $^3/_4$ mile east of the ancient stannary town of Chagford four tin lodes have been exploited by open-cast workings in the neighbourhood of **Great Week** (OS 90 NW). Two of these lie adjacent to the road-side near Westcott farm, others have been tried as far east as Drewston Cross and in the woods near Lower Drewston. The main stockwork stands a short distance SW of the hamlet of Great Week and is of impressive size being 30 to 40ft deep and approximately 50ft wide. From the bottom of this now tree-lined excavation the ore body was followed down on the northerly underlie in Lydia's Shaft to a depth of 24fm below the 12fm adit, the latter having been driven by the old men through almost the entire length of the sett. A second shaft, 65yd SW of Lydia's reached only to adit level. A plan of Great Week Consols at the County Record Office, Truro, shows three drives on the main lode vizÀ«t adit, 12fm and 24fm but does not indicate any stoping. Nothing is known of the early history of the mine, the only record of output being 56 tons of black tin in the years 1887-92.

The latest working took place about 1904 when a small steam-engine was erected for hoisting on Lydia's Shaft. The water was drawn by a wheel near the stamps and drove a line of flat-rods operating Cornish pit-work in the shaft, the wheel being kept turning at the required speed by an arrangement of balance boxes. The dressing floors, marked 'Tin Works' on the map, adjoined the stream a short distance east of Great Week and included six heads of stamps. After crushing, the ore was fed on to shaking tables and thence to buddles; final concentration being obtained by tossing and packing in kieves (tubs). Due to increasing costs or a falling-off in the grade of ore, operations were abandoned after a short trial, no output being recorded.[49]

CHAPTER 6

BUCKFASTLEIGH

On Huntingdon Warren near the south-eastern border of Dartmoor and adjacent to the margin of the Avon dam (OS 113 NE, SE), a group of tin lodes has been worked in open-cast trenches and by mining. Of the early operations which were doubtless carried out by alluvial streamers no record has survived, nor is anything known of the underground development of the lodes before the middle of the last century.

In 1851-54 the sett was being worked as **Avon Consols** and an adit had been driven some 200 fathoms. Below adit the 10fm level extended 75fm and in the 25fm level, east of Engine Shaft, the lode was reported to be rich. From a 'sink' 5ft beneath this level a small shoot of tin 12ft long yielded 35cwt of concentrate. The mine at this date was drained by a 40ft water-wheel.

About 1858 work was resumed on part of the same sett under the catch-penny title of Devon Wheal Vor. The principal lode was said to be hard and embedded in a soft granite formation. In 1863 the stopes in the back of the 10fm level were producing good tin-stuff for the stamps, as was similarly the case in the 20fm level. The lode varied in width from 3 to 6ft and in the bottom of the 20 level 'rocks weighing up to one hundredweight contained more than half tin'. (MJ 12 December 1863).

In 1864, as the Huntingdon Mine, working was renewed on some of the more southerly lodes. Here according to the plan, dated 1866, Engine Shaft situated at a point near the eastern bank of the stream opposite Warren House was 35fm deep. Adit level extended 190fm east of the shaft and was connected to surface by at least seven air shafts. From Engine Shaft the 10 and 20fm levels were driven for lengths of 82 and 48fm. Stoping was extensive from surface to a little below the adit, but in the deeper levels the stopes were small. The company, later known for a brief period as Devon Consols Tin, was finally wound up in the Stannary Court in 1868.[2] None of the shafts are visible today and the fairly extensive open-cast workings are much overgrown.

In a small woodland on the south side of the road from Buckfastleigh to Wallaford Down, and immediately south-east of **Hannaford's Barn** (OS 114 SW), may be seen an open shaft with its attendant whim-plat and wheel-pit. Locally known as 'Tin Mines', the workings almost certainly correspond with the Dean Prior and Buckfastleigh Mine which was started in 1847 – primarily for copper. Reports issued in that year state that the adit was 30fm deep, beneath which the 10 and 20fm levels were being driven west on a copper lode valued, in places, at £80 per fathom. In July 1847 it was decided to erect a larger water wheel in order to deepen the engine shaft below the 50fm level (20fm under adit) and at the same time to sink a new shaft in the western part of the sett to develop the lode there at 30 fathoms. Due, however, to the non-payment of calls, the materials were advertised for sale in the following year. These included three water-wheels (the largest 40 x 3½ft), stamps, a grinder and 50 fathoms of pumps.[3] In 1856 a correspondent of the *Mining Journal* stated that the mine in its former working was reputed to have sold £40,000 worth of copper ore from above the 50fm level and that a new company was then being formed to rework it. That these statements bore any relation to the truth appears unlikely. No mention of the mine is made by Collins or Dines.

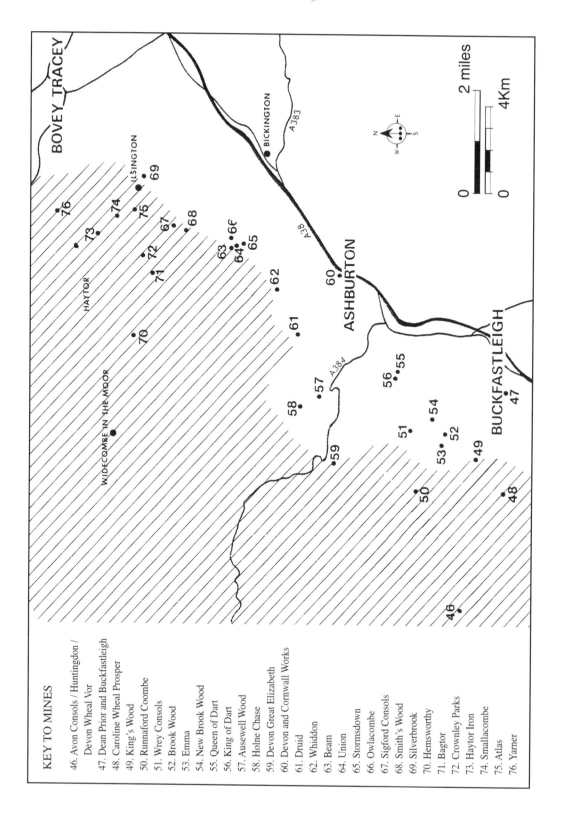

KEY TO MINES

46. Avon Consols / Huntingdon /
    Devon Wheal Vor
47. Dean Prior and Buckfastleigh
48. Caroline Wheal Prosper
49. King's Wood
50. Rumaford Coombe
51. Wrey Consols
52. Brook Wood
53. Emma
54. New Brook Wood
55. Queen of Dart
56. King of Dart
57. Ausewell Wood
58. Holne Chase
59. Devon Great Elizabeth
60. Devon and Cornwall Works
61. Druid
62. Whiddon
63. Beam
64. Union
65. Stormsdown
66. Owlacombe
67. Sigford Consols
68. Smith's Wood
69. Silverbrook
70. Hemsworthy
71. Bagtor
72. Crownley Parks
73. Haytor Iron
74. Smallacombe
75. Atlas
76. Yarner

On a tributary of the Dean Burn some $2^1/_2$ miles west of Buckfastleigh, trials for tin were carried out in the 1850s under the name of **Caroline Wheal Prosper**. The workings were described as situated in a gorge midway between Lamb's Down and Wallaford Down (OS 114 SW) and affording backs of nearly 70 fathoms. The principal lode was 3ft in width, striking eastward at right angles to the main river. In 1854 a 40ft water-wheel and 24 heads of stamps were supplied by Messrs Gray & Oatey of the Wadebridge Foundry and in November of that year the adventurers assembled to witness the starting up of the machinery. As the water was turned on, Mrs Hamilton, wife of the purser, pronounced success to the mine, 'ratifying the same by the sacrifice of a bottle of champagne on the wheel which immediately commenced its majestic gyrations'.[4]

In the following year six miners and three labourers were employed in sinking and stoping at Williams' Shaft, then 15fm deep, the lode being over 5ft wide in places and producing 'good stamps work'. In the Deep Adit level the lode was more settled but the values were poor. Surface pitting later revealed a number of other lodes crossing the Dean Burn and in the next few years the quantity of tin discovered was claimed to have been so great that 30 heads of stamps were erected and a railway laid down from the shaft to the floors. In actual fact the only sale of tin recorded totalled a mere 10cwt. Working ceased in the latter part of 1859 by which time more than £8,000 is said to have been spent – and lost.[5]

A short distance east of **Bowerdon farm**, near the NW corner of King's Wood, two shafts originally sunk in prospecting for copper are shown on the OS map 114 SW. About 1,000yd to the eastward an adit was started in 1918 and driven north from the stream flowing through the wood. At 27fm from its portal an E-W copper lode was intersected which was opened up for short distances in both directions. The adit was later continued a further 21fm north where a second lode was encountered. In addition to copper and zinc blende, this contained a small lens or pocket of pitchblende. The latter discovery being a closely guarded secret at the time naturally evoked a widespread interest. The fact that nothing more was done, however, suggests that the uranium proved of little economic importance.[6]

In 1857 a company was formed to work an iron mine or quarry on the **White Cleave** estate just south of Buckfastleigh (OS 114 SW). The lode or fissure was said to consist of a mass of exceedingly rich ore 'of a rare kind producing metal so hard as to be nearly akin to steel'. A sample assayed in Bristol gave a produce of 60% to 68% iron and offers were made to extract it at the low rate of 1/- per ton, the ironmasters having expressed their willingness to purchase the same.[7] According to local tradition an adit was driven and a shaft sunk. The latter is shown on the 1904 edition of the OS map but has since been filled.

To the north-west of Buckfastleigh, the Holy Brook and the River Mardle flowing eastward from the Moor follow a roughly parallel course before uniting their waters with the Dart between Buckfast and Buckfastleigh. At Combe Bridge on the north bank of the Mardle a number of cassiterite lodes were developed in the **Runnaford Combe Mine** (OS 114 NW). Earlier worked as an open-cast excavation 100yd long and 50ft deep, the lodes were subsequently exploited by at least two shafts. A specimen of the ore in the writer's possession shows that the tin was of excellent quality and notable for its fine crystals.

The sett was originally granted by the Earl of Macclesfield in 1834 but little appears to have been done until 1848 when the manager reported that four men were driving an adit and two others stoping the 'backs' east of Jeffrey's Shaft. In the adit-end the lode was 8ft wide with several leaders of tin running through it and the mine was producing a greater quantity of ore than the 14 heads of stamps were capable of crushing. In the following year Morris' Shaft was sinking in hard ground 3fm below the adit and a cross-cut was being driven north towards another lode. During 1849 the number of stamps was increased to 26 and an engine-house was erected. In it was placed a single-acting, horizontal Sims' compound engine with cylinders of 19 x 36 inches, this being connected to the shaft by 100fm of flat-rods.[8] The engine not proving entirely satisfactory was later sold and replaced by a large water-wheel. Working was suspended in 1853 and arrangements were then being made to re-float the company with increased capital.

The 'chimney' shown on the map was felled in 1915 and falling nearly intact, could recently be seen lying on its side in the garden of an adjoining cottage.

In the valley of the Holy Brook, one mile NE of Runnaford Combe Mine, work was restarted in 1857 at **Wrey Consols**. The mine was situated on the Shuttaford estate midway between Holne Mill and Hembury South Gate (OS 114 NW) and was held under grant from Sir Bouchier Palk Wrey. The sett contained at least four lodes and was traversed at its western end by a northward extension of the Wheal Emma cross-course. By the latter part of 1860 the principal lode had been proved for a length of 60fm and an adit had been driven into the steep valley side where it afforded backs of up to 180ft. The lode was claimed to be 5 to 11ft in width and composed of quartz, peach (chlorite), gossan, with black and yellow copper ore. The latter was very 'vughy' (honeycombed) and letting down a stream of highly mineralised water. The cross-course was 12ft wide where intersected by the adit which was then continued a further 5 fathoms on an elvan.

In the following year it was reported that £1,400 had been spent in driving the adit upwards of 60fm on lode, erecting a 36ft water-wheel and sinking and timbering the engine-shaft to a depth of 14 fathoms. Working appears to have ceased in the latter part of 1861, the only recorded output being one ton of copper ore sold for £8 in November of that year.[9] No mention of the mine is made by Collins or Dines although in 1959 the mouth of the adit, together with the site of the shaft and a small adjacent dump were still clearly visible.

Copper, so far as is known, was first produced in the Buckfast district shortly before 1814 when it was announced that an adit had been driven for 300fm in the **Buckfastleigh Copper Mine**. Although still in its 'infant state' about £1,300 worth of ore had been raised from the adit level where the lode was 10 to 12ft wide. There was as yet only one shaft and this had been sunk 10fm below the adit. A stream of water brought in from a distance of 7 or 8 miles [sic] supplied power for the mill which was capable of crushing 20 tons a day. The ore was then fetching about £9 a ton and values were expected to increase as the workings were deepened. Under the name of Buckfastleigh 505 tons of copper ore was sold in the years 1822-31.[10] No indication is given as to the site of the mine which was regarded by Collins as a forerunner of the group later to become known as Brookwood and Emma.

Situated in a wooded valley about two miles NW of Buckfastleigh, **(Old) Wheal Emma** or the **Brook Mine** was started in 1845 near Brook farm at the western end of Hepney Wood, where an old shaft is marked on the OS map 114 NW on the north bank of the River Mardle. By the following year North Lode had been cut in the 22fm level where it was 4-6ft in width and contained mundic and copper ore of promising appearance.[11] A few years later a larger sett was obtained on the south side of the river extending through the woodlands for a length of 3,000ft. Known at that time as the Macclesfield Mine from the title of the mineral owner, the Earl of Macclesfield, a shaft was sunk to 32fm and three lodes were discovered of 'extraordinary promise'. North Lode was passed through in the shaft at about 8fm depth and the junction of Middle and South Lodes was seen some 10fm deeper. About this time another copper lode was discovered 600fm to the west.[12]

The potentialities of the sett were now thought sufficiently encouraging to warrant its development in three mines: Wheal Treeby on the west, Wheal Emma in the centre, and Brookwood adjoining the latter to the east. This division of the property took place about 1854, after which the name of Macclesfield Mine was dropped.

Wheal Emma (not to be confused with the previously mentioned Old Wheal Emma) lay in the woods directly opposite Brook House; its lodes striking nearly E-W and underlying south. Work was carried out through Whim Shaft, Emma (or Old Sump) Shaft and Pixton's Shaft; the two last to depths, respectively, of 123 and 135 fathoms on the underlie.[13] From Wheal Emma the ore ground pitched eastward into the Brookwood sett, the two properties being separated only by a small transverse valley near which the great cross-course passes north. By 1856 both mines had entered the list of producers, 65 tons of ore from Wheal Emma being sold at Swansea in that year for £550.[14] Writing at this time to Pascoe Grenfell the South Wales copper smelters, Alfred Jenkin their 'cashier' or principal agent in Cornwall, stated the ores were to be delivered at Totnes 'where there is as yet no shipping agent but I think it likely that considerable quantities will be sent there. The mines are situated near Buckfastleigh – the ores contain silver'.[15]

In 1858 a new 50 x 5ft water-wheel was ordered by the Wheal Emma adventurers from Nicholls & Williams' Foundry at Tavistock. Pending its delivery the 46ft wheel then standing idle at the Brook Mine (Old Emma) was connected by flat-rods, nearly half a mile in length, to Wheal Emma where a 13 inch working-barrel and 13 inch plunger drained the shaft to a depth of 46 fathoms. On the wheel being started the rods moved off so quietly that those with their backs to them were unconscious of their being in motion. In the evening of the same day the men who had been engaged in their erection were regaled with a supper of roast beef and strong beer.[16]

By this date the flow of water through the original leat from the Mardle being insufficient to drive all the various wheels, arrangements were made with the Duchy to obtain additional supplies by constructing a new leat from a point on the Swincombe River, near Whiteworks Mine (OS 107 SW). Following the contours of the hills its meandering course can still be traced in many places – notably on the Hexworthy to Holne road which it crosses at four different points. Variously estimated as nine-and-a-quarter and twelve miles in length it constituted the longest artificial water-course on record in the west of England, and was alike remarkable as a feat of engineering and surveying. In 1860 it was stated that the bed of the leat was still 'scarcely sufficiently staunched to convey one-half of the stream which runs into it at the weir-head'.[17]

In 1862 Wheal Emma was employing 125 people and six years later reached a depth of 116fm below adit (18fm). The mine was drained by the 50 x 5ft wheel; hoisting and crushing being carried out by two other wheels of 30 and 29ft diameter. During 1866 785 tons of copper ore were sold for £4,666, resulting in a small profit of £160.

Brookwood was similarly worked at this time entirely by water-power and in 1866 returned 1,440 tons of ore which realised £6,567.[18] In 1868, however, it was decided to purchase a 50in steam engine. Four years later the *Mining World* reported that for some nine years past the Brookwood sett had been in the hands of a small group of adventurers, chiefly residents of Liskeard. The dividend had lately been raised from 2/6 (12½p) to 5/- (25p) per share but this had been increased at the last meeting to 10/- (50p), leaving more than £300 to be carried forward as a balance in hand. 'Brookwood, therefore, is the prize of the Emma sett'. That the lodes were very rich at this time is confirmed by Kelly's Directory of Devon (1873) which states that 'most of the ore was sent to market in nearly the same state as received from the shaft' i.e. without any need for dressing.

Due to the continuing use of water-wheels, the 50 inch engine was then working at only three quarters of a stroke per minute.[19] This would suggest that steam was only employed on a limited scale. The ruins of a substantial engine house are visible on the property today, and close to the stack is a mound containing traces of what appears to be clinker.[20] No reference, however, to any extensive use of steam power at any period was made when the mines were advertised for sale in 1877.

Prior to 1873 Wheal Emma had been idle for some years but shortly before that date working was resumed and the proprietors were sinking a new shaft in the hope that by 'tunnelling to the old workings a new vein would be discovered'. By this time the mine had returned a total of approximately 11,500 tons of ore.[21] The two mines continued in operation until 1877 when their combined output of copper ore, from 1856, amounted to not less than 34,000 tons.[22] This figure is much in excess of that given by Dines which, however, relates only to the years 1861-77.

Although Brookwood and Emma ranked as the largest copper producers in this part of Devon, the various trials carried out in their immediate vicinity had little success. Wheal Treeby to the west of Wheal Emma and believed to have the same lodes, was started in 1855 when an adit was driven some 40 to 50 fathoms and several small shafts were sunk. In this area, however, the lode was found to be hard and capelly, having more the character of a tin than a copper lode. Finding nothing to encourage exploration in depth, work was abandoned in 1859.[23]

Old Emma or the Brook Mine had been sunk by this time to 42fm. At that depth a cross-cut was put out north but apparently to little purpose and in 1859 operations were also suspended here.[24]

New Brookwood Mine on the south bank of the Holy Brook, ½ mile NE of Old Emma (OS 114 NW), was opened up by an adit extending 60 fathoms on the course of the lode. Here an incline shaft was sunk to 10fm under the adit where a level was driven a short distance east and west. The plan shows only one small stope at this horizon. The mine, however, would appear to have been worked intermittently over a fairly long period since it was not finally abandoned until 1891.[25] Little remains to be seen on the site today other than a few small dumps with traces of the adit.

East Brookwood was another mine of equally little success. The sett contained four lodes and was worked in the 1860s to a depth of 20 fathoms below adit (10fm) by means of a 40ft water-wheel. From the shaft bottom a cross-cut driven 14fm north intersected a south-dipping lode which was opened up for 12fm east. No stoping is shown on the plan and working had ceased by 1868.[26] The site of the mine remains uncertain, the only clues to its position being that it lay in the parish of Holne, was held under grant from Sir Bouchier Wrey and comprised the estates of Steart and Shuttaford (OS 114 NW). This points to a location exactly conforming to that of

Wrey Consols (as described above). For what reason the mine should have been re-named East Brookwood is hard to understand seeing that it lay, not east, but almost due north of the Brookwood sett.

In 1878 a company entitled South Devon United Copper Mines was registered in Truro with a capital of £30,000 for the purpose of acquiring the Brookwood and Emma setts. As explained in the prospectus these had formerly been worked as separate mines 'always at variance, each endeavouring to control the valuable water-power to the detriment of both'. This state of affairs had since been regularised by the Earl of Macclesfield taking over the water-rights and granting the two properties as one sett, at a royalty of 1-24th.[27]

During the next two years a new shaft, named Martin's, was started on the eastern part of Brookwood. This was eventually sunk to 110 fathoms, and replaced the old skip-shaft which was then in a ruinous condition and served only by a horse whim. At the same time Pixton's Shaft on the former Wheal Emma part of the sett was deepened from 140 to a 155fm level although without meeting any ore of much consequence. The machinery consisted of two pumping wheels of 40 and 26ft diameter together with a small portable steam engine for hoisting, the latter wholly inadequate for a mine of any size as the *Mining Journal* pointed out.

By 1883 although the directors still professed confidence in the ultimate success of the undertaking, their view was not generally shared by the adventurers. As one of them remarked 'they had been in the Heaven of expectation over and over again but had now come down to the Hell of disappointment'. In November 1884 the mines were stated to be losing £300 per month and shortly after additional capital was raised by means of a debenture. On this being exhausted, it was decided to go into voluntary liquidation.[28] Cleaning up operations continued into 1885 by which time production had amounted to 8,190 tons of copper ore and 84 tons of mispickel.

Following their appointment, proposals were made by the liquidators to sell the property as a going-concern 'together with the fine machinery, water-wheels, dressing floors and water privileges'. Tenders for the erection of a new plant were invited on at least three occasions but these met with no response and by June 1885 dealings in the shares had ceased.

ASHBURTON

River of Dart, River of Dart,
Every year she claims a heart

is a saying not without truth as testified by those who have gambled their lives in its swift currents and dark, treacherous pools. Fatalities such as these, however, are small in number compared with those who have happily 'lost their hearts' to this loveliest of Devon rivers.

In one of its most secluded reaches, about 1½ miles SW of Ashburton, lies the short-lived but fittingly-named **Queen of Dart Mine** (OS 114 NW). The valley at this point is crossed by an E-W lode whose outcrop is said to have been first noticed in the bed of the river during a season of exceptional drought. In 1854 a trial shaft was started near the eastern margin of the stream and at a depth of only 5 fathoms a level driven westward proved the lode to be sufficiently rich in copper to justify working.

Fifty tons of ore were raised in July of that year and in the following month three consignments were shipped to Swansea via Totnes to which it was carried in a procession 'preceded by flags and a band of music'. Later in the same year another lode was cut containing a leader of copper 2 inches wide and in 1855 a further parcel of 124 tons was sold in Swansea for £435.[29]

The ore seems generally to have occurred in 'squats' or bunches in a dark and somewhat uncongenial stratum but it was thought that this was probably underlain by a kindlier-natured country rock.

Initially, the mine was drained by a small Robey engine. In March 1856, early on a Sunday morning, the house in which it stood was burnt to the ground, a not infrequent occurrence in the days when candles served as the only means of lighting and more especially, as in this case, when the engine-driver had fallen asleep.[30] The machinery was not extensively damaged and continued working until it was replaced by two water-wheels of 30 and 35 ft diameter, supplied by Messrs Webber of the Newton Abbott foundry. These did duty for pumping, winding and crushing.

In 1858 the lode was being developed to the eastward where an adit was driven into the rising ground of Shere Wood. Here another shaft was put down to a depth of 30 fm. By 1859 the principal shaft had been sunk on the underlie of the lode to 40 fm, with levels driven at 5, 10, 20 and 30 fm from surface. A 42 fathom level was expected to be opened up shortly. East of Boundary Shaft a small shoot of ore, 6 fm long, was passed through in the 30 fm level, and there was another small bunch in the same level west of that shaft.[31] Very little, however, was doing at this time.

As a *Mining Journal* correspondent wrote in March 1859 'it is a great misfortune that property bearing so high-sounding a title should be in abeyance from want of revenue but such has been the case. Now, we understand, the difficulty has been removed by the liege subjects of Her Majesty and the Queen of Dart is likely to emerge from the obscurity in which she has been for some time immured'. Despite this assurance little more was done and in January 1860 the sett and materials were advertised for sale. From 1854-7 output amounting to 579 tons realised £2,127.[32] No plans are known to exist of the underground workings but an illustration purporting to show the direction of the lodes and cross-courses is reproduced in the *Mining Journal* of 8th March 1856.

The site of the mine now lies in the garden of a private house. When visited by kind permission of the owner in 1959 two shaft dumps were to be seen containing copper and iron pyrites, together with what may have been the foundations of the engine-house. On the edge of Shere Wood the mouth of the adit was also visible.

In Hembury Plantation (OS 114 NW) on the west bank of the river, immediately opposite the Queen of Dart, may be seen the adit of **King of Dart** which was driven in 1857-8 on a presumed extension of one of the lodes of the former mine. A short distance from the adit's mouth a small shaft was sunk and carried down to 8½ fathoms below the level. Here the lode had a good appearance and the prospects were regarded as 'far superior to those at the Queen, the stratum being different'.[33] In 1859 a re-working of the sett was contemplated with the aid of a water-wheel but there is no evidence to suggest that this ever took place.

Further down the river, south of the King of Dart, another adit has been driven westward beneath the slopes of Hembury Woods. Named the **Knight of Dart**, the sett belonged to a Captain Billing who worked it single-handed, displaying a 'praiseworthy, if misapplied, perseverance' in his self-imposed task. His progress in driving was naturally slow but to the end he remained confident that some day or other he would cut the lode which was to reward his arduous labour.[34]

In contrast to Captain Billing working in solitary obscurity, the starting of **Wheal Blackpool** some years earlier was heralded with a blaze of publicity. The christening of the mine took place on Whit Monday 1850 when in the presence of a large party, Miss S A Sawdye performed the ceremony by casting a bottle of 'bright champagne' into the shaft, following which about sixty persons dined together in a marquee erected nearby.

For the rest of the afternoon the mine continued *en fete* – 'songs, glees and toasts were given and the valley re-echoed sweet sounds in the lovely woodland scene by the side of the River Dart. The merry dance and loud continuous cheering for the success of the mine terminated the proceedings'.[35] No trace of any workings can now be seen near Blackpool (OS 114 NW) and it is to be feared that despite the loud continuous cheering the mine was an instance of 'more cry than wool'.

On the west bank of the river about one mile north of the Queen of Dart trials were initiated in 1849 at the **Holne Park Mine** where four lodes had recently been discovered. On one of these two men were then employed in driving an adit, the lode being proclaimed as 6 to 7ft wide and containing yellow and peacock ore 'going 18 to 30 per cent' (copper).[36] In the following year the name of the sett was changed to South Plain Wood presumably to avoid confusion with the nearby Holne Chase Mine. In July 1850 Nicholson's Lode was reported to be 3ft in width and two shafts had been sunk to a depth of a few fathoms. The water being low at that time, the lode could be seen crossing the bed of the river and on the strength of this a sett was acquired of the Horsey Hill (now Horsehill) estate on the east bank of the Dart (OS 108 SW)[37] where Gabriel's Shaft was sunk to a depth of 8 fathoms. To reach this part of the mine a bridge was constructed 66ft in length across the river.

Working continued in a desultory fashion for the next three or four years, the maximum depth recorded being 17 fathoms at Todd's Shaft. In 1854 16 tons of low grade copper ore were sold for £35[38] – apparently the only sale that was ever made. Commenting on the mine some years after its closure a correspondent wrote 'Promising stones of ore were raised and an immense 'scream' made about it, resulting in the desired end – the bagging of no small sum in premiums by the promotors'.[39] Proceedings were subsequently taken against the secretary of the company for fraudulent conversion of shares into his own name and, in general, the mine would have appeared to have been a 'bubble company' of the worst type.

High above the east bank of the Dart, a quarter of a mile NW of Holne Bridge, a rocky eminence known as the **Cleft Rock** stands out prominently against the background of Auswell Wood (OS 108 SW). Two nearly parallel copper and iron lodes extend through and alongside the Rock where they have been developed in open gunnises and by underground mining. On the river bank immediately below, a map of the parish of Ashburton dated 1605 marks two buildings bearing the words 'Iron Mill', with a leat taken up from the Dart passing behind them. In 1924 the foundations of the buildings still remained, together with the base of furnaces vitrified by the heat and with large heaps of slag lying alongside. Analyses of the latter showed no traces of copper or tin, the slag being solely derived from the smelting of iron ore. Some of this was presumably obtained from the Cleft Rock itself 'where the sides of the miners' excavations still yield specimens of spathic iron'.[40] Many years have elapsed since these words were written and it is possible that excavation today may reveal further traces of the features so circumstantially described in 1924. At the Cleft Rock itself, a deep gunnis, which seems to split the rock almost in two, is dramatic evidence of the one-time mining activity there.

The Cleft Rock workings, as it would appear, were already more than a century old when they were seen by Kahlmeter in 1725. He describes them as being on a point of land projecting westward beyond the wood and nearly vertical on either side. The veins of copper, striking NE-SW, dipped north and appeared to unite towards the extremity of the point. Here they had been worked for some distance in length and to a depth of 14 or 15 fathoms. Trials had been conducted on the lodes by various parties, the latest being the 'Welsh company' who held a 20 years lease from the mineral lord on the following terms viz. an annual rental of £400 for the first $3^1/_2$ years, together with $1/7^{th}$ dues on the ore raised – this being additional to any profit arising from the $1/6^{th}$ share held by the lessor. The company was further obliged to keep 100 men at work during the first $3^1/_2$ years and thereafter not less than 20 men.

Shortly after acquiring the lease, the company sublet the property to their manager who from Christmas 1724 contracted to keep the said 100 men at work and to pay the company 20/- per ton on the ore raised. The company also reserved the right to purchase ore at a maximum price of £6 per ton even if a higher price were offered by an outside party. From December 1724 to May 1725 output amounting to 170 tons was sold at £4.5.0d per ton. The cost of delivering this on board ship at Dartmouth was 9/4d per ton and the freight to the copper smelting works at Neath 6/- per ton.[41]

Locally, the pronunciation of Auswell approximates to 'Azel'. In 1763 the mine which had then been idle for some time was advertised for sale as Haswell[42] and two years later appears on Benjamin Donn's Map of Devon as 'Hazel Copper Mine'. By the middle of the last century the property had become generally known as **Wheal Hazel**. During this latter period the lodes were developed by two adits and a like number of shafts.

Upstream from Auswell Wood the River Dart describes a huge double-bend, its northern loop nearly encompassing the prehistoric encampment of Holne Chase. Just south of the latter, on the 600ft contour, the **Holne Chase Mine** (OS 108 SW) developed a tin/copper lode by means of a shaft and an open gunnis 15ft wide. About 40yd SW of the shaft lies the mouth of a shallow level which appears to have driven along the course of the lode. According to Dines the sole recorded output consisted of 5 tons of black tin in 1875, the mill at that time being situated on the east bank of the Dart 1,000yd SW of the mine.[43] The writer has been unable to find any particulars relating either to this last or the earlier working of the mine.

In September 1857 as a correspondent of the *Mining Journal* was crossing New Bridge on the road from Buckfastleigh to Poundsgate, his attention was attracted by shouts proceeding from further down the Dart near Lower Hannaford (OS 108 SW). Here he found several men, with Captain William Williams, 'rejoicing over the christening of a new mine, called **Devon Great Elizabeth**'. The 'splendid' specimens of copper ore which he saw displayed convinced him that a rich deposit existed here at a shallow depth. A week later another correspondent claimed that an E-W lode found when sinking a pit contained rich yellow and black ore worth at least £7 per ton. Further north good 'orey' work standing on the footwall of the lode was valued at £40 per fathom, the lode at this point being 6ft wide. During the following month it was reported that over twenty tons had been raised from a depth of less than 12ft.

In January 1858 a shaft was started about 100fm distant from the original discovery and it was decided to erect a water-wheel. By this time, however, doubts were being cast on the extravagant claims made for the mine, more especially when a cross-cut driven south from the shaft at a depth of 23fm failed to encounter any ore values. The shaft moreover lay within 20fm of the boundary of another property over which the company had no control --a fact which the directors omitted to mention.

In September 1858 a lengthy report by Patrick Buchan, M.E. while claiming that the sett comprised 'almost the whole of the parish of Widecombe-in-the-Moor', shows that little had been done beyond making various openings on the back of a lode. In one of these extending about 9 fathoms the lode width was 5 to 8ft and had yielded a few tons of ore but 'not worth taking into consideration'. In June 1859 8 tons of ore were sold for £24 but other than this no returns are officially recorded. By the end of that year work had virtually ceased and in July 1861 the materials consisting of a 30ft water-wheel, a horse whim and 24fm of ladders were advertised for sale by order of the Vice-Warden of the Stannaries.[44]

On the outskirts of Ashburton a deposit of umber was formerly developed to the north-east of the town where the workings are shown on the OS map 108 SE (Edn.1906) at the rear of the hospital. The bed was 30ft thick and was excavated by sinking large rectangular pits, each one being infilled before starting another close alongside. Operations were carried out by two companies known as the **Devon and Cornwall Works** and the **Roborough Works**: the former owned in 1891 by Beer Musgrave & Co and the latter by the Truro Colour Company. Between 1873-83 output by the Devon and Cornwall is recorded at 6,946 tons and from the smaller Roborough Works 850 tons in 1874.[45] These figures are manifestly incomplete since both companies continued in operation well into the present century. The tall stack which marked the site of a pit near East Street remained standing for a number of years after the last war. The umber was principally used for paint manufacture and was prepared for that purpose in grinding mills situated in the nearby valley of the Yeo or Ashburn river.

Near the eastern corner of Auswell Wood adjoining the road from Ashburton to Auswell Cross, the **Druid Copper Mine** (OS 108 SE) developed two principal lodes by means of adits and at least three shafts. Worked on numerous occasions and under a variety of names the sett was acquired by a new company in 1853 from John Sparke Amery, owner of the Druid estate, and was then entitled the Arundell Mine. On Christmas Eve of that year the employees numbering sixty miners were invited by Mr Amery to a supper in the hall of his residence when, in addition to the fare provided by their host, the adventurers contributed a large American cheese and warm clothing for the men.

A similar feast took place that night at the **Devon Tin Mines** on Dartmoor which was under the auspices of the same company. Here the menu consisted of a large side of Wiltshire bacon together with a 60lb American cheese, while each man was offered the choice of a Guernsey frock (jersey) or a woollen waistcoat. Both mines were in advance of their time in possessing a benevolent fund and as there had been no serious accident at either during the year a portion of this was distributed 'in a genial way' at these Christmas gatherings, leaving a balance in hand of £100 at the Arundell Mine and about £20 in the fund of the Devon Tin Mines.[46]

By September 1854 considerable progress had been made at the **Arundell Mine**. An engine house had been erected on Druid Hill where it formed a prominent feature of the landscape and the engine was reported to be working well. Williams' and Watson's

Shafts were being sunk at this time and a new shaft, named the 'Queen Victoria', had been started, the latter event being celebrated by a gift of 2/- and strong ale to each of the miners 'by whom the toasts were drunk with loud cheering'. Shortly after Victoria Shaft was reported to be 35 fathoms deep and Carey's Lode was yielding 'saving work' for copper. A 25 fathom level had been driven 25fm and was showing considerable quantities of malleable and grey copper ore. Little development had been carried out on the other lodes, stoping being deferred until the engine shaft had been sunk below Carey's Lode and the Great Lode cut at the 25fm level.[47]

Due to the failure of Strahan, Paul & Co, the company's bankers and large shareholders in the mine, work was suspended in the autumn of 1855. By that time the adit had been driven 140fm, passing through the Great Lode near the middle of the sett. Elsewhere two lodes of 'great size and fine mineral indications' had been opened up at 25, 35 and 46fm below adit, working cost being in the neighbourhood of £200 per month. Thereafter the sett remained dormant until the latter part of 1856 when operations were resumed under the title of the Arundell Copper Mining Company.

It would appear that this last was of short duration since in April 1860 the *Mining Journal* announced that 'the Druid Mine, worked a few years ago as the Arundell Mine, is now renamed the Devon New Copper Mine and about to resume its periodical working'. The new company, 'under the auspices of several gentlemen of considerable wealth and standing' had acquired the property for £15,000 credited in fully-paid shares, together with a cash sum of £1,000 for the engine.

Shortly after the mine was drained to the 46fm level and preparations were being made to resume the sinking of Victoria Shaft. Due to shortage of capital operations were suspended again in October of that year but were resumed in March 1861, following which the pitwork was completed to the 58 fathom level. Samples of ore taken from the 25fm level on Great North Lode assayed 9 ounces of silver to the ton, 3 $\frac{1}{8}$ per cent nickel, 3 $\frac{1}{4}$ per cent cobalt and 1 $\frac{1}{4}$ per cent bismuth. Further sampling in the 36fm level on New South Lode gave 10 ounces of silver per ton, with slightly lower percentages of nickel, cobalt and bismuth.[48]

During the summer of 1861 Engine Shaft was being sunk below the 78fm level by nine men at a cost of £16 per fathom. At the 78 level Great North Lode was composed of capel, spar (quartz), mundic with spots of yellow copper ore, and cross-cuts were being extended at this depth and also at the 68 level. In the early part of 1862, 36 people were employed and Victoria Shaft reached a depth of 96 fathoms,[49] the first 56fm being vertical and the remainder carried down on the hanging wall of Great North Lode. Throughout this working no sales of ore were recorded and the expenditure on development, amounting to some £15,000, appears to have exhausted the funds of the company which went into liquidation in 1863.

The mine remained idle until November 1866 when it was purchased for £4,000 by the Druid Mining Company. In the course of the next few years about £6,500 was spent in developing the shallower part of the mine above the 68fm level, by the end of which time it was estimated that not less than £35,000 had been laid out on the property since 1854.

On the assumption that the failure of the Druid Mining Company had been chiefly attributable to its neglect in working the deeper levels, a fresh company named the New Victoria (South Devon) Mine was formed in 1869. Among its first tasks was the replacement of the existing engine which had originally been thought capable of developing the mine to over 100 fathoms. In consequence, however, of the increase of water resulting from extension of the upper levels, this was no longer the case. A new 56in cylinder engine with larger pitwork was accordingly purchased for £2,500 and set to work before the end of the year.[50] After this nothing more was heard of the mine and by 1870 its shares had ceased to be listed in the *Mining Journal*. No record is known of the output of the mine throughout its numerous trials and although Collins states that some copper ore was produced the amount must have been wholly disproportionate to the outlay involved.

A short distance east of the Druid Mine, the Yeo or Ashburn River flowing southward from the Moor, takes its meandering course towards Ashburton. On the eastern side of the valley near Waterleat Bridge (OS 108 SE) the portal of an adit with various small shaft dumps and overgrown surface workings marks the site of **the Widdon Smelting House, Tin and Copper Mine** as it was named in 1765 on Benjamin Donn's Map of Devon. The sett was worked on a number of occasions during the 18th and 19th centuries and when reopened in 1845, the principal lode was stated to be 4 to 5ft wide. This was served by a deep adit driven east from the valley, affording backs of up to 40 fathoms at its inner end. During that working the adit was cleared and a cross-cut extended south towards four tin lodes which had lately been revealed by costeaning (surface pitting). In 1849 another cross-cut driven north from the shallow adit was reported to be 'within three feet of the great tin lode'. The mine at this date was equipped with a 40 x 14ft water-wheel and continued in operation until January 1851 when the sett and materials were advertised for sale.

In 1859 arrangements were made to rework the property under the name of Whiddon and Brownshill (or Brownswell) and in the same year a new sett, called **Bowdley Consols**,[51] was acquired with a view to exploring the presumed extension of the lodes to the westward. Up to this time the Whiddon lodes had been worked only above adit but it was now intended to test their values by sinking below that level. It appears, however, that this proposal came to nothing since in 1870 when small-scale working was again in progress no evidence was found of any development deeper than adit level.[52]

In 1861 a company pretentiously named **Devon Great Wheal Ellen Tin and Copper Mine** was formed to prospect the estate of Lower Bowdley (OS 108 SE), an area virtually identical with that of the above-mentioned Bowdley Consols. Work started by clearing the adit where the lode was described as 'kindly', 18 inches wide and composed of gossan, 'very pretty quartz' and mundic (pyrite). In the following year the shaft was said to be 50 fathoms deep and six men were employed in driving on a caunter lode. The working, however, was of short duration and by the end of 1862 all activity had ceased.[53]

About 1½ miles NE of the Whiddon group and some two miles north of Ashburton, a number of setts totalling nearly a mile square have been developed under the name of Owlacombe Mines or, later, Ashburton United. The oldest workings, traditionally dating from the seventeenth century, lie in a plantation bordering the north-west side of the road from Owlacombe Cross to Sigford Bridge (OS 108 NE). Here before the introduction of blasting and by manual labour alone a mass of tin-bearing ground was excavated in an open-cutting 1,200ft long, 30 to 40ft deep and from 50 to 100ft wide,[54] the formation being drained by an adit brought up beneath it from the neighbouring stream. Seen today as a tree-lined gorge the site still affords a surprising example of early mining in Devon, despite a recent attempt, fortunately stopped, to fill it in completely.

Near the bottom of the stockwork the ore body contracted in width, exposing two parallel well-defined lodes which at a later period were developed by shaft mining. During the 1840s the **Beam Mine**, or Wheal Beam as it was then known, was worked by four partners who are said to have raised £6,000 worth of tin stuff from the relatively shallow depth of 31 fathoms below adit. The machinery consisted of a 40 x 4ft wheel which in addition to drawing the water drove 12 heads of stamps, the latter connected to the wheel by a sweep-rod, 'plumocks' and 90 fathoms of 2½in iron rods.[55]

Adjoining the Beam Mine, **West Beam** near Halshanger Wood was started about 1836 when a shaft was sunk on an extension of the old Beam lodes. In the course of the next ten years sales of black tin realised £10,600 but owing to insufficient water-power to drive the pumping-wheel the company was unable to sink deeper than 40 fathoms and in 1848 working was suspended. In June 1851 a small 21-inch steam engine was erected and the shaft eventually reached a depth of 66fm. In 1866 a production of 30 tons of black tin and 22 tons of copper ore was recorded,[56] soon after which the mine was abandoned.

On the south side of the road, opposite the entrance to Owlacombe Beams, the **Union Mine** exploited an extension of the North and South tin lodes of Wheal Beam but apart from being served by a branch of the same adit was an entirely distinct sett. Although the lodes here proved less productive than in the Beam Mine they were extensively developed; Parry's, the original engine shaft, being sunk vertically to 76 fathoms and Murray's Shaft to 45fm, figures relating in each case to depths below adit.

In its earlier days the mine was worked solely by water-power, with two wheels for pumping and stamping and another for hoisting, all three driven by the same stream. While the latter provided ample power during the winter months it was liable to fail in dry summers when operations were brought to a stand. About 1839 a new centrally-placed vertical shaft named Hobson's was started 290yd north-east of Owlacombe Cottage and was eventually carried down to 78 fathoms under adit (here 17fm deep). North Beam Lode was passed through just below adit, South Beam Lode at the 78 level.

After a period of idleness, a company entitled **Ashburton United** was formed in 1857 to take over all the former setts consisting of the Beam Mines, Wheal Union and the Wheal Brothers copper mine. Included in the grant was one of the last 'tin bounds' extant at that time, comprising an area between West Beam and the original Owlacombe Beams workings. Ownership of these bounds pertained to the Earl of Mount Edgcumbe and was preserved in accordance with ancient Stannary custom by turning up a turf at each of the boundary corners on a fixed date annually.

By the early part of 1858, the mines had been reopened to deep adit, of which about 100 fathoms had been cleared. Six pitches were being worked on tribute for tin and a water-wheel stamps was in operation. In the following year a 56in cylinder steam engine from Perran Foundry was installed on Hobson's Shaft. In this a 12in plunger was fixed at the 45fm level, with a 10½in drawing lift below. With the engine working at only a stroke and a half per minute it sufficed to keep the water for the greater part of the year. Shortly afterwards it was announced that 800 fathoms of adits and shafts had been secured and preparations made for reopening the workings of the Beam Mine and the Wheal Brothers copper lode,[57] despite the fact that the latter had proved a failure in its earlier trial.

In 1860 a good bunch of tin was passed through in the 55fm level west of the engine-shaft where the lode was nearly 3ft wide and yielding over a ton of ore per fathom. The 67fm level had already been extended 14fm west of the shaft with a view to developing the downward extension of this bunch. At the 55 level East the lode had been taken away for 50fm in length in a former working. A winze had been sunk from this level to the 67 and the latter was then being extended to a point immediately under the 55fm level end.[58]

Throughout the next few years progress was hampered by continual squabbling, disputes and recriminations over the mineral and water-rights, the sett being referred to by a contemporary critic as 'one of the most complicated and unsatisfactory mining holdings in the West of England' – and as the present writer has cause to know, one of the most difficult to describe intelligibly. Another correspondent after inspecting the property remarked that Ashburton United 'seemed but a poor job and from what they say in the neighbourhood, the present party would appear to be only picking out the tin discovered by the late management'. In 1861 160 people were employed and in the following year when the mine was 100 fathoms deep, it became apparent that further capital would be required. As the existing shareholders showed no inclination to provide the money, working was suspended in 1867. After this, apart from some slight activity in 1887 nothing more appears to have been done until the beginning of the present century.

In 1906 a company was formed to take over the former Owlacombe sett, together with the **Stormsdown Mine** adjoining on the south. Of the three known lodes in the latter, working was confined to South Lode which was served by a branch of the Owlacombe adit. The Stormsdown main shaft lay on the 600ft contour, a quarter of a mile north-east of Owlacombe Cross (OS 1008 SE) and was drained by the adit to a depth of 30 fathoms from surface. Below this the lode was developed in No. 1 level ($12^{1}/_{2}$fm under adit) and No. 2 level 15 fathoms beneath No. 1. Eastward the lode was worked as far as a N-S cross-course beyond which it was not seen. To the west, the adit was extended 185 fathoms, No. 1 level 180fm and No. 2 85 fathoms. Stoping was fairly extensive in each of these levels, the lode being very arsenical but also carrying tin, the latter chiefly in No. 2 level where values from 76 to 170lb to the ton were recorded. The lode, however, was patchy and its average yield is thought to have been little more than 10lb of black tin to the ton. It is estimated that about 11,000 tons of ore was left standing underground when working was abandoned in 1912.

Little or nothing is known of the two other lodes to the south, although the more northerly shows signs of having been worked open-cast by the 'old men' in Stormsdown Plantation. The third lode was seen only in an old cross-cut adit from the end of which a level had been driven 45 fathoms east.[60]

Due to the altitude of the mine the ore was conveyed by a tramway, still traceable in the woodlands, to a site near Owlacombe Bridge (OS 108 NE) where water was available for dressing purposes. The foundations of the stamps and buddles can still be seen here, together with remains of the calciner where the concentrate was 'burnt' for the recovery of arsenic. The calciner stack built of white brick and about 30ft high is shown on the OS map and was demolished in 1973.

During the last working electric power was generated by a coal-fired gas engine. Output is quoted by Dines as 348 tons of black tin and 11,460 tons of arsenical pyrite in the years 1854 to 1912.[61] As will be seen these dates cover the working life of the Owlacombe group as a whole but fail to distinguish the production derived from the last period of activity in the Stormsdown section. In one other respect the recorded output of tin is necessarily incomplete since it takes no account of the production obtained from the original Owlacombe Beams. Whilst this must certainly have been very large, the actual amount can never be known due to the antiquity of those workings.

To the east of Ashburton United a mine named **Wheal Lemon** was restarted about 1854 when a shallow adit driven by the 'old men' was cleared to the point where it intersected a lode 4ft in width. At the same time the old deep adit was secured for a length of 100fm and a number of air shafts situated on the hillside were cleared. The results proving unsatisfactory the work was soon after abandoned. In 1858 the sett was again taken up, being then known as East Ashburton United. On this occasion the deep adit extending from the River Lemon was reopened for its full length of 120 fathoms and investigations were made of several more shafts. During 1859 a cross-cut was driven south from the adit level where it was expected to cut the Union Lode of the Owlacombe mines.

Further east other ancient workings were visible at this time in a wood on the south bank of the Lemon. Known as **Cranover Works**, trials were similarly carried out here during the 1850s but to little purpose since nothing of value was discovered. No further record has been found of either of these small forgotten mines whose sites have not been identified.[62]

About one mile NE of Owlacombe Beams as the crow flies and a short distance upstream from Cocksland Bridge, the River Lemon is crossed by several E-W lodes, some carrying tin and others copper. These were prospected in **Sigford Consols** on the eastern side of the valley and **Smith's Wood Mine** on the west (OS 108 NE). The former was started in 1859 following the discovery by two miners, when exploring old workings, of a lode yielding rich stones of copper ore. On this a number of trial pits were sunk to depths of about 4 fathoms and an adit was begun at river level to drive east on its course. Soon afterwards a second lode was met with some 50fm to the north. This was similarly opened up by an adit, with communicating air shafts. On reaching a depth of $8^{1}/_{2}$fm work was impeded by an influx of water and arrangements were made to purchase a 20in cylinder pumping engine and a 10in steam whim from the neighbouring Silver Brook Mine.

The workings were eventually carried down to a depth of 20 fathoms, with a recorded output of 20 tons of copper ore which realised £95 in the first quarter of 1861. Two years later the sett and machinery were advertised for sale by auction.[63] Ochreous water still oozes from each of the adits, while the site of two shafts may be traced near the 700ft contour a short distance west of Sigford Cottages.

On the opposite side of the valley Smith's Wood Mine was similarly started in 1859 when an adit was driven into the steep-sided western bank in search of the south copper lode of Sigford Consols. Although this was never found, a large tin lode was encountered. Known as Browning's Lode after the name of the mine captain, it was first seen in a short cross-cut from the adit where its width was not less than 20ft and showed an average value of 46lb of black tin to the ton. Adjacent to this on the south another tin lode, 3 to 4ft wide, was soon afterwards found in sinking a shallow pit. This second lode underlay north and was expected to form a junction with the 'Great Lode' at a shallow depth. As a result of these discoveries an order was placed with Messrs Nicholls Williams & Co foundry at Tavistock for a water-wheel capable of driving 24 heads of stamps. The wheel pit was completed in 1861 by which time the

Great Lode had been developed westward in an open-cast working extending to the summit of the hill. Here the lode still maintained its original width but at this point was 'not tinny'.

Meanwhile a shaft had been sunk from which a 10fm level was driven 13fm west and 3fm east. Beneath this a short drive was extended west at the 20fm level. In 1863 work was in progress at the 34fm level where the lode in the end was reported to be 1½ft wide and producing rich stones of copper as well as tin. Operations appear to have ceased in the following year when the machinery was acquired by a neighbouring mine. No record is known of the amount of ore produced.[64]

Indications of the lay-out of the property are still in evidence, including what was formerly the mine count house and an ivy-covered stack on the apex of the hill.

ILSINGTON

Half a mile south-east of Ilsington Church, in a deep secluded valley, two lead-zinc lodes trending NE were formerly worked in the **Silver Brook Mine** (OS 109 NW). The lodes at surface lay 35yd apart and were developed by an adit 2,000ft long and by two shafts. Engine Shaft, about 550yd WNW of Lenda farm, was vertical for the first 16fm and thence followed the hanging-wall of the lode to a depth of just over 80 fathoms from surface. From it levels were driven on the lode at 11, 22, 33, 44, 55 and 66fm below adit. The other shaft, 120yd SW of Engine Shaft, lay on higher ground and was sunk to about 11fm under adit (here 16fm from surface).[65]

The mine is an old one. In the middle of the last century deeds were in existence to show that work had been carried out here and in the nearby Silver Wood, at least 200 years earlier. Operations were resumed about 1757 the lodes on that occasion being exploited to a depth of 15½ fathoms below adit, with a 'sink' in one place extending 7 fathoms deeper. Apparently this working was abandoned in a hurry. In 1852 an old man then living in the district had heard his grandfather say that the miners left behind them all their tools (which he enumerated) and that these would be found if the mine was ever worked again. He added that in the bottom of the sink there was a course of lead ore as 'big as a hogshead'.

The most recent working started about 1851 and continued for seven years. In November 1852 a 20in cylinder pumping engine was installed being the 'first steam engine ever erected in the Ashburton area'. On forking (draining) the mine, the tools were found exactly as the old man had predicted. Clearing the 'sink' also brought to light two sets of wooden hand-pumps, accurately bored and with their leather valves almost as hard as the oak from which the pump columns were constructed. During 1853 the lode was cut through in several places, 80 fathoms south of Woodley's Engine Shaft, where it was reported to be 2ft to 8ft wide. Similar widths were recorded in the adit level north of the shaft. Assays of the ores about this time gave the following produce:

No. 1 Undressed ore, 10cwt 2qrs lead and 10 ounces of silver per 20cwts;
No. 2 Undressed ore, 10cwts, 3qrs lead and 6 ounces 18dwts of silver per 20cwts;
No. 3 Stones crushed and dressed, 72 ¼ per cent lead and 9 ounces of silver per cwt;

No. 4 Crushed ore not dressed, 32½ per cent zinc, 9 per cent lead and 6 ounces of silver to the ton.[66]

Zinc blende was then selling at about £3 and lead ore at £14 per ton. Above the 22fm level the lode produced rich bunches of lead ore but from that level down to the 44 was less productive. Below the 44 zinc ore predominated, scarcely any galena being found except in association with the blende, which in some places yielded as much as 4 tons per fathom.

One of the principal objectives in this working was to deepen the new Engine Shaft to the point where the Main and Western lodes were thought to unite at 75fm from surface. In sinking, however, the Western Lode was found to dip more steeply than had been expected and on reaching the depth of 80fm the mine was abandoned, being then in all probability within a few fathoms of the anticipated junction. Production is recorded as 93 tons of 65 per cent lead ore and 80 ounces of silver in the years 1854-56, together with 1,474 tons of zinc ore between 1854 and 1858. In October 1859 the 20in pumping engine and 10in rotary for hoisting and crushing were still standing on the mine but the pitwork had been drawn up and the rest of the plant sold.[67]

In 1967 the ivy-covered pumping-engine house with its separate stack still remained intact but the whim house had been largely demolished. Below these lay the dressing floors adjoining the stream, and nearby some fairly extensive tailings dumps containing lode material. Two interesting water-colours of the mine were formerly in possession of the late Sir Arthur Russell. Said to have been painted by the purser of the company shortly before the mine was stopped, the whereabouts of these pictures is now unknown.[68]

Although Ilsington has never been regarded as a manganese locality, the ore has in fact been worked in at least two sites in the parish. Some two miles SE of the village a small deposit exists ¼ mile NW of **Stancombe farm** where a shaft is marked on the OS map 109 NW. This was drained by an adit brought up from a point on the 300ft contour, 300yd north of the farm house. Little is known of the mine beyond the fact that it was being worked in 1879 by two partners named Richards and Power who in the following year sold 40 tons of ore for £80.[69]

About ½ mile north of Ilsington another manganese working was accidentally revealed in 1967 when a subsidence took place in the orchard of a farm referred to as **Narrowcombe or Higher Brimley**.[70] Investigations made at the time disclosed an adit or level 200ft long, at the end of which was found a piece of an old drill and the remains of a miner's candle. No record is known of when the mine was worked and although probably of no great antiquity its existence appears to have been entirely forgotten until brought to light in the above manner.

A short distance east of Hemsworthy Gate at the northern foot of **Rippon Tor** (OS 108 NE), a number of small tin-bearing lodes or quartz-tourmaline 'strings' have been worked in the granite country. Originally opened up on the backs by alluvial streamers, they were further developed in the 1840s and 50s by various short-lived companies bearing such names as the Hemsworthy, Somerset, Ilsington and Teignmouth mines. Work carried out by these consisted of little more than sinking small shafts and driving levels rarely exceeding 10 fathoms deep.

In 1851 operations were renewed on a pretentious scale by a company entitled **Haytor Consols** (not to be confused with the subsequently mentioned Haytor Iron Mine). In addition to the Hemsworthy workings the sett included the Bagtor Mine on the south-east and thence eastward to Crownley Parks. Here in a shallow valley near the head-waters of the River Lemon an extensive area of ground had been worked away by the 'ancients' for alluvial tin, leaving a great irregular excavation up to 30 fathoms deep. Adjacent to this dressing-floors were laid out on a lavish scale with a 30ft wheel driving 32 heads of stamps, later supplemented by a second wheel designed to increase their number to 48 heads. The floors were connected to the Hemsworthy workings and other points of operation by a railway 1 3/4 miles in length.

In contrast to this impressive display at surface, underground development was trifling and incompetent. By 1854 an engine shaft had been sunk on the Hemsworthy North Lode to 18 fathoms below the old men's adit (10 fathoms) where a level was driven 120ft east and west. On South Lode the backs above the 15fm level were stoped for 200fm but apparently to small purpose, output from this part of the property amounting to little more than 3 tons of black tin per month.

At the **Crownley Works** two adits were driven with a view to exploring beneath the old men's open pit. The higher adit known as Lord Cranstoun's, was extended to a length of 115 fathoms – 20fm as a cross-cut and the remainder on lode. A little tin was raised here together with a small quantity of copper ore, the latter containing a leader 1 to 6in wide yielding 49 to 397 ounces of silver to the ton. The second adit was driven some 90 fathoms but failed to produce anything of note, having for some unexplained reason been carried alongside instead of on the lode. At one period about 80 people were employed on the property which ceased work in 1856 with a recorded output of black tin totalling a mere 16 tons.[71] In view of its obvious mismanagement it is surprising to learn that Mr Finney 'the able engineer of the mine' was rewarded for his services with the gift of a silver snuff-box in 1853 (M.J. p556).

Shortly before 1862 working was resumed by the **Bagtor Mining Company**. In the course of that year two levels were being driven on the Wheal Prosper lode at the eastern end of the sett. The lower level was designed to come up beneath the 'Pixie Pits', the open-cast working near Crownley Parks referred to above. Another adit was in course of driving on a recently discovered lode some 50 fathoms to the south. The mouth of this adit being adjacent to the floors laid down by the Haytor Consols company, supplied water for dressing purposes. In September 1863 a new 60 x 2½ft wheel was erected here to drive the stamps, also serving by means of flat rods to operate pumps in the Wheal Prosper and Engine shafts. By the following year the adit on Prosper Lode had been driven 96 fathoms and the adit on the new lode 14½fm, while on the Quickbeam Lode the Eastern and Western Engine-shafts had been sunk respectively to depths of 14 and 16 fathoms.

In April 1864 it was decided to purchase the machinery and dressing plant from Smith's Wood Mine and in the following year a 30fm level was being driven west from Wheal Prosper and a 20fm level east from Quickbeam Shaft. Towards the end of 1866 it was decided to wind up the company, returns of black tin to that date having amounted to little more than 25 tons.[72] Two chimney stacks adjacent to Bagtor Cottages are shown on the 1885 edition of the OS map 108 NE. These were presumably erected during the last working of the mine but for what purpose is not clear.

The area adjacent to Haytor Vale is characterised by beds of iron ore interstratified with sandstones and shales. These extend from Kiln Shotts Wood north of the Rock Hotel and thence in a south-easterly direction to Lewthorne (or Loothorne) Cross, a distance of something over a mile (OS 100 SE, 108 NE). Cassiterite also occurs sporadically throughout the region although never extending to any great depth so far as yet proved. The iron ores were of two kinds – brown haematite (limonite) and magnetite – the former occurring in nodules deposited in irregular beds. The magnetic ore where exposed at surface was probably recognised at an early period and may have provided a source of 'lodestone' which, due to its natural magnetic polarity, was used in antiquity for navigation. The earliest form of Mariners' compass consisted of a splinter of magnetite floating on a bowl of water.[73] Development of the ore beds by mining is thought to have started by the sixteenth century, although no plans or records of the workings are known before the last century. By that time a number of the older scattered workings had been consolidated into two main groups comprising the Haytor Iron Mine near the valley head and the Smallacombe Cutting to the south-east.

Haytor Mine, 200yd south of the Rock Hotel, had been developed opencast and by means of an incline shaft before 1828. Some time later an adit was driven from near the valley bottom about 200yd east of the hotel, striking the ore beds 20 fathoms below the open pit. The deposits consisted of four layers varying in thickness from 6 to 14ft with intervening strata of barren ground between. Output during the years 1858-61 and 1869-82 is recorded as 26,500 tons of magnetite, brown haematite and specular iron ore. Additional sales of ore totalling 12,106 tons are given under the names of Haytor and Haytor Vale, with a further 1,400 tons in 1908.[74] It is thought that some of this ore was obtained by purchase from other workings outside the area.

From the Haytor Mine the outcrop of the iron ore has been traced southward more or less continuously to **Smallacombe** where the beds of limonite were exploited by adits ventilated by a number of air shafts. The site was subsequently developed as an open quarry known as the Smallacombe Cutting, its position shown on the OS map (100 SE) half a mile south-east of the Rock Hotel. Due to the large amount of overburden that had to be removed the resultant excavation was described by a writer in 1859 as more nearly resembling a 'great railway works than West of England mining'. During the eighteen seventies an adit was driven obliquely through the ore body for a length of 90 fathoms with the object of reaching the magnetite beds beneath the rising ground to the north and westward.[75]

In an attempt to reduce the cost of transporting the ore to the coast a traction engine had been purchased before this time but the latter proving a failure it was decided in 1860 to smelt the ore on the mine, using lignite from Bovey Tracey. The difficulty, however, of finding a process for converting this into charcoal caused an abandonment of the project. Output from the Smallacombe workings is recorded as 73 tons of magnetite in 1868 and 11,770 tons of brown haematite, ochre and umber in 1874-9. The mine was restarted in 1917 when some further limonite was raised but the amount is not known.[76]

A short distance east of the Smallacombe Cutting three tin lodes and two beds of iron ore have been exploited in the **Atlas Mine**. In 1858 working was resumed under the name of Atlas Iron and Tin Mines, a subsidiary of the South Devon Iron and General Mining Company which at that time owned furnaces and coking ovens on the Bovey Heath. The main centre of activity lay adjacent to Lewthorne Cross about 600yd east of Ilsington Church (OS 108 NE). Development consisted of an adit and at least three shafts. Among these White's Shaft was vertical to 30 fathoms where it intersected White's Lode on which it was carried down on the underlie to the 35fm level. At 18 fathoms from surface the shaft passed through South Lode and the lower ironstone bed a little below the 25 level. In Sarl's Shaft which was equipped with a 30in engine, the upper ironstone bed was cut through at 10fm from surface and intersected Warren's Lode at 35fm.

A first sale of black tin from this lode was recorded in February 1860. Later in the same month a cross-cut driving towards White's Lode encountered a new lode containing bismuth. From the shafts and adit level the ore was conveyed by a tramway to Middlecott Wood (OS 100 SE), a short distance to the east, where a 60ft stamps wheel, together with two calciners and an accompanying stack were erected by the side of a small stream.[77] In 1862 the mine was employing 40 people and in 1864 returned an output of 1,300 tons of brown haematite.

During the following decade the Native Iron Ore Company was formed with a capital of £50,000 to acquire the Smallacombe workings and the Atlas Mine, together with the red haematite mines of Pawton near Wadebridge.[78] The Atlas Mine according to the prospectus was expected to yield 10 tons of black tin per month at an estimated profit of £40 per ton. Total output of tin, however, is officially recorded as 60 tons between 1890-1902. An additional 5 tons is known to have sold in 1903 but in the following year the mine was dismissed with the remark 'nothing doing'.[79] Due to the dense undergrowth the workings of the Haytor Mine like those of Smallcombe are now largely obscured, while at the Atlas Mine White's Shaft lies today in the garden of a private house.

One mile north-east of Haytor Vale, Yarner or **Yarrow Mine** situated near the south-eastern end of Yarner Wood (OS 100 SE) developed two copper lodes adjoining the granite-killas contact. Work started in the early part of 1857 and by May of that year Engine Shaft was six fathoms below the adit and sinking on a lode yielding payable ore, the water being drawn by a 30ft wheel. In September 1857 the 10 fathom level was in course of driving beneath the hill where it was estimated to give 60 fathoms of backs. Concurrently with this two cross-cuts were started from the same level with a view to intersecting Watt's Lode and another (unnamed) lode to the eastward. Ore dressing began in April 1858 and 155 tons were sold in that year. During 1861 the 30 fathom level on North Lode was producing 5 tons of ore per fathom and the 30 level east on South Lode about 2½ tons.

By 1862 the mine had reached a depth of 50 fathoms and 50 people were employed. The machinery at this time consisted of a 60in cylinder pumping engine, one 40ft wheel and another of 25ft, the latter having a drawing machine and crusher attached. Water for driving the wheels and for dressing purposes was presumably obtained from the Bovey Pottery leat which passed through the sett. In December 1864 it was decided to wind up the company which by that date had returned a total of 2,300 tons of 3 ¾ per cent ore, realising £6,200.[80]

In the following year a new company was formed to take over the mine. According to the prospectus the sett contained four lodes 'embedded in the killas at the junction of the granite', together with a large elvan course. The previous company had raised 'almost sufficient ore to make the mine self-supporting'. The flotation, however, appears to have been unsuccessful and in October 1865 the machinery, including 60fm of pitwork, was put up for sale. The mine with its ruined engine-house, two shafts and, until recently, extensive burrows now lies in a nature reserve and should be visited only by permission of the local warden.

Due to its remote situation, much hardship was formerly experienced by the men in coming and going to their work in the cold and wet of Dartmoor winters. In 1864 a Yarner miner stated that 'many of the men have to walk two miles to the mine over an exposed road. They then go underground for eight hours, come up fatigued and freely perspiring and have to put on their cold wet clothes in which to go home'.[81]

Devon Wheal Frances (or Francis) assumed by Dines to be an alternative name for the Yarner Mine, was in fact a quite distinct sett although it closely adjoined the latter on the high ground to the west. Working began about 1859 and in 1866 it was decided to purchase the Yarner Mine (then recently abandoned) for the sum of £250. As a consequence of this it was claimed that by extending the Yarner adit, Devon Wheal Frances would be able to develop its lodes to a depth of 90 fathoms without the aid of machinery.

About this time the property was inspected by two visiting captains who reported that the mine lay near the summit of a high hill and contained eleven lodes, four of which where exposed at surface showed widths of 4 to 14ft. In the cross-cut adit the lodes were principally composed of gossan and mundic (iron pyrites), with spots and leaders of green silicate of copper (chrysocolla). The mine was still active in 1870 when it was 30 fathoms deep and employing 40 people.[82] No record of production has been found nor is it known when working finally ceased.

CHAPTER 7

THE TEIGN VALLEY

The mineral deposits of the Teign valley consist of two main types; manganese occurring chiefly on the east and south-east, whilst on the western side two productive lead-zinc lodes extend northward and roughly parallel with the river for a distance of nearly six miles. Barytes (barite) is also present in commercial quantities, and iron ore has been returned from E-W lodes extending from the Dartmoor granite.

At the turn of the last century the valley as a whole was entirely pastoral in character. By 1810, however, following the partial exhaustion of the manganese mines of Newton St Cyres and Upton Pyne near Exeter, search for that mineral had started in the parishes of Ashton, Christow, and Doddiscombsleigh, where signs of old workings can yet be traced. Among these are the pits and shallow gunnises near Higher Barton farm where three lines of outcrop have been exploited, close to the 400ft contour some 550yd north of Higher Ashton Church (OS 91 SE). At the western end of one of these an openwork (marked 'Old Quarries' on the OS map) is 60ft deep, whilst 300yd NE of Higher Barton a shaft has been sunk in another excavation known as Wells Head Great Pit.

In the parish of Doddiscombsleigh manganese deposits were developed on a more extensive scale in the **Teign Mine** 800 yards east of Christow Station (OS 91 NE). The northernmost workings here commence a short distance SE of Woodah farm and extend for 280fm SW in the form of shallow pits, the deepest about 6fm. Near the eastern boundary of Scanniclift Copse, 200 yards SW of the Woodah workings, an adit has been driven south-eastward into the steeply-rising hillside where at 23fm from surface it meets a deposit on which a level was extended 50fm along the strike. Other manganese workings are known to exist in Harehill Plantation, 400yd south of Doddiscombsleigh Church. Here a small shaft on the northern boundary of the wood probably connects with an adit having an entrance 30 yards to the north-west.[1]

In 1821 according to Lysons the total manganese output of the parishes of Ashton, Doddiscombsleigh and Christow amounted to 426 tons and in the course of the next twenty years a number of fresh setts were granted. Among these was a licence in 1829 to the Cornish industrialist, John Williams of Scorrier House, to search for manganese in the parish of Christow. The site of the operations is thought to correspond with the **Aller Mine** (OS 91 SW) which had earlier produced small quantities of manganese. From 1829-41 some 2,460 tons of ore were returned, on which dues of £2,964 were paid to the mineral lord.[2]

On 17 December 1836 the *Mining Gazette* announced the sale of 40 tons of manganese from the **Ideford Mine** near Chudleigh. Six years later advertisements appeared of the **Channiwell Copper and Manganese Mine** in Doddiscombsleigh where three large lodes were said to be standing at only 6fm from 'grass' (surface). Situated on a lofty hill 'commanding a fall of 70fm' it was claimed that these could be worked simply by driving adits.[3] The site of this last mine is uncertain but was thought by Ramsden to refer to Harehill (OS 91 NE).

In 1859 a lease was granted by Lawrence Palk Esq of Haldon House to James Hampton, mine agent, of Christow, to search for manganese at Shippen Town Barton and Ogden in the parish of Doddiscombsleigh. This is believed to be the last reference to

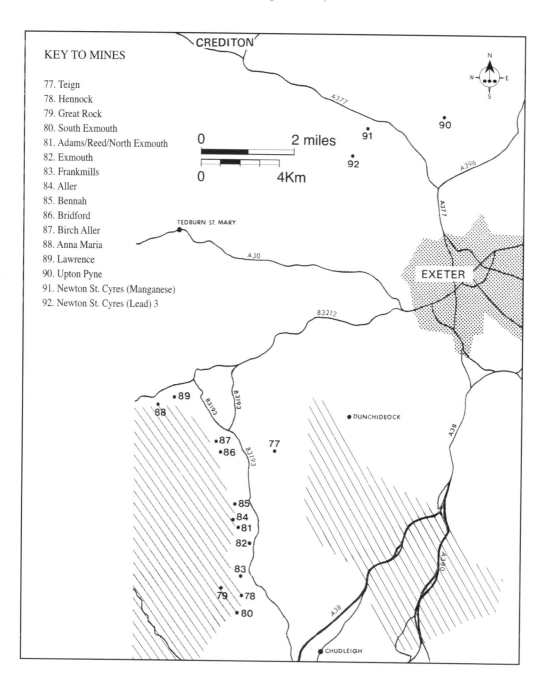

KEY TO MINES

77. Teign
78. Hennock
79. Great Rock
80. South Exmouth
81. Adams/Reed/North Exmouth
82. Exmouth
83. Frankmills
84. Aller
85. Bennah
86. Bridford
87. Birch Aller
88. Anna Maria
89. Lawrence
90. Upton Pyne
91. Newton St. Cyres (Manganese)
92. Newton St. Cyres (Lead) 3

manganese working in the Teign Valley, the main centre of production having shifted many years before that time to the area north-west of Tavistock.[4]

There is reason to think that lead was first mined on the west bank of the Teign in the vicinity of Franklyn or Franklands farm, on a site which was later to become known as the **Hennock Mine**. Towards this point a shallow adit dating from an unknown period had been driven south on the course of a lode from the valley near Hyner Bridge (OS 101 NW). On 3rd June 1812 the Hennock sett was granted to a certain John Gullett of Exeter with liberty to search for lead and other minerals. Although an experienced miner, Gullett at this time was already advanced in years and through lack of capital did little more than erect a water-wheel and extend the adit from which a small quantity of manganese was raised.[5]

In 1836 an enlarged sett was acquired by a company entitled the **Wheal Hennock Silver, Lead, Copper and Manganese Mine**, with an authorised capital of £15,000. A new adit was commenced at this time, the adit driven by the old men (i.e. Gullett's miners) for 300fm alongside the lode having collapsed. The former engine-shaft, however, was considered well placed for the future development of the property, and the existing wheel-pit was of sufficient size to accommodate a 36ft wheel. The leat which served it was also in good condition.[6]

In 1839 the mine was reported as having two lodes. On the western one South Whim Shaft had been sunk to a 30fm level from surface where a cross-cut driven east intersected the second lode. The latter was 18in wide and showing good values for silver-lead. This had been opened up by a level driven 10fm north. Lead ore was also encountered south of the engine shaft which was then in course of sinking. 'At our new shaft' wrote the manager 'a little to the west of the old workings, we have discovered some fine branches of manganese'. Shortly after a parcel of manganese ore was sold for £458, another valued at £500 was ready for market, whilst a third parcel then being dressed was expected to realise £350. In addition £250 worth of lead ore was awaiting sale.[7] Despite the many optimistic reports issued at this time, however, it is clear that the mine was yielding little or no profit and early in the 1840s operations were suspended.

In 1849 a fresh lease was granted to a Mr Vatcher of Exeter who sank a trial shaft a short distance south of the former workings. At the 20 and 30fm levels the lode displayed values of up to £18 worth of lead ore per fathom and in February 1852 it was decided to purchase a 50in steam engine from the Tavistock foundry of Nicholls, Williams with a view to deepening the mine. The engine was ready for dispatch by August but instead of being sent by road was carried via the Tavistock canal to Morwellham whence it was shipped down the Tamar and around the south coast of Devon to Newton Abbot. From there it was drawn in waggons to the mine.[8]

Soon after the engine had been put to work the shaft reached a depth of 40fm and eventually 60fm. At this horizon, however, the lode values showed a serious decline and three years later the machinery including the engine, 70 fathoms of pumps and two water-wheels were advertised for sale. The sole recorded output from this working consisted of 29 tons of lead ore and 36 ounces of silver in the year 1853.[9]

Under the name of **South Exmouth** (OS 101 NW) working was resumed in 1861 and during the next seven years the mine was developed on a considerable scale. The sett at this time extended 600fm south from the Hyner Brook and thus included the sites of all the earlier trials. None of these being considered sufficiently promising to warrant reopening, a new shaft named Westcomb's was commenced in virgin ground,

630yd ESE of Hennock church. By the early part of 1862, the shaft was already down to 33fm and a 40in engine had been erected. At the 45fm level, north, connection was made with the old Hyner Bridge adit which was cleared and maintained by the mine throughout this working. In the 45fm level the stopes gave an average yield of 3 tons of ore per fathom and £2,800 worth was sold. Encouraged by this, dressing floors were laid down and two further shafts were sunk to provide ventilation as the levels were extended north and south. By the early part of 1863 Westcomb's Shaft was 60fm deep, and in the previous quarter 260 tons of lead ore had been returned. Although values at the 60fm level showed a falling off sinking of the shaft was continued to 90fm. At this horizon the lode was 2ft wide, principally composed of quartz, blende and barytes but in general was poor. Of the two lodes, the western one was chiefly exploited the longest drives on this being over 200 fathoms north of the shaft and 120 fathoms south.

At the height of its activity the mine employed 122 people and in one year showed a profit of £1,500. Notwithstanding this and a recorded output of 760 tons of lead ore and 1,150 ounces of silver between 1862 and 1867 the overall cost of working exceeded the returns. As a consequence, operations were abandoned in 1868, when the 40in pumping engine, 25in steam whim and crusher, together with two water-wheels of 20 and 8ft diameter were offered for sale.[10]

In addition to the **Hennock** lead mine described above, another mine in the vicinity was formerly worked under the same name, a fact which has tended to much confusion. The Hennock twin lay adjacent to the densely-wooded Beadon Valley, 750 yards NNW of Hennock Church (OS 101 NW) where, as stated by Lysons in 1822, a lode of micaceous iron ore 2ft wide was found embedded in the granite. Locally known as 'shiny ore' its principal use before the invention of blotting paper was for drying ink on documents, being sold for that purpose under the name of 'Devonshire sand'.[11]

The distinction between the two Hennock mines was first made clear in 1849 when working was resumed on the Beadon Valley lodes under the name of the Hennock Iron & Tin Mine. The sett at this time claimed to possess an unlimited quantity of rich micaceous peroxide of iron, yielding 50 per cent of iron 'of a type eminently suited for the manufacture of steel'. From one lode averaging 7ft in width at a depth of only 10fm, 1,600 tons had already been raised at a cost not exceeding 2/- per ton and it was estimated that output could be increased to 2,000 tons per month to return a profit of £4,000 to £5,000 a year.

About this time experiments were made by a Mr Prince in smelting the ore to which lime had been added, with lignite from Bovey Tracey. The process, however, failed to give satisfactory results due to the brown coal containing traces of sulphur with a high proportion of ash.[12] Despite this the mine continued in operation until 1889, the output finding a ready market in the manufacture of non-corrosive paint.

In 1902 the Hennock iron mine was taken up by the Ferrubron Company who gave it its present name of Great Rock.[13] The sett containing at least five known lodes was developed principally by adits – the deepest being 72fm below the highest point of outcrop. The ore occurred in pockets often separated by considerable lengths of barren ground, a fact which tended to raise the working costs. The latest period of activity came to an end in 1969. Output from 1902-7 is recorded as 650 tons. After 1907 it was worked in conjunction with the Kelly Mine near Lustleigh which was under the same ownership, production being then about 400 tons a year.[14]

Near Hyner Bridge (OS 101 NW) trial was made in 1842 by an Exeter company in the hope of finding a northward extension of the lodes of South Exmouth. At this point, however, the ground was disordered by iron courses emanating from the granite and although a small quantity of galena was returned, the mine as such was a failure.[15]

In contrast to this **Frank Mills** with its immediate neighbour **Wheal Exmouth & Adams**, a short distance only to the north, were destined to prove by far the richest and most productive of all the lead mines of the Teign Valley. Wheal Adams otherwise known as the Reed Mine and, later, North Exmouth, adjoined the 400ft contour, $^{1}/_{2}$ mile north of the Tudor mansion Canonteign Barton or Old Canonteign (OS 91 SW). Operations started here about 1839 when large quantities of lead ore and blende were revealed in the 8, 18 and 28fm levels. Working was resumed in 1845 and by the following year a 30in pumping and 16in winding engine had been erected, and New Engine Shaft was sunk to an eventual depth of 85fm from surface.

Between the 50 and 60fm levels the lode was very productive returning over £30,000 worth of ore. In February 1847 10 tons of lead ore and 100 tons of 'rosin jack' (a variety of zinc blende) were reported to be ready for sale.[16] In the 18fm level driving north the lode was 2ft wide and consisted mainly of barytes, with a small leader of galena and mundic on the footwall side. The ground in Wheal Adams was predominantly weak and unstable. In April 1847 an extensive run took place between the 40 and 60fm levels in New Engine Shaft. By good fortune the fall took place during the night, involving no danger to the men, and within a few months the damage had been repaired. The water, however, was very quick and the mine was with difficulty kept in fork with the engine working at 10 strokes per minute.[17]

Production from 1845-52 is officially recorded as 1,220 tons of lead ore and 680 ounces of silver.[18] Towards the end of that period output showed signs of falling off, the ore shoot in the deeper part of the mine having pitched southward beyond the boundary in the direction of Wheal Exmouth. As a consequence, in 1853 Wheal(s) Adams and Exmouth were amalgamated to form one sett.

Wheal Exmouth had been started about 1828 by the Cornish firm of Messrs Williams of Scorrier on the site of some small-scale earlier workings. In 1848 an adit was commenced near the margin of the Teign a little to the north of Canonteign Barton and was driven west in a dead straight line for 277fm (1,662ft). The work occupied a period of four years but on its completion drained Wheal Adams to the 50fm level and Wheal Exmouth to 25fm from surface. After raising a quantity of ore from the back and floor of the adit the mine was sold by the Williams' to the Exeter firm of Bidwell & May.

In seeking to develop the mine on a larger scale the new company was faced with the problem that the back of the principal lode outcropped only 60ft from the windows of Old Canonteign, still at that time the seat of Viscount Exmouth. Short of actually sinking the shaft on the lawn before the house, the nearest feasible site lay at a corner of the road forming the boundary of the park. Here a new shaft, named Porter's after the Chairman of the company, was started on 12 March 1853 when a large assembly including the committee and 150 miners gathered to witness the cutting of the first sod. After breaking a bottle of wine to mark the occasion, the Chairman addressed the men, warning them against wasting their substance in public-houses – following which the committee retired to the King's Inn for refreshments, whilst the miners were regaled with bread and cheese and ale.[19]

By 1860 the shaft had reached a depth of 84fm below adit or 108fm from surface and a 70in pumping engine from the Plymouth Foundry of Mare & Co had been erected, with a 22in whim engine close alongside. As the engine houses were in full view of the mansion they were constructed in castellated style and both externally and in their internal fittings were probably the most sumptuous and imposing buildings of their kind ever erected in England. Other machinery included a 22in stamps engine and a 24in crusher with a very short stroke, the latter being among those originally put up by Brunel in his ill-fated attempt to use a vacuum as a propelling force on a section of the old South Devon Railway. The dressing floors of the mine were constructed near the site shown on the OS map (91 SE) as Exmouth Cottages where the outflow from the adit provided water for preparing the concentrates.

Although the position of the shaft was the best that could have been reasonably expected in the circumstances it was still some way off the lode, necessitating a cross-cut of 50fm in length at the 20fm level. Realising the need to provide ventilation Lord Exmouth went so far as to allow an air shaft to be sunk on the lawn immediately fronting the house, stipulating only that the dumps were removed and the shaft surrounded by ornamental iron railings. In permitting such development in a situation where many proprietors would have refused consent under any terms it might seem that Lord Exmouth was influenced by something more than royalty considerations alone and one wonders if his compliance was attributable in part to his West Cornwall ancestry and the inherited sympathy of a Cornishman towards mining enterprise.

In the course of sinking, the lode proved highly productive from the 50 to 60fm levels. At the 72 the ground was disordered but on reaching the depth of 85fm the lode gave indications of becoming larger and richer again. Cross-cuts were extended at the 20, 40, 60, 72 and 84fm levels, with intermediate drives at 10, 30 and 50fm. Little work, however, was done below the 84 level under adit (25fm), although the shaft was carried down to an ultimate depth of 145fm from surface.[20] Development was chiefly confined to the East Lode, work on the West Lode being on a smaller scale. Between the two lodes lay a number of branches, including the so-called Antimony Lode and the Jack Lode, all of which came together at the 70fm level making 'ore against ore' in a mass of mineralised ground 10 to 100ft wide.

In 1860 a 24in horizontal engine was added to the existing plant in order to drive 36 heads of stamps for treating the halvans (discarded ores) remaining in the burrows.[21] From 1854-57 sales of 2,761 tons realised £36,000 and in the latter year the mine was returning 150 tons of lead ore per month. The greater part of this was conveyed in waggons to Teigngrace on the Stover Canal and thence down the river to Teignmouth for transhipment.[22]

In 1857 the levels at Wheal Adams having run together that part of the sett was abandoned and the machinery comprising a 30in pumping engine and 16in winding engine together with two horse-whims was advertised for sale.

Wheal Exmouth reached the peak of its activity in 1859 when 265 people were employed and sales of 1,345 tons of lead ore were recorded. This exceptional output suggests that the 'eyes of the mine had been picked' and in the following year when only 630 tons were returned, it was stated that little ore of value remained in sight. As a consequence it was decided in 1862 to wind-up the company and sell the machinery. Working, however, had been resumed by 1870 but on a much reduced scale, the mine being unwatered only to the 50fm level with a maximum of 20 people employed.[23] The latter consisted mainly of tributers 'fossicking' in and above the old deep adit. From 1870-74 sales amounted to a mere 515 tons of lead ore with 997 ounces of silver and by 1875 the mine had been finally abandoned.

Total output in the years 1851-74 is officially recorded as 11,573 tons of lead ore and 118,000 ounces of silver, together with 1,564 tons of sphalerite (zinc blende) between 1859-74. To this should be added 1,220 tons of lead ore and 680 ounces of silver returned by Wheal Adams during the time when the latter formed part of the Wheal Exmouth sett.[24]

Adjoining Wheal Exmouth on the south working commenced in 1854 at **Frank Mills**, a mine which was destined to out-rival its neighbour in size and productiveness. Named after Francis Mills, a banker and at one period the largest shareholder in Wheal Exmouth, the sett covered 600 acres on the course of the lodes, extending north from the Hyner Brook (OS 101 NW) to the Wheal Exmouth boundary. At an early stage when the shaft was still only 30fm deep, the directors showed their confidence in the property by installing a 60in cylinder pumping engine. This was housed in a building of similar ornamental style to those of Wheal Exmouth. Other machinery included a 42in winding engine and 28in crusher.[25] By 1862 the shaft had been sunk vertically to 8fm and 150 people were employed.[26] Among these were many Bere Ferrers miners who had migrated to this district after the flooding of South Tamar Consols in 1856.

The engine shaft was sunk between the outcrops of the East and West Lodes which were 23fm apart at the 30fm level but drew closer together in depth. Noteworthy values were first encountered at the 60fm level and continued equally rich at the 70. At these horizons the levels were extended for lengths of over 330fm. At greater depths the values of West Lode declined, the 115 and 150fm levels being relatively short.

The two lodes varied considerably in their characteristics. West Lode was composed of gossan, carbonate of lime, quartz and white iron – the lead ore consisting of fine-grained galena with a fairly high proportion of silver. East Lode between the 45 and 84fm levels showed a preponderance of barytes and the lead ore, known as Potters' Lead (lead carbonate) was almost without silver. The average width of both lodes was from 2 to 4ft but expanded in places to as much as 30ft – the whole of this ground being 'orey' if not rich.[27] The barytes occurred chiefly in vughs (cavities in the lodes). A visitor to the mine in 1868 was told by one of the men that when working in one of these chambers he 'suddenly came upon a splendid show of white carbonate of lead, from ten to twelve feet square, the needles suspended from the roof as in a limestone cavern'.[28] A statement by Collins suggests that these were in continuous process of formation, he himself having observed newly formed crystals in parts of the mine which had only been abandoned for a relatively few years.

At the northern end of the sett the lodes extended beneath a 'pan' or basin of ground forming part of Old Canonteign park. Here a small stream cascading eastward from the Moor had been dammed up to form an ornamental pond or lake. To reach this point levels were driven for 20fm, mainly through barren ground, with the further necessity of sinking at least one intermediate shaft to provide ventilation. The cost and perseverance entailed in carrying out this work was amply rewarded when just beneath the margin of the lake 'as fine a lead lode was met with as I have had the pleasure of seeing' the *Mining Journal's* correspondent reported in September 1860.

The values contained in this ore shoot being exceptionally rich, the ground was apparently stoped too far upwards beneath the pond and in June 1861 it was learnt that the water had broken in. Happily this took place during the night when there was no one underground, and since the amount of water in the pond was small the workings were soon drained and the breach sealed, with no serious consequences to the mine as a whole.[29]

In the initial stages of working the Frank Mills ores were treated at Wheal Exmouth but by 1856 the floors there were becoming overburdened by the increasing output of the latter mine. New floors were accordingly laid down to the west of the Frank Mills Shaft, adjoining the site of the present Frank Mills cottages (OS 101 NW) which at that time constituted the count house and workshops of the mine. By consent of Lord Exmouth, water for driving a wheel and for dressing purposes was brought in through a leat from the ornamental pond referred to above.[30]

Throughout the next twelve years the output of lead and silver from Frank Mills continued to increase, gradually drawing ahead of Wheal Exmouth as the production from the latter declined. Frank Mills reached its zenith in 1868 when sales of 1,519 tons of lead ore and 39,865 ounces of silver were recorded. About this time the mine also attained its maximum depth of 150fm from surface and 180 people were employed. In the following decade a decline set in, production of lead ore falling from 957 tons in 1870 to 237 tons in 1874.[31]

Working, however, continued for another six year during which time the produce consisted mainly of brown haematite, spathic iron ore and fluor-spar. From 1857-79 output totalled 14,800 tons of lead ore and 248,520 ounces of silver; whilst 873 tons of barytes, 179 tons of fluor-spar and 240 tons of brown haematite were returned in the course of the mine's last years.[32] On 21 August 1880 the setts and machinery of Frank Mills and Wheal Exmouth were jointly advertised for sale in the *Mining Journal* and by that date lead mining throughout the Teign Valley had ceased.

At Frank Mills the waste and tailings dump are still of huge extent, grab samples taken from the latter being said to show 8 to 10 per cent barytes and 1 per cent galena. (Barclay & Toll MS). Assuming these values to be consistent throughout, their treatment might well prove a viable proposition at the present day prices of base metals.

In contrast to these last two mines the lead lodes in the upper reaches of the valley were small in size and the trials made thereon proved generally unsuccessful. In 1844 a sett bearing the catch-penny title of **East Wheal Friendship** was taken up immediately north of Wheal Adams and on driving an adit a lode was intersected 5 to 6ft in width which was said to be of sufficient promise to warrant the erection of a 40in engine to test it in depth.[33] Beyond making this announcement, however, little if anything appears to have been done. In 1859, a mine named **Wheal Amery**, similarly described as adjoining Wheal Adams on the north, claimed to have cut a number of promising branches when driving an adit. These were composed of blende, lead and copper ores; the principal lode being thought to lie only a short distance ahead.[34] In the following year some work was carried out on this property by the Wheal Exmouth company but apparently without seeking consent of the shareholders. On this irregularity being pointed out operations were immediately suspended in order to avoid the risk of litigation.

The exact site of Wheal Amery is uncertain but probably formed part of the Aller Mine, the latter as shown on the OS map 91 SW, being three-quarters of a mile south of Christow Church. The Aller sett was held under grants of 1850 and 1852 and an undated plan marks Engine Shaft, 200yd W by S of Aller Cottages, as 30fm in depth. Deep Adit passes this shaft at 33fm from its portal and intersects four lode branches all of which were opened up for a few fathoms north. From the shaft-bottom a cross-cut extending 33fm E by N cuts a fifth lode. Shallow Adit was driven 145fm west but apparently all in barren ground, and is not connected with the other workings. Old Engine Shaft, 140yd ESE of (new) Engine Shaft was thought by Dines to lie within the boundary of the adjoining Reed Mine, otherwise Wheal Adams. In addition to the above several other shafts are shown to the north of New Engine Shaft. Orchard Shaft, the only one named, was 10fm deep, with short E-W cross-cuts from the bottom.[35] In 1856 the sett was advertised for sale but according to Collins (p403) was at work again in 1879 when its sales of silver-lead ore were described as 'very small, if any'. The ruined engine-house here probably dates from that period.

A quarter of a mile SW of Christow village, **Christow Lead Mine** or Bennah as it is named on the OS map 91 SW, was started in 1851 by an Exeter company. During the next two years a steam engine was erected and the shaft sunk to 40fm. At a depth of 30fm cross-cuts were driven 43fm west and 2fm east. Although traces of galena and pyrite were seen in the shaft no production was recorded and in August 1854 the plant comprising a 26in pumping engine, boiler, pumps and 50fm of ladders were advertised for sale. In 1860 the Truro correspondent of the *Mining Journal* stated that the mine had been commenced by a Mr Christopher Robins but that little was done and the extent of the workings was 'trifling'.[36]

Some three-quarters of a mile eastward of Bridford Church, trials were started in 1849 at **Wheal Bridford** where an adit was driven in search of lead. There is no record of any such ore being found and at the end of twelve months working was abandoned. In the following year the mine was taken up by a new company and entitled Bridford Consols. In January 1851 a lode of barytes, 40ft wide, was cut near the western boundary of the sett where the gossan 'back' yielded 11 ounces of silver to the ton. Two men were then employed in bringing up an adit to and beyond the lode and a site had been chosen for sinking an engine-shaft. By 1853 the lode had been proved to some depth and was said to be of good quality 'free from injurious tints, uniform in texture, brittle and easily broken'. The controlling interest in the mine was held at this date by an Exeter solicitor, Mr R T Head who worked it occasionally, selling the ore at about £1 per ton as and when he could find a market.[37]

The many uses which barytes now serves, notably as a non-poisonous substitute for white lead in paint, as a 'filler' for heavy paper and more recently in sinking oil wells, were as yet unknown and consequently the demand was small. Despite this 35 tons were sold in 1855, the ore body from which it was raised being 40ft wide, 600ft long and 300ft deep.[38] This was developed in an open-cast excavation just south of Bridfordmills Lane, and by a 400ft deep shaft 100yd south of the pit. The workings are named on the OS map 91 NW (Edition 1906) as Teign Valley Barytes Mine and the open-cast excavation as 'Stone Quarry' – the latter of course from its proximity to Stone farm. On the 1884 edition of the same sheet the pit is more correctly designated 'Stone Mine, Barytes'.

The ore-body was later exploited by a second shaft, 60yd NE of the old shaft. This was sunk to 380ft and development carried out at three levels, although due to intrusions of country rock only the wider, well-defined veins were removed. From 1882 when regular production first began output increased steadily, rising from 2,000 tons per annum in 1890 to a peak of 21,000 tons in 1940. In the ensuing decade production averaged 12,000 tons a year.[39]

During its more recent working the mine was operated on behalf of Laporte Industries, the barytes being used for the manufacture of hydrogen peroxide. Two main ore-channels and a number of minor branches were exploited over a strike length of 800ft and to a depth of 600ft, total production amounting to over 370,000 tons. At the 600ft level the ore body showed signs of exhaustion, due not only to the diminishing size of the shoots but also to an increase in the sulphides of lead, zinc and iron bordering the veins. Whilst it was thought that barytes in association with lead and zinc existed in payable quantities at greater depth, to prove this would have necessitated sinking a new shaft or else a long and costly repair job on the existing haulage shaft. As the company was unwilling to put up the money for either of these alternatives the mine was closed down in 1958.[40]

Birch Aller or Ellers (shown as **Birch Mine** on the OS map 91 NW) lies some 2,000ft north of Bridford Consols. Work was started or restarted here by a Mr Pye and a small group of Exeter adventurers early in 1851. By July 1853 a shaft had been sunk and a 30in engine erected, working costs being estimated at £315 per month. Negotiations were then in hand for constructing a tramway to the mine. During the second quarter of 1854 25$\frac{1}{2}$ tons of lead ore were sold for £370 and in 1855 Engine Shaft reached its maximum depth of 46fm and Pye's (or Whim) Shaft 50fm. The two shafts were connected at the 15 (adit), 30 and 40fm levels.

The lode is said to have been 3$\frac{1}{2}$ft wide at the 40 level where it consisted of galena, blende and fluor-spar. From the 40 down to the 50fm level 30 tons of lead ore were raised. A lens or locket of barytes 3ft wide and over 200ft in length was also proved, although never worked, in the southern part of the mine.[41] In 1855 the sett and materials were advertised for sale, the latter including the pumping-engine, a horse whim, 30ft wheel and about 50fm of pumps.[42] Remains of the engine-house with a well-preserved stack now lend character to the garden of a private house.

Near Dunsford Mills (OS 91 NW) on the Exeter-Moretonhampstead road, 1$\frac{1}{2}$ miles NW of Bridford Village, **Wheal Anna Maria and Wheal Lawrence** lay respectively on the north and south banks of the Teign which at this point flows in an easterly direction from its source within the Moor. The setts comprised the northernmost extremity of the Teign Valley N-S lead lodes which are here crossed by a number of E-W copper veins.

The lease of Anna Maria was granted in 1847 by Baldwin Fulford Esq of Fulford House, the lord of the soil, who with his family held a majority of the shares. By August of that year several copper-bearing lodes varying in width from 4 to 7ft had been opened up at surface and on one of these named Woon's a pit had been sunk about 9ft. During the next six months further pits excavated in the river alluvium revealed no less than nine lodes within a transverse distance of 80fm. Two of these were said to contain cobalt and on one of them a sink was put down 11ft below the river bed. In July 1850 a 32 x 6ft water-wheel operating 200fm of flat-rods was draining the shaft to 20fm at which depth it was proposed to cross-cut all the lodes. In the course of sinking, the shaft passed through a solid mass of mundic (pyrite) showing assay values of up to 3$\frac{1}{2}$ per cent copper. Due, however, to their proximity to the river the workings were greatly impeded by water which rendered progress 'very troublesome and expensive'. Operations, moreover, were carried out in a desultory fashion and as the *Mining Journal* remarked, the adventurers needed to adopt a far more vigorous policy if they were ever to make a mine of their concession.[43]

Wheal Lawrence was similarly started in 1847, under a grant from Sir Lawrence Palk, Bt. The sett lay opposite Anna Maria with rights extending for about a mile along the south bank of the Teign. By November 1847 seven lodes showing copper staining were claimed to have been discovered, these being traversed in at least one instance by a N-S vein, 12 inches wide, yielding cubes and fine-grained lead ore of very pure quality. During 1848 an adit started near the river had been driven for a length of 80fm and in the following year the engine-shaft was 13fm deep. From this a cross-cut extending 33fm south intersected a copper lode on which a level was driven 2fm E-W. Later in the same year Whim Shaft on the high ground, 375yd ESE of Dunsford Mills, was down to $19^{1}/_{2}$fm and in February 1850 holed to the adit at 30fm from surface. In 1852 the two mines which had always been at loggerheads over the water rights of the Teign were brought under one control.[44]

Working continued for a short time after this although little development appears to have been carried out other than driving a few cross-cuts from the adit to prove the width and nature of the lead lodes, together with short drives on some of the copper lodes. No plans of the workings are known nor are there any records of output although some lead ore is reputed to have been sold by Wheal Lawrence in 1851. Little trace of the workings is visible today, the shaft at Anna Maria having long since been filled, whilst search by the writer in 1959 failed to detect the sites of the Wheal Lawrence Adit and of Whim Shaft, although the latter is shown on the OS map 91 NW.

UPTON PYNE – NEWTON ST CYRES

Some three miles north of Exeter an E-W fault in the New Red Sandstone has been traced for a distance of nearly seven miles yielding as De la Beche observed in 1839, 'much valuable manganese at Huxham, Upton Pyne and Newton St Cyres'.[45]

According to Lysons (1822) manganese was first discovered at **Upton Pyne** about the year 1770 and at **Newton St Cyres** somewhat later. The earliest documentary evidence relating to the former appears in a letter of the 1780s when Samuel Kingdon, ironmonger of the City of Exeter, requested leave of Sir Stafford Northcote to take over the management and sales of the Huxham lode at a spot called the Pound Living, a name shown on the parish tithe map and corresponding to the site now known locally as the Black Pit. After some discussion an agreement was drawn up in March 1788 whereby Kingdon was granted liberty to dig for manganese at the Pound Living tenement for a term of ten years, paying Sir Stafford a royalty of ten shillings per ton on the ore raised and undertaking to restore the land by filling in the pits resulting from his operations. On being made merchantable, the ore was to be delivered at Exeter Quay but in the event of any consignment being carried elsewhere, Kingdon was to make oath of its quantity and how it was sent.

Insight into the working of the mine can be gained from a cost book covering the period 1788-96. Accounts appear to have been made up every second year and from 1788-90 the returns realised £546.11.3¼d. The mine captain was named William Blamey and was evidently a Cornishman. Weekly wages of the men varied from £1.11.0 to £1.18.0, which was considerably above the average rate for miners at this period. Other emoluments included a 'Hogshead of Cider £1.16.0' and 'Given to the men and women at Christmas 1790 2/-'. Among sundry costs are listed picks, shovels and brooms and, in lighter vein, a 'Pair of old boots to wash manganese in 8/-'.

From the frequent mention of cooperage it appears that after washing the ore was packed in barrels some of which were conveyed to Teignmouth and in other cases to Topsham for shipment. In the latter part of the term covered by the cost book the net income from the mine, after payment of royalty, showed a slight falling off, the credit balance of £328 for the two years ended 1792 declining to £320 in the corresponding period to 1796.[46]

In 1795-6 the Upton Pyne workings were inspected by Charles Hatchett and the Rev W G Maton, both well-qualified observers. Hatchett's account is brief, merely stating that the manganese was found in nodules immediately under the surface and extending to a maximum depth of 20ft. At the time of his visit most of the pits had been filled in. Maton provides a more detailed description. 'The manganese mine or rather pit' he writes 'is not far from the village, the soil surrounding which is a deep red viscid clay and in this the ore is dug. There is no occasion for a shaft as the ore diminishes so much in richness in proportion to its depth that it is worked only in a horizontal direction. We observed that the ore was in nodules of various dimensions and generally crystallised in the inside. It was used in the glass-houses [glass-works] formerly established at Exeter but is now sent chiefly to London. The manufactory at Bristol undersold that of Exeter.[47]

In February 1802 a lease was granted by Sir Stafford Northcote to a new syndicate consisting of Richard Oates of London, merchant, together with five other adventurers hailing from as far afield as Peterborough. Rights were extended to work in numerous localities within the parish of Upton Pyne. The indenture, however, specifically excepted the Pound Living tenement which by this date had been granted to Nicholas Williams, a corn factor of Exeter, and also a small area in which Jane the widow of Samuel Kingdon still retained the mining rights. At what date the Upton Pyne deposits were finally abandoned is not known. A small output of 30 tons was recorded in 1821 and it seems probable that working by that time was drawing to an end.

Pieces of ore can still be picked up around the Black Pit. A typical nodule analysed in recent years by the Geology Department of Exeter University gave a produce of 34.22 per cent manganese. Russell (*op. cit.*) describes this site as now resembling a pond covering an area of half an acre, shallow at its eastern side but becoming deeper towards the west in an adjacent field another flooded pit about 40 feet deep and surmounted by a brick arch could lately be seen. This has now been levelled owing to frequently recurring subsidences.

In the adjoining parish of **Newton St Cyres** there were formerly two distinct mines, one being worked for manganese and the other for lead, the mineral rights in each case being owned by the Quicke family. The manganese deposits formed an extension of those of Upton Pyne and as shown on the Old Series one-inch Geological map, strike E-W through Ford, Hayne and westward to Woodley. In this area the Tithe Schedule records such names as Buckey or Bucket Pit, Bucket Pit Orchard and Black Pit. In the field numbered 1019 on the Tithe map, manganese floors are indicated adjacent to Hayne Farm where the nearby stream was dammed in two places to make pools for washing the ore. Further west at a site known locally as The Landings the ore was tipped down a shute where it was picked clean by women.[48]

Charles Hatchett who visited the workings on 4th May 1796 in company with Mr Kingdon, noted that in 'some of the new pits lately opened the manganese was found at 4 to 12 feet from grass [surface] in a red clay. The quality of the manganese is not at present so good as that which was found at Upton Pyne but much resembles it and probably may equal it when digged deeper'. The ore was principally used at this time for bleaching, the refuse being strewn over the fields where it acted as a fertiliser causing the grass crop to be much increased, as Hatchett was informed by Mr Kingdon.[49]

In their earlier years the output of manganese from Upton Pyne and Newton St Cyres was not inconsiderable, exports from Exeter Quay to London, Liverpool and Bristol rising from 500-700 tons annually in the last decade of the 18th century to 3,000 tons in the years 1800-1810.[50] Next to bleaching the chief use of manganese at that time was in the manufacture of glass to which it gave a characteristic green tint. If added to excess it tended to impart a purple colour as seen in the apothecaries' drug jars manufactured in Bristol during the period 1730-50. Manganese was also employed as a pigment for printers' ink. Its service to the chemical and metallurgical industries evolved later.

After a preliminary washing at the mines it appears that in some cases the ore was given a further dressing on the outskirts of Exeter. Russell (*op. cit.*) notes that a crazing or grinding mill formerly existed near Hamlyn's Marsh between Exwick and Cowley Bridge. Here the nodules were reduced to a fine sand and rid of its impurities by 'buddling'. The road leading towards Exwick from Exeter is still known locally as Buddle Lane.[51]

The Newton St Cyres deposits continued to be worked intermittently until a comparatively late period. On 22 August 1840 the *Mining Journal* reported that miners driving an adit in the Newton St Cyres Manganese Mine holed into old workings and were swept back to the shaft-bottom by a rush of water, as the result of which several of the men are believed to have been drowned. The sett at that time was under grant to the Cornish firm of Williams & Son of Scorrier who surrendered their lease in 1849.[52]

In 1872 it was announced that the Simms brothers of Calstock 'the fortunate owners of the manganese mines at Chillaton (in West Devon) had for many months been prospecting in old and new works at Newton St Cyres and have now come to an arrangement with Mr Quicke who owns the principal part of the parish, for the working of these valuable mines which were first brought under their notice by the Rev. C May, the Rector of the parish'.[53] The mines were still in operation in 1878 as noted in the Second Edition of William White's Directory of Devonshire. From 1872-79 1,260 tons of ore were sold for £5,465 but the price gradually fell from £4.10.0 to £1 per ton at which latter figure working became unremunerative, although the lode was reported to be fully 10ft wide at one point only 3fm from surface (Collins p.273).

In 1881 John Quicke decided to offer the mining rights of all his land around Ford where it was stated that an adit existed of sufficient depth to drain the whole of the property. The manganese was claimed to be of first class quality, with large portions of the lode standing near surface. A map in the Exeter City Record Office of about this date shows the manganese works and floors adjacent to Hayne Farm. It is not know whether the sett was taken up.[54]

In the Culm Measures about half a mile south of the manganese deposits, a lead lode striking a little south of east is shown on the 1-inch Geological Map (Old Series 325) extending from a point near the Newton St Cyres-Exeter road and westward to Venny Cleave. The existence of this lode had long been recognised and is reputed to have been worked at the time of the Roman occupation. In 1958 Mr L E Braddick of Nadderwater, whilst gathering information for an intended paper on mining in Newton St Cyres, was granted access to the Quicke archives among which was a map of the Newton Tin Mines dated 5 November 1765 but based on information derived from an earlier source. From an estate book of 1767 it appears that the mines at this date were being operated by a syndicate known as the Fraternity of Exeter Gentlemen.[55]

The map displays two adits and a number of shafts on one of which surprisingly at this date is depicted a Cornish-type engine house. The main centre of activity lay in the area locally known as **Tin Pits Hill**, a short distance south of Widden Cottage. On being brought to surface the ore was conveyed by a tramway to a nearby spot where it underwent a 'first calcining'.[56] That they were described as 'tin mines' was, of course, a misnomer but one still favoured by the popular press which habitually refers to the industry in Cornwall as Cornish 'tin mining' oblivious of the fact that here, as in Devon, a preponderance of the mines were worked for copper or minerals other than tin.

In 1853 a company entitled the **Newton St Cyres Silver-Lead Mine** was granted a lease by John Quicke covering an area of 600 acres. The prospectus recalled that 'about 80 years since' a shallow and a deep adit had been driven for lengths, respectively, of 150 and upwards of 200fm. Some ten or a dozen air shafts were sunk and several tons of ore raised, work being only abandoned through want of funds to purchase machinery. In 1823 the sett was acquired by a Captain Opie who deepened the mine to 26fm below adit. A quantity of argentiferous galena averaging 30 ounces of silver to the ton,[57] was returned from a lode about 20 inches wide. On this occasion also operations were brought to a stand by lack of capital.

Preliminary investigations by the company of 1853 confirmed that the old men had started by driving the north adit where good values were found. They were then induced 'at enormous expense' to bring up another adit, from the west, which on being extended for 220 fathoms resulted in a gain of only 2fm depth – the north adit-end being 25fm below surface and the western or so-called deep adit a mere 27fm.[58]

During the summer of 1853 the adit was being cleared east of Mary's Shaft by 17 men. Good stones of lead ore were encountered and although the main part of the lode had been taken away, numerous branches were standing on the north side of the level. In September of that year the manager, Captain W P Nicholls, whilst ascending the shaft in a kibble (mining bucket) caught his foot in the timbering and was precipitated 13 fathoms to the shaft bottom and killed. Working appears to have been suspended in the winter of 1853-54 but was resumed in March 1855. In the following month at least one pitch was being worked on tribute and hopes were entertained of the mine shortly paying cost. A ladder-road was installed at this time in Maxwell's Shaft which was cleared to 15fm below Deep Adit or 42fm from surface. Operations had ceased by 1858 with a recorded output of only two tons (Spargo 1868). According to White[59] the mine was active again in 1878, but with what result is unknown.

On Tin Pits Hill a number of open shafts can still be seen, with specimens of galena and other associated minerals in the small surrounding dumps. Prospecting shafts and adits are also traceable in the dense plantations extending west to the Suttern Brook, more particularly near Coombland Quarry adjacent to Venny Cleave. In the absence of any plan the full extent of the underground development can never be known, although it appears likely that this was considerable in view of the long history of working throughout the area.

NOTES & SOURCES

CHAPTER 1 (p12)

1   University of Liverpool. *A Relation of the English Mines*, 1725. Partial and extremely poor translation of the old Swedish script, Bergs Kollegium, Stockholm.

2   Still thus pronounced locally, although spelt Net Stakes on the OS map (Corn wall 30 NW). 'At Nuttstack on the Tamar there was some years ago a smelter to melt copper, tin and lead ore – now disused.' Kahlmeter (November 1724).

3   *MJ Supplement* (25 May 1844).

4   Booker, Frank. *Industrial Archaeology of the Tamar Valley* (1967).

5   Phillips and Darlington. *Records of Mining and Metallurgy* (1856).

6   Spargo (1868); Dines, p 669.

7   Hamilton, Henry. *The English Brass and Copper Industries to 1800*. Dr John Lane of Bristol (b.1678), was a pioneer of the copper industry. In 1717 he established a smelting works at Landore near Swansea which continued until he was ruined by the bursting of the 'South Sea Bubble'.

8   Booker, op cit, p139.

9   *MJ* (7 March 1846).

10   Jenkin, A. K. H. *Mines and Miners of Cornwall*, Pt 14 (1967), pp 65-9. It is not known definitely which of the Bere Alston group of mines is referred to under this name.

12   *Sherborne Mercury* (6 August 1781; 7 September 1795).

13   *RIC Journal* Pt 2 (1952), Sir Arthur Russell

14   *Royal Cornwall Gazette* (13 June 1812).

15   CRO Truro MS notebook apparently belonging to Joseph Carne.

16   *Royal Cornwall Gazette* (26 May 1821; 7 September 1822).

17   *MJ* (12 December 1835).

18   *Royal Cornwall Gazette* (25 July 1851).

19   In addition to local output, the works smelted ores from Wales, Ireland, Sark, Isle of Man, and as far afield as Mexico and Australia. Toll, R. W. *Mining Magazine* (June 1948); McDonald, Donald. *Percival Norton Johnson* (1951) *passim*.

20a   Dines, p 682

21   Watson, J. Y. 'Cornish Notes for Out-Adventurers', *MJ* (1861), pp 18-19.

22   *MJ* (July 1876).

23   *MJ* (14 October 1843; 10/24 November 1855).

24   Dines, p 683.

25   There was formerly a smelting house at Tuckermarsh Quay the sale of which was advertised in the *Royal Cornwall Gazette*, 16 January 1808.

26   *MJ* (30 May 1846).

27   *MJ* (15 February, 12 July 1851; 6 October 1855).

28   Toll, R. W. *in litt* (2 April 1958).

29   Watson, J. Y. *MJ* (3 February 1849).

30   *MJ* (1 May 1847; 3 February 1849; 23 September 1854); Dines, p 684.

31   Among the older generation of local people the mine itself is still invariably known as 'Cow-ez'.

32   *MJ* (1846-9) *passim*.

33   Murchison (1854).

34   *MJ* (16 June 1860).

35   *MJ* (29 December 1849). At a subsequent sale in 1855 the auctioneer was questioned as to the values claimed for the mine, to which he replied that

although he had never before sold 'a Virtuous Lady, or any other lady, he was satisfied she was worthy of notice'. *Devonport Weekly Journal* (27 December 1855).

36   Bray, Mrs. *Tamar and Tavy*, Vol 3 (1836), pp 257-8, quoting Dr Edmund Pearse of Tavistock.
37   Toll, R. W. 'The Virtuous Lady Mine', *Western Morning News* (31 October 1956).
38   *MJ* (13 September 1845).
39   *MJ* (12 March 1859).
40   *MJ* (23 June 1860).
41   The supporting cables of the bridge came from an old battleship then under demolition at Devonport.
42   Redruth Public Library, Barclay and Toll MS.
43   *MJ* (23 December 1880).
44   Report *penes* W. J. Sleeman of Albaston in 1957, copied by A. K. H. J.
45   *MJ* (26 June 1860).
46   RIC Truro. HJ/7/6; *MJ* (13 June 1857).
47   RIC Truro. HJ/7/6.
48   Toll, R. W. *in litt,* (29 September 1953).
49   *MJ* (25 June 1853; 6 May 1854).
50   *MJ* (17 November 1855).

CHAPTER 2 (p33)

1   *MJ* (December 1845; January 1846; December 1848).
2   *MJ* (7 July 1860; 3 December 1864), *passim.*
3   *MJ* (5 December 1863; 28 November 1868); Captain Jos Paull, 'Report Book', formerly *penes* the Bedford Estate Office, Tavistock.
4   *MJ* (18 May 1850).
5   *The Mining World and Engineering Record* (11 May 1889).
6   Dines, p 671.
7   MS at Redruth Public Library.
8   Spargo, (1868); Williams J. *Mining Directory of Cornwall and Devon* (1870). Williams, J. *Cornwall and Devon Mining Directory* (1862). Dines, p 673.
11   Bray, Mrs. *Tamar and Tavy*, Vol 3 (1836), p 254.
12   Barclay, C. F. 'Notes on the West Devon Mining District', *Trans Roy Geolog Soc Cornwall* (1930).
13   *MJ* (8 November 1879).
14   Booker, op cit, p 136.
15   *Royal Cornwall Gazette* (23 March, 22 June 1811).
16   Phillips and Darlington, op cit.
17   *MJ* (27 March 1858).
18   *MJ* (13 October 1849; 22 June 1850).
19   *MJ* Prospectus (30 October 1880).
20   CRO Exeter, Bedford Papers. Justin Brooke extract.
21   *MJ* (3 April 1858).
22   *MJ* (21 April 1860).
23   Watson, J. Y. *Cornish Notes for Out-Adventurers* (1861), p 21.
24   Spargo (1868); Williams, op cit.
25   Dines, p 690.

26   *MJ* (21 June, 5 July, 20 September 1851, *et seq).*
27   *MJ* (19 February 1853).
28   *MJ* (May 1853), Extracts by Justin Brooke.
29   *MJ* (19 January 1861).
30   Lysons. *Magna Britannia, Devon* (1822); *Royal Cornwall Gazette* (5 May 1810).
31   *MJ* (1 November 1856).
32   Murchison, op cit; *MJ* (23 June 1860).
33   *Plymouth and Devonport Weekly Journal* (12 April, 26 July 1855).
34   Booker, op cit, p 136.
35   Dines, p 696.
36   *MJ* (December 1868).
37   *MJ* (January 1846; January 1851); *Kelly's Directory* (1856).
38   Phillips and Darlington, op cit; Murchison (1854).
39   Collins, p 568.
40   Barclay MS.
41   CRO Exeter, 'John Swete MS' (1797-8), p 53 Extract by Justin Brooke.
42   Stoke-on-Trent, original with Josiah Wedgwood & Sons. *Common Place Book I,* 28408-39. Copy *penes* A. K. H. J.
43   Russell, Sir Arthur. *Journal of the Royal Institution of Cornwall,* Pt 2 (1952).
44   *Royal Cornwall Gazette* (18 June 1814).
45   *Royal Cornwall Gazette* (4 May 1816).
46   *Trans of the Roy Geolog Soc Cornwall,* Vol I, pp 124-5.
47   *Royal Cornwall Gazette* (17 May 1817).
48   The reason for the mine being called Willsworthy is more difficult to explain, but it may well have formed part of the Manor of Willsworthy – manors commonly extending throughout different parishes – and sometimes more than one county.
49   *Royal Cornwall Gazette* (4 April 1818).
50   *MJ* (21 March 1846).
51   Murchison, op cit, 1856 edition, p 698.
52   Henwood. *Trans of the Roy Geolog Soc Cornwall,* Vol 5 (1843), p 475; Watson, J. Y. *Compendium of British Mining* (1843), p 56.
53   Collins, p 484.
54   *MJ* (12 February; 28 May 1870).
55   *MJ* (22 June 1861).
56   Spargo (1868); Dines, pp 699-700.
57   *MJ* (11 August 1838; 6 February 1847).
58   *Plymouth and Plymouth Dock Weekly* (2 October 1823).
59   Calvert, John. *On the Production of Gold in England,* quoted in *MJ* (10 September 1853).
60   Harris, Helen. *The Industrial Archaeology of Dartmoor,* (1968), p 220.
61   Richardson, P. H. G. MS notes of 'Mines of West Devon' (1935-9); Greeves, T.A.P. 'A Mine in the Deancombe Valley', *Trans Devonshire Association* (1969).
62   Carrington. Burt's Preface to *Dartmoor* (1826).
63   *MJ* (1838-48) *passim.*
64   *MJ* (28 April 1849).
65   *MJ* (19 April, 31 May, November 1851; 29 May 1852).
66   Worth, R. Hansford, *Dartmoor* (1953) pp 303-4.
67   Exeter City Library.
68   *MJ* (13 June 1863), *et seq.*
69   *Royal Cornwall Gazette* (2 January 1808).
70   *MJ* (21 October 1848; 7 February 1852).

71   *MJ* (24 February 1877).
72   CRO Exeter, 'John Swete MS', Vol 16, (1797-8).
73   *MJ* (20 June 1846; 23 August 1862).
74   *MJ* (1849-52), *passim;* Dines, p 728 (under Devon Tin Mine).
75   *MJ* (1853-6), *passim.*
76   *MJ* (1836-40); Watson, op cit; Dines, p 728.
77   *MJ* Supplement (28 February 1874).
78   *MJ* (1852-5), *passim.*
79   *West Briton* (5 November 1891); *Parliamentary Papers,* Mineral Statistics (1892).
80   CRO Truro, 'Trestrail Coll: Hexworthy, Summary of its Later History'.
81   *The Hatchett Diary,* ed Arthur Raistrick (1967), pp 21-3.
82   CRO Truro, Davey correspondence.
83   Baring-Gould. *Devonshire Characters and Strange Events,* 2nd series (1908), p 296.
84   Henwood, op cit, pp 132, 476.
85   Spargo, 1868; Williams, op cit.
86   Broughton, D. G. 'The Birch Tor and Vitifer Tin Mining Complex', *Trans Cornish Institute of Engineers,* new series, Vol XXIV (1968-9), pp 25-49.
87   *MJ* (18 March 1848), *et seq.*
88   Broughton, op cit.
89   'London and West Country Chamber of Mines' (1904-8), p 236.
90   King's Oven, otherwise *Furnum Regis* – a medieval blowing-house.
91   Williams, op cit.
92   Broughton, op cit.
      MJ (26 August 1876, 1887, p 259; 21 February 1880); Dines, p 724.

CHAPTER 3 (p59)

1   *MJ* (20 August 1853).
2   Kelly (1856); Murchison (1856).
3   *MJ* (17 January 1863).
4   *Records of Mining and Metallurgy,* (1857).
5   Edwards, E. *Life of Raleigh,* Vol II, p 211.
6   *MJ* (5 November 1853).
7   Murchison (1856).
8   *MJ* (26 November 1853).
9   Report Book, Tehidy Minerals Office, Camborne.
10   Murchison (1856).
11   *MJ* (1881-9), *passim.*
12   *MJ* (2 October 1858; 31 December 1859; 28 January 1860).
13   *Royal Cornwall Gazette* (19 May 1821; 8 February 1823).
14   *MJ* (23 May 1857; 31 December 1859; 28 January 1860).
15   Spargo (1868).
16   That part of the Plym above Shaugh Bridge is sometimes styled the Cad – W. Crossing. *One Hundred Years on Dartmoor* (1901).
17   *MJ* (31 March 1838; 2 May 1840; 31 December 1859).
18   Dines, p 686.
19   Now in the Archives Department, Plymouth Central Library.
20   *Royal Cornwall Gazette* (17 July 1824).
21   *MJ* (16 July; 22 October 1836).
22   *MJ* (31 December 1859); Murchison (1854).

23 *MJ* (31 December 1859).
24 Lysons, op cit.
25 *MJ* (3 December 1859).
26 Murchison (1856).
27 *MJ* (15 September 1860).
28 *MJ* (4 August; 20 October 1855).
29 *MJ* (15 September 1860).
30 Dines, pp 686-7.
31 Not to be confused with the Hemerdon Ball Wolfram and Tin stockwork.
32 *MJ* (31 December 1856; 31 December 1859).
33 *MJ* (17 October, 14 November 1868); Kelly (1873); Dines, p 688.
34 Deed at County Museum, Truro.
35 Justin Brooke. *Mining Journal* (1850-5), extracts.
36 Barclay, C. F. *Notes on the West Devon Mining District, (1931).*
37 *MJ* (31 December 1859); Kelly (1873).
38 *MJ* (27 June 1846; 10 April 1847; 31 December 1859).
39 *MJ* (7 August 1847; 31 December 1859).
40 *MJ* (30 April 1853).
41 *MJ* (9 January, 20 July, 17 August 1850; October 1851; 8 May 1852).
42 *Geolog Mem Tavistock and Launceston*, p 120.
43 *MJ* (September/November 1859; 4 February 1860).
44 *MJ* (May, June, August 1850; 21 June 1851).
45 *MJ* (10 June, 14 October 1848).
46 *MJ* (26 September 1857).
47 *Plymouth and Devonport Weekly Journal* (8 August 1850); *Western Morning News* (2 December 1960).
48 Berry, A. K. 'Lost Caves of Stonehouse', *Western Morning News* (2 August 1968).
49 *West Briton* (2 July 1841).
50 MJ (4 August 1877).
51 *MJ* (8 May 1858).
52 *An Account of Antimony Mines of Great Britain*, MS *penes* British Museum Natural History.
53 *MJ* (9 June 1849; 23 November 1850).
54 Dines, p 689.
55 At County Museum, Truro.
56 *MJ* (17/31 December 1859).
57 *MJ* (28 October, 5 December 1843; 15 February, 18 March 1845).
58 *Plymouth Mail* (7 October 1854).
59 Murchison (1854); *MJ* (6/20 December 1856).
60 *MJ* (6 May, 19 August 1854).
61 'Near the Blackdown entrenchment is a copper mine but it is not now worked.' Fox, S. P. *Kingsbridge Estuary* (1864), p 143.
62 Shown on Bartholomew's 1/2 inch map of South Devon, sheet 36.
63 Fox, S. P. *Kingsbridge and its Surroundings* (1874), pp 184-5. This volume constituted an enlarged edition of *Kingsbridge Estuary,* op cit.
64 *MJ* (27 March 1858; 31 December 1859; 4 February 1860, *et seq).*
65 *MJ* (7 February 1857; 3 April 1858).
    The Geology of Kingsbridge and Salcombe (1904).

CHAPTER 4 (p76)

1   *MJ* 3,10 January, 13 June 1846. *et. seq.*
2   *MJ* 21 June, 20 December 1845; 1 May 1847.
3   *MJ* 29 March, 14 June, 26 July 1851.
4   *MJ* 18 September 1852 *et. seq.* 9 April 1859.
5   *MJ* 1845-55
6   *MJ* 18 October 1845, 12 September 1846
      West Briton 8 December 1848.
7   *MJ* 2 July 1836.
8   *MJ* 23 September 1843.
9   *MJ* 1845-48. Extracts by Justin Brooke.
10   Kelly's Directory 1856. *MJ* 7 July 1855; 28 July 1860; Murchison, *Progress of British Mining*, March 1861.
11 *MJ* 1863-66 *passim.*
12 *MJ* 16 October 1880.
13   Dines pp 662-3.
14 *MJ* December 1845-August 1847.
15 *MJ* April 1853-September 1856.
16 *Report on the Geology of Cornwall, Devon & West Somerset*, p609.
17   Russell, P.M.G. Manganese Mining in Devon, *Devon & Cornwall Notes & Queries* Summer 1970.
18 *Mineralogical Magazine*, September 1946.
19 *MJ* 5 February 1847.
20   Dines pp 712, 715.
21   Jenkin, A.K.Hamilton. *Mines & Miners of Cornwall*, Pt.XV pp 18-19.
22   Booker, *Industrial Archaeology of the Tamar Valley*, p.29.
23 *MJ* 22 August 1846.
24 *MJ* 24 July 1852; 2 December 1854.
25 *MJ* 22 August 1846.
26 *MJ* August, September 1852.
27 *MJ* 1, 15, 29 May 1858.
      Dines p.711
28 *MJ* 29 March 1851, 7 August 1852, 6 August 1853.
29 *MJ* 11 September, 27 November 1847, 13 October 1849.
30 *MJ* 15 November 1845, 23 August 1851, 13 May 1854.
31   Dines p.711
32 *MJ* 20 December 1845, 13 March 1852, 7 February 1857 *et passim.*
33 *MJ* 6 October, 10 November 1849; 1850 *passim*, Williams, J. *Cornwall & Devon Mining Directory*, 1862.
34 *MJ* 24 January 1846, 11 October 1856.
35   *Western Morning News* 15 January, 1 February 1954.
36   Now *penes* Justin Brooke.
37   Moore, Rev. T. *History of Devonshire* 1829-36.
38 *MJ* 23 July 1842.
39 *MJ* 28 May 1864.
40 *MJ* 28 May, 25 June 1864. Spargo.1868.
41 *Sherborne Mercury*, 1 March 1790.
42 *Diary of Charles Hatchett*, edited by Raistrick, Arthur 1967, pp 22,23.
43 *Royal Cornwall Gazette*, 15 October 1825.
44   Moore, Rev. T. *op.cit.*
45 *MJ* 23 July 1842.

46   Toll, RW. 'Water Power in West Devon'. *Mining Magazine*, March 1948.
47   Evans, Rachael. *Home Scenes: or Tavistock & Its Vicinity*, 1846.
48   Watson, JY. MJ 13 June 1863.
49   *Diary of Charles Hatchett*, edited by Raistrick, Arthur 1967 p.23.
50   Dines, p.710.
51   As the writer was informed in 1957 by the then Mr Batten.
52   *MJ* 1845-51.
53   *MJ* 19 July 1851.
54   Phillips & Darlington, *Records of Mining & Metallurgy*, 1856.
55   *MJ* 5 September 1863 *et passim*.
56   *MJ* 23 September 1848 *et passim*, Justin Brooke extracts.
57   *MJ* 15 August 1846.
58   *MJ* 1847-54 *passim*.
59   Dines. Pp 708-9.
60   Lysons. *Magna Britannia*, vol.6, 1822.
61   *MJ* 8 May 1847.
62   *MJ* 25 October 1835.
63   Phillips & Darlington. *op. cit.* p.259.
64   Toll, RW. *Sands, Clays & Minerals*, April 1938.

CHAPTER 5 (p94)

1   *MJ* 31 August 1850, 22 February 1851, 1861 pp 632, 736 *et passim*.
2   Russell, Sir Arthur, *An account of the Antimony Occurrences of Great Britain*, *MJ*.
3   *MJ* 10 August 1850.
4   Spencer, E. *MJ* 18 April 1857
5   *MJ*. Supplement. 7 December 1861, paraphrasing paper read at a meeting of the Miners' Association of Cornwall & Devon.
6   *MJ* 18 June 1836. Dines p.751.
7   *MJ*. 1851-54 *passim*.
8   *MJ*. 9 May 1857
9   Spargo 1868. Harris, Helen *Industrial Archaeology of Dartmoor, 1972*.
10   Geolog.Mem. *Around Okehampton*, 1968.
11   *West Briton* 23 May 1828.
12   *MJ*. 11 October, 8 November 1845; 24 March 1849, and 1851-54 *passim*.
13   *MJ*. 21 December 1850, 19 June 1852.
14   *MJ*. 2 April 1853.
15   Geolog.Mem. *Around Okehampton* 1968
16   *MJ*. April 1852. Williams, J. *Cornwall & Devon Mining Directory*, 1870.
17   *MJ*. 23 April, 2 July, 10 September, 10 December 1864; December 1865.
18   *MJ*. 21 March 1857, July 1867, June 1868, October 1869, Spargo 1868.
19   *MJ*. 27 August 1864.
20   *MJ*. 11 February 1865.
21   *MJ*. 2 March, 13 July 1878.
22   Williams, J. *Cornwall & Devon Mining Directory* 1862, *MJ* 11 February 1865.
23   *MJ*. 28 January 1865, Letter initiated N.C.H.
24   *MJ*. 25 April 1874.
25   *MJ*. 5 February, 25 March 1876.
26   Letters dated 19 February 1880, 22 August 1881 copies *penes* Justin Brooke.
27   Dines p.752. The *MJ* (29.11.1879) gives the dimension of the wheel as 60ft but

the great size of the pit suggests that 70ft was correct. Ferguson, as contributor to the Barclay & Toll MS also confirms the diameter as 70ft.

28   Collins p.414.
29   Geolog.Mem. *Around Okehampton* 1968.
30   Letter initialled N.C.H. *MJ.* 28 January 1865.
31   *MJ.* 10 June 1854.
32   *MJ.* 10 April, 28 November 1858.
33   *MJ.* 25 February 1860.
34   *MJ.* 1857-59 *passim*, Williams, J. 1862, Spargo 1868.
35   Kelly, *Directory of Cornwall & Devon* 1873.
36   County Museum, Truro. HJ/7/7.
37   London & Westcountry Chamber of Mines vol. I p.192.
38   Geolog.Mem. *Around Okehampton* 1968.
39   *MJ.* 28 January 1865. Letter initialled N.C.H. Dines p.753.
40   *MJ.* 15 May 1852
41   *MJ.* 1851-4 *passim*.
42   Geolog.Mem. *Around Okehampton* 1968.
43   Worth, R. Hansford, *Dartmoor* 1953 pp 170-71.
44   *Sherborne Mercury* 28 April 1783.
45   *MJ.* 27 February 1847, 26 August 1848, 10 March 1849; White, *Directory of Devon* 1850 p.191.
46   Rowe, Rev. Samuel. *A Perambulation of the Antient & Royal Forest of Dartmoor*, 1848.
47   Ormerod, G.W. *Trans.Devon Assoc.* 1867.
48   *MJ.* 1853-56 *passim*. Dines p.754.
49   Broughton, D.B. *Western Morning News* 27 February 1961. Dines p.750.

CHAPTER 6 (p109)

1   MJ 1851-1854 *passim*.
2   Dines p.729. Spargo 1868.
3   *MJ.* 6 March, 10 July 1847 *et passim*.
4   *MJ.* 25 November 1854.
5   *MJ.* 22 October 1859. Dines p.739.
6   Dines p.740.
7   *MJ.* 28 February 1857.
8   *MJ.* 11 November 1848, 25 August 1849.
9   *MJ.* 21 March 1857, 10 November 1860, 30 November 1861.
10   Phillips & Darlington, *Records of Mining & Metallurgy* (1857) p.257-67.
11   *MJ* 23 January 1846.
12   *MJ.* 3 May 1851.
13   Dines p.738.
14   Phillips & Darlington. *op. cit.* p.268.
15   County Museum, Truro, Hamilton Jenkin Coll:
16   *MJ.* 29 May 1858, 19 November 1859.
17   *MJ.* 19 November 1859, 12 May 1860.
18   Williams, J. *Cornwall & Devon Mining Directory* 1862. Spargo 1868.
19   *MJ.* 5 September 1868. *Mining World* 6 July 1872.
20   Booker, Frank: *in litt* 24 October 1972.
21   Kelly, *op. cit.* 1873.
22   Realising a sum of £157,018, Collins p.425.

23   *MJ*. 26 November 1859.
24   *MJ*. 19 & 26 November 1859.
25   Catalogue of Plans of Abandoned Mines, 1929, Devon p.6.
26   Dines p.739. Spargo 1868.
27   *MJ*. 7 February 1880.
28   *MJ*. 9 December 1882, 30 June 1883, 22 November 1884.
29   Phillips & Darlington, *op. cit.* p.270.
30   *MJ*. 5 April 1856.
31   *MJ*. 3 December 1859, *et passim*.
32   Phillips & Darlington, *op. cit.* County Museum Truro, Hamilton Jenkin Coll:
      HJ 7/6.
33   *MJ*. 26 November 1859.
34   *MJ*. 22 October, 26 November 1859.
35   *MJ*. 1 June 1850.
36   *MJ*. 5 May 1849.
37   *MJ*. 20 July, 5 October 1850, *et passim*.
38   County Museum Truro, Hamilton Jenkin Coll: HJ/7/6.
39   *MJ*. 26 November 1859.
40   Amery, J.S. *Trans.Devon Association* vol.6 (1925) pp 53, 54, 94.
41   Bergs Kollegium, Stockholm: *A 'Relation' of the English Mines* 1725. Partial and
      poor quality translation *penes* University of Liverpool.
42   *Sherborne Mercury* 1 August 1763. 'To let:copper mine at Haswell – unworked
      for some years'.
43   Dines p.737.
44   *MJ*. 12 September, 31 October 1857; 2 January, 4 September 1858; 6 July 1861.
45   Parl. Papers 1892, *Mineral Statistics*. Dines p.739.
46   *MJ*. 7 January 1854.
47   *MJ*. 9 September 1854.
48   *MJ* March-December 1860 *passim*. Brooke, Justin: extracts.
49   Williams, J. *Cornwall & Devon Mining Directory* 1862.
50   *MJ*. 19 June, 11 December 1869.
51   *MJ*. 12 February, 12 March 1859.
52   *MJ*. 20 December 1845; 23 July, 3 September 1859; 1870-71 *passim*.
53   *MJ*. 2 March, 27 April 1861. Williams, J. *op. cit.* 1862
54   *MJ*. 1862 p.743.
55   *MJ*. 30 September 1843; 19 June 1847.
56   *MJ*. 25 March 1848; 1851-2 *passim*. Spargo 1868 p.182.
57   *MJ*. 20 August, 3 September 1859.
58   *MJ*. 8 September 1860.
59   Williams, J. 1862.
60   Dines p.736.
61   Dines pp 735-6. In 1908 sales were recorded of 140 tons of a 9 per cent copper
      ore. London & Westcountry Chamber of Mines, Vol. 3, p.87, Harris, Helen.
      Industrial Archaeology of Dartmoor, pp 56-7.
62   *MJ*. 6 May 1854; 3 September 1859.
63   *MJ*. 17 July 1858; 1 October 1859; 16 October 1863.
64   *MJ*. 1 October 1859; 10 November 1860; 1 August 1863.
65   Dines p.734.
66   *MJ*. 27 November 1852. The gossan on the hanging-wall of the lode also showed
      traces of gold.
67   Murchison (1854) pp 153-6. *MJ* 27 November 1852; 14 May 1853; 13 February
      1858; 1 October 1859.

68   But see Harris, Helen *The Industrial Archaeology of Dartmoor* p.36.
69   Information per the late Sir Arthur Russell, Bt.
70   *Western Morning News* 5 June 1967. Harris, Helen *op. cit.* p.201.
71   *MJ.* 21 January 1854; 1 October 1859.
72   *MJ.* 1862-66, extracts by Justin Brooke.
73   James, W.R. *Minerals in Industry*, Pelican Books 1945 p.64.
74   Dines pp 732-3.
75   Collins, J.H. *The Miners' Association of Cornwall & Devon* 1872-3 p.71.
76   Dines p.733
77   *MJ.* 23 July, 22 October 1859; 21 April, 8 September 1860.
78   *Royal Cornwall Gazette* 7 June 1873.
79   Records of the London & West Country Chamber of Mines 1901-04.
80   *MJ.* 1857-66. Geolog. Mem. Newton Abbot (1913). Williams, J. *op. cit.* 1862.
81   Parl: Pap: 1864. Commission Appointed to Enquire into the Condition of All Mines in Great Britain (not coal).
82   *MJ.* 23 July 1859; 29 September 1866. Williams, J. *Mining Directory of Cornwall & Devon* 1870.

CHAPTER 7 (p131)

1   Dines pp 747-8.
2   Schmitz, C.J. *The Teign Valley Lead Mines* pp 13-14 (Northern Cavern & Mine Research Society, Sheffield. Occasional Publication No. 6, 1973-cyclostyled) (second edition published 1980, NMRB – British Mining No. 15).
3   *MJ.* 7 May 1842, 8 July 1843.
4   Russell, P.M.G. 'Manganese Mining in Devon', *Devon & Cornwall Notes & Queries*, summer 1970.
5   Schmitz *op. cit.* p.9 *et seq.*
6   *MJ.* 15 October 1836.
7   *MJ.* 3 August 1839. James, Henry. 'Mining Report Book' *penes* F. Bice Michell, Redruth.
8   Schmitz, C.J. *op. cit.* p.36.
9   *West Briton* 8 June 1855. Geological Memoir, Newton Abbot, p.132.
10   *MJ.* 1861-68 *passim.* Spargo, 1868.
11   Lysons, *Magna Britannia* Vol 6. De la Beche, *Report on the Geology of Cornwall, Devon & West Somerset*, 1839 p.617.
12   *MJ.* 4 August, 1 September 1849.
13   Schmitz *op. cit.* p.100.
14   Dines, p.727.
15   *MJ.* 1842 p.204, 1 September 1860.
16   *MJ.* 21 October 1854.
17   Schmitz, *op. cit.* p.32.
18   Geolog. Mem. Newton Abbot, p.132
19   *MJ.* 1853 p.163.
20   Geolog. Mem. Newton Abbot, Fig 12, p.131.
21   *MJ.* 21 October 1854, 1 September 1860. From these two sources the foregoing account of Exmouth & Adams has been principally derived.
22   Toll, R.W. *in litt* 18 September 1954.
23   Williams, J. *Cornwall & Devon Mining Directory*, 1870.
24   Dines, p.746.
25   Spargo, 1868.

26 Williams, J. *Cornwall & Devon Mining Directory*, 1862.
27 *MJ*. 1 September 1860. Dines p.746.
28 Andrew, T. *Geological & Archaeological Papers*, 1875 pp 52-3.
29 Schmitz. *op. cit. p*.67.
30 Schmitz. *op. cit*. pp 58, 59, 65.
31 Schmitz. *op. cit. p*.114.
32 Dines, p.746.
33 *MJ*. 9 November 1844, quoting the Plymouth Journal.
34 *MJ*. 5 March 1859.
35 Dines. P.745. *MJ*. 1 February 1856.
36 *MJ*. 1851-54 *passim*, 1 September 1860.
37 *MJ*. 29 September, 8 December 1849, 1851-55 *passim*. 1 September 1860.
38 Hunt, R. *Mineral Statistics*, 1855.
39 Dines pp 743-4.
40 Vipan, P.G.L. 'Symposium on the Future of Non-Ferrous Mining in Gt. Britain & Ireland' pp 337-52. *Institute of Mining & Metallurgy*, 1959.
41 *MJ*. 1851-4 *passim*. Murchison, J.H. *British Mines considered as a Means of Investment* 1856. Vipan, *op. cit.* p.343.
42 *West Briton*, 8 June 1855.
43 *MJ*. October 1847, March 1849, July 1850, July 1859.
44 *MJ*. November 1847, April 1848, November 1849, August 1852, July 1857.
45 *Report on the Geology of Cornwall, Devon & West Somerset* p.295.
46 Russell, P.M.G. 'Manganese Mining in Devon', *Devon & Cornwall Notes & Queries*, summer 1970 pp 205-13.
47 Maton, W.G. *Observations of the Western Counties of England* (1797) Vol.I, p.94.
48 Braddick, L.E. *in litt* 12 November 1958.
49 *Diary of Charles Hatchett*, edited by Arthur Raistrick 1967, pp 18, 19.
50 Russell *op. cit.* p.208.
51 A buddle consisted of a circular cone-centred pit in which the finely-crushed ore was distributed by revolving arms and graded in accordance with its specific gravity.
52 Russell, P.M.G. *op. cit.*
53 *MJ*. 26 October 1872.
54 Russell, P.M.G. *op. cit.*
55 *Western Morning News*, 31 October 1958.
56 Braddick, L.E. *in litt*, 12 November 1958, 13 May 1959.
57 Lysons, *op. cit.*
58 *MJ*. 11 June, 9 July 1853.
65 *Directory of Devonshire*, second edition 1878.

GRID REFERENCES

The following list gives the grid references for the current 2½ inch OS maps of the principal mines mentioned in the text.

ALBERT	SX 568 595	CAROLINE WHEAL PROSPER	SX 702 659
ALLER	SX 834 840	CARPENTER	SX 414 766
ALLERFORD	SX 423 853	CHILLATON AND HOGSTOR	SX 431 812
ANDERTON	SX 485 723	CHILLATON, EAST	SX 465 819
ANNA MARIA	SX 807 883	CHRISTOW	SX 833 845
ANNE	SX 512 786	COLCHARTON	SX 450 730
ARUNDEL	SX 744 716	COLLACOMBE DOWN	SX 433 771
ASHBURTON UNITED	SX 771 733	COLLACOMBE, WEST	SX 414 766
ATLAS	SX 778 762	COMBE	SX 702 682
AUSEWELL WOOD	SX 728 710	CONCORD (CONQUER)	SX 427 770
AVON CONSOLS	SX 667 677	CONCORD, NEW	SX 433 771
AYLESBOROUGH (EYLESBARROW)		COPPER HILL	SX 632 945
	SX 599 682	CORYTON	SX 477 851
BACHELOR'S HALL	SX 597 734	COURTENAY	SX 460 724
BAGTOR	SX 761 758	CREBOR, EAST	SX 478 726
BATTISHILL DOWN	SX 515 862	CREBOR, SOUTH	SX 464 714
BEAM	SX 767 734	CREBOR, WEST	SX 452 721
BEDFORD UNITED	SX 441 728	CREBOR, WHEAL	SX 460 724
BEER ALSTON	SX 437 647	CRELAKE	SX 478 736
BELSTONE	SX 632 945	CROWNDALE	SX 470 725
BENNAH	SX 835 847	CROWNDALE, EAST	SX 478 726
BEREALSTON UNITED	SX 437 678	CROWNLEY PARKS	SX 764 760
BETSY	SX 510 812	DARTMOOR CONSOLIDATED	SX 599 682
BICKLEIGH VALE PHOENIX	SX 531 642	DARTMOOR CONSOLS	SX 649 728
BIRCH ALLER (ELLERS)	SX 828 869	DEAN PRIOR & BUCKFASTLEIGH	SX 729 657
BIRCH TOR AND VITIFER, NEW	SX 682 815	DENHAM BRIDGE	SX 475 682
BIRCH TOR, EAST	SX 694 810	DEVON AND CORNWALL WORKS	
BLACK DOWN	SX 512 823		SX 761 705
BORINGDON PARK	SX 531 584	DEVON AND CORNWALL	SX 463 701
BORINGDON, EAST	SX 537 584	DEVON AND COURTENAY	SX 472 717
BOTTLE HILL	SX 564 587	DEVON BURRA BURRA	SX 514 742
BOWDEN HILL COMMON	SX 465 819	DEVON CONSOLS, NORTH	SX 418 743
BRADFORD (BRADMERE) POOL	SX 700 910	DEVON COPPER AND BLENDE	SX 414 766
BRIDFORD	SX 830 865	DEVON FRIENDSHIP	SX 506 794
BROOK WOOD	SX 718 675	DEVON GREAT CONSOLS	SX 426 733
BROOK WOOD, NEW	SX 721 678	DEVON GREAT ELIZABETH	SX 710 707
BULLER AND BERTHA	SX 487 696	DEVON KAPUNDA	SX 403 754
BUTTSPILL	SX 437 678	DEVON NEW COPPER MINE	SX 744 716

DEVON TIN	SX 668 740	FURSDON	SX 650 930
DEVON UNITED COPPER, SOUTH		FURZEHILL	SX 517 692
	SX 718 675	GATEPOST	SX 514 742
DEVON UNITED	SX 513 788	GEORGE AND CHARLOTTE	SX 454 699
DEVON UNITED, SOUTH	SX 512 785	GEORGE, EAST	SX 529 703
DEVON WHEAL BULLER	SX 503 670	GOBBETT	SX 649 728
DEVON WHEAL FRANCES	SX 778 783	GOLDEN DAGGER	SX 679 803
DEVON WHEAL VOR	SX 667 677	GOLDSTREET	SX 467 664
DREWSTEIGNTON	SX 730 912	GOOSEFORD	SX 672 925
DRUID	SX 744 716	GRACE	SX 425 769
DUKE OF CORNWALL	SX 668 740	GREAT ROCK	SX 837 816
EASTON'S	SX 681 386	GREAT WEEK	SX 713 875
ELEANOR, GREAT	SX 732 833	GREEN VALLEY	SX 437 678
ELIZA	SX 514 830	GUNNISLAKE (EAST) & SOUTH BEDFORD	
EMILY	SX 542 498		SX 435 719
EMILY	SX 650 930	HARRIS (CHILLATON)	SX 430 813
EMMA	SX 715 675	HARRIS (LIFTON)	SX 373 829
EXMOUTH	SX 838 829	HASWELL (HAZEL)	SX 728 710
EXMOUTH, NORTH	SX 836 837	HAYTOR IRON	SX 773 771
EXMOUTH, SOUTH	SX 835 807	HEMERDON CONSOLS	SX 572 588
EYLESBARROW (AYLESBOROUGH)		HENNOCK IRON AND TIN	SX 828 816
	SX 599 682	HENNOCK MINE	SX 836 814
FANCY	SX 437 678	HENNOCK, WHEAL	SX 834 808
FANNY	SX 521 883	HENS ROOST	SX 652 711
FILLHAM	SX 647 551	HEXWORTHY	SX 656 718
FLORENCE	SX 514 847	HOCKLAKE	SX 469 688
FLORENCE	SX 568 595	HOLNE CHASE	SX 723 715
FORD	SX 647 931	HOOE, NORTH	SX 427 661
FOREST	SX 561 912	HOOE, SOUTH	SX 425 657
FORTUNE	SX 672 925	HOPE COVE	SX 675 389
FRANCO	SX 508 702	HUCKWORTHY BRIDGE	SX 533 707
FRANK MILLS	SX 836 820	HUGO, GREAT	SX 425 783
FRIENDSHIP	SX 508 793	HUNTINGDON	SX 667 677
FRIENDSHIP, DEVON	SX 506 794	IMPHAM	SX 439 715
FRIENDSHIP, EAST	SX 519 794	INDUSTRY	SX 613 710
FRIENDSHIP, NORTH (MARY TAVY)		IVY TOR	SX 628 936
	SX 512 823	IVYBRIDGE CONSOLS	SX 647 551
FRIENDSHIP, NORTH (PETER TAVY)		JEWELL	SX 526 814
	SX 519 784	JULIAN	SX 551 597
FRIENDSHIP, SOUTH	SX 509 784	KING OF DART	SX 733 688
FRIENDSHIP, WEST (LAMERTON)	SX 433 771	KING'S WOOD	SX 711 666
FRIENDSHIP, WEST (MARY TAVY)	SX 485 796	KIT	SX 562 675

KITTS	SX 517 845	TAMAR SILVER-LEAD	SX 425 657
LADY BERTHA	SX 471 689	TAMAR VALLEY, NEW	SX 437 678
LADY BERTHA, SOUTH	SX 477 682	TAVISTOCK CONSOLS	SX 485 723
LAWRENCE	SX 813 885	TAVY CONSOLS	SX 469 688
LEAWOOD	SX 521 883	TAVY, NORTH	SX 471 695
LITTLE DUKE	SX 471 695	TOR WOOD	SX 537 891
LOCKRIDGE	SX 439 665	TUNNELL	SX 431 642
LODDISWELL	SX 732 485	UNION	SX 768 733
LOPES	SX 517 633	UPTON PYNE	SX 911 977
LOPWELL	SX 471 649	VICTORIA, NEW	SX 744 716
LUSCOMBE	SX 436 716	VIRTUOUS LADY	SX 474 698
MACCLESFIELD	SX 718 675	VITIFER, WEST	SX 677 828
MARIA	SX 713 990	WALTER	SX 432 783
MARISTOW	SX 471 649	WARD, NORTH	SX 427 687
MARY EMMA	SX 533 852	WARD, SOUTH	SX 427 677
MARY HUTCHINGS	SX 565 581	WATERHILL AND KING'S OVEN	SX 676 812
MELDON	SX 570 918	WEEK	SX 451 811
MID-DEVON	SX 632 945	WHITCHURCH DOWN CONSOLS	
NUN'S CROSS	SX 604 699		SX 511 740
PORTLEMOUTH CONSOLS	SX 758 389	WHITE WORKS (DARTMOOR)	SX 613 710
PRAWLE, EAST	SX 772 353	WHITEWORKS (PLYMOUTH)	SX 568 595
RAVEN ROCK	SX 471 695	WHITLEIGH	SX 483 598
REYNARD (RENARD)	SX 588 585	WHITSTONE	SX 464 818
RIX HILL	SX 482 723	WIDDON (WHIDDON) & BROWNSHILL	
ROBERT, NORTH	SX 513 708		SX 757 721
RUSSELL, NEW EAST	SX 464 714	WILLIAM AND MARY	SX 463 701
RUTH	SX 599 682	WILLIAMS, GREAT	SX 409 761
SHAUGH IRON	SX 533 633	WOOD	SX 478 663
SIDNEY	SX 551 594	WORTHY	SX 827 816
SORTRIDGE CONSOLS	SX 510 708	WREY CONSOLS	SX 716 684
SURPRISE	SX 511 740	YARNER (YARROW)	SX 783 783
TAMAR CONSOLS, EAST (FURZEHILL)		YENNADON	SX 543 684
	SX 434 633	YEOLAND CONSOLS	SX 561 663
TAMAR CONSOLS, SOUTH	SX 437 645		